# insight

**Elementary Workbook**

OXFORD
UNIVERSITY PRESS

Kate Haywood

# OXFORD
## UNIVERSITY PRESS

Great Clarendon Street, Oxford, OX2 6DP, United Kingdom

Oxford University Press is a department of the University of Oxford.
It furthers the University's objective of excellence in research, scholarship,
and education by publishing worldwide. Oxford is a registered trade
mark of Oxford University Press in the UK and in certain other countries

© Oxford University Press 2013

The moral rights of the author have been asserted

First published in 2013

2017 2016 2015 2014 2013

10 9 8 7 6 5 4 3 2 1

**No unauthorized photocopying**

ISBN: 978 0 19 401111 2

Printed in Spain by Just Colour Graphic S.L.

This book is printed on paper from certified and well-managed sources

ACKNOWLEDGEMENTS

*The authors and the publisher would like to thank Jane Cammack for the material she
contributed to this book.*

*The authors and the publisher would also like to thank the many teachers who
contributed to the development of the course by commenting on the manuscript, taking
part in lesson observations, focus groups and online questionnaires.*

*The authors and publisher are grateful to those who have given permission to reproduce
the following extracts and adaptations of copyright material:* pp.92–93 Extract
from *Oxford Bookworms: The Adventures of Tom Sawyer* adapted by Nick Bullard.
© Oxford University Press 2008. Reproduced by permission; pp.94–95 Extract
from *Oxford Bookworms: The Wizard of Oz* adapted by Rosemary Border. © Oxford
University Press 2008. Reproduced by permission; pp.96–97 Extract from
*Oxford Dominoes: Macbeth* adapted by Alistair McCallum. © Oxford University
Press 2010. Reproduced by permission; pp.998-99 Extract from *Oxford
Bookworms: The Withered Arm* adapted by Jennifer Bassett. © Oxford University
Press 2008. Reproduced by permission; pp.100–101 Extract from *Oxford
Bookworms: Sherlock Holmes and the Duke's Son* adapted by Jennifer Bassett .
© Oxford University Press 2008. Reproduced by permission.

*The publisher would like to thank the following for their permission to reproduce
photographs:* Alamy Images pp.9 (woman playing sitar/Lebrecht Music and
Arts Photo Library), 13 (Teen boys in football kit/Beyond Fotomedia GmbH),
14 (students/Janine Wiedel Photolibrary), 15 (students reading/INSADCO
Photography), 15 (boy texting/Radius Images), 15 (classroom/PhotoAlto),
15 (sleeping student/Image Source), 15 (bored girl/RubberBall), 16 (Electrician
with stage lighting system/PhotoStock-Israel), 18 (Child reading/Christina
Kennedy), 21 (Beach volleyball/imagebroker), 21 (Indoor winter sports/
Robert Stainforth), 24 (Family with gadgets/ONOKY - Photononstop), 26 (Teen
girls with bikes/MBI), 33 (loft conversion/Elizabeth Whiting & Associates),
34 (Brighton Pier/Art Directors & TRIP), 34 (Liverpool/Powered by Light/
Alan Spencer), 40 (storm chasers/Ryan McGinnis), 48 (acrobats/Jeff Morgan
16), 52 (Broadway/Maria Green), 54 (pop up shop/Jeffrey Blackler), 63 (Man
consoling friend/ONOKY - Photononstop), 64 (Illustration of medicinal leech
treatment/Everett Collection Historical), 77 (Man walking dogs/Big Cheese
Photo LLC), 80 (High school environmental club meeting/Martin Shields),
85 (Cave rescue team/Peter Storh), 87 (Lindisfarne Castle/Dan Tucker),
89 (Backpackers/Alaska Stock), 97 (Macbeth/Mary Evans Picture Library),
107 (mountain biker/Westend61 GmbH); ardea pp.36 (Emperor penguins/
Graham Robertson), 37 (Polar bear/Geoff Trinder), 84 (Penguin/Kenneth W.
Fink); Corbis pp.7 (footballers/Hero Images), 13 (Ballet dancer/Erik Isakson),
24 (Woman with phone and iPad/B. Boissonnet/BSIP), 31 (Hanging Rock/
Nick Rains), 34 (The Beatles Story sign/Paul Thompson), 36 (Sonoran desert
toad/Kike Calvo/National Geographic Society), 38 (flood/Romeo Ranoco/
Reuters), 50 (Chinese dragon/Melvyn Altwarg/Demotix), 60 (Woman in gym/
Hybrid Images/Cultura), 65 (17th-century illustration of a physician wearing
protective clothing/Bettmann), 88 (Mountain bikers in the desert/Doug Berry),
93 (illustration from a 1910 edition of The Adventures of Tom Sawyer/Worth
Brehm/PoodlesRock); Getty Images pp.7 (baby carriers/Daly and Newton),
10 (headshots/Brand New Images), 15 (teacher in classroom/Svetlana Braun),
17 (Roadie/Martin Philbey/Redferns), 21 (Swimmer/Fuse), 23 (Business woman/
Dimitri Vervitsiotis), 25 (Teen boy playing video game/Schedivy Pictures
Inc.), 29 (Wigwam hotel/Tom Bean), 31 (couple with map/Image Source),
32 (building plans/Solidago), 42 (King penguins/Martin Harvey/Gallo Images),
42 (giraffe/Martin Harvey), 47 (Couple at cafe/Panorama Media), 53 (fashion
show/Thomas Samson), 61 (Girl on zip line/SJKoenig), 62 (Artist's conception
of Titanic sinking/Time Life Pictures/Mansell), 68 (Mahatma Gandhi/Dinodia
Photos/2010 Getty Images), 70 (Marie Colvin/Arthur Edwards - WPA Pool/2010
Getty Images), 71 (Father teaching son to drive/Ryan McVay), 72 (Roald Dahl/
Tony Evans/Hulton Archive), 76 (The Beatles waxwork, Madame Tussauds/
VisitBritain/Britain on View), 78 (Students with digital tablet/PhotoInc),
79 (Students checking test resutls/Eric Audras/ONOKY), 95 (The Wizard
of Oz/Authenticated News/Archive Photos), 99 (Apparition illustration/
helenecanada), 109 (Birthday party/Fuse), 109 (Nightclub crowd/Chris
Ryan); Oxford University Press pp.12 (Cow grazing/Fuse), 22 (Violin/Ingram),
22 (Acoustic guitar/music Alan King), 22 (Grand piano/Corbis), 92, 94, 96, 98,
100 (book covers), 105 (trekking/Image Source); Press Association Images
p.90 (Rosie Swale-Pope/Al Grillo/AP); Rex Features pp.32 (underground room/),
48 (Love-bug salad/Paul Grover), 55 (clothes shop/View Pictures), 56 (teens
shopping/OJO Images), 73 (*Matilda, a Musical*, Kerry Ingram as Matilda/Geraint
Lewis), 101 (*The Return of Sherlock Holmes*, 1986/ITV); Shutterstock pp.4 (World
map/Hibrida), 5 (teen band/auremar), 10 (alphabet/iralu), 10 (mandarin/James
Stuart Griffith), 22 (Drum kit/Dario Sabljak), 45 (food pyramid pie chart/
ifong), 46 (Woman in supermarket/Pressmaster), 48 (Tutankhamen mask/Ross
Wallace), 58 (wedge shoes/Guzel Studio), 76 (Mannequins/Raisa Kanareva),
104 (hydroponic salad/Bplanet); SuperStock pp.6 (boys with cookies/Corbis),
29 (Ice Hotel/age fotostock), 37 (kangaroo/fStop), 53 (family lined up/
PhotoAlto).

*Cover:* Nikali Larin/Image Zoo/Alamy.

*Illustrations by:* Gavin Reece pp.12, 20, 23, 52; Norbert Sipos/Beehive Illustration
pp.28; Jane Smith pp.30, 31.

*Although every effort has been made to trace and contact copyright holders before
publication, this has not been possible in some cases. We apologise for any apparent
infringement of copyright and, if notified, the publisher will be pleased to rectify any
errors or omissions at the earliest possible opportunity.*

# Welcome

## Welcome A  Hello

**V** The alphabet

**1** 🔊 **3.01** Write the letters that you hear. What word do the letters spell? Put the words in the correct category.

| Sport | Music | Country |
|---|---|---|
| | | Japan |
| | | |
| | | |

**V** Countries and nationalities

**2** Complete the table with countries or nationalities.

| Countries | Nationalities |
|---|---|
| France | 1  French |
| 2 | Spanish |
| 3 | Belgian |
| Poland | 4 |
| Turkey | 5 |
| Italy | 6 |
| 7 | Canadian |
| 8 | Dutch |
| Thailand | 9 |
| Egypt | 10 |
| 11 | Luxemburgish |
| Ireland | 12 |
| Hungary | 13 |
| the Czech Republic | 14 |
| 15 | Slovakian |
| 16 | Argentinian |
| Mexico | 17 |
| Kenya | 18 |
| 19 | New Zealander |
| Morocco | 20 |

**V** Talking about interests

**3** Choose the correct words to complete the sentences.

1  I love / don't like football. 😊
2  I like / 'm not into karate. 😐
3  I like / 'm not into hip hop music. 😐
4  I love / don't like computers! 😨
5  I'm into / don't like baseball. 😨

**4** Complete the sentences so that they are true for you.

1  ......................... football.
2  ......................... music.
3  ......................... baseball.
4  ......................... computers.
5  ......................... karate.

**V** Numbers 1–30

**5** Write the numbers.

1  1  .....one.....
2  2 ....................
3  13 ....................
4  21 ....................
5  10 ....................
6  27 ....................
7  12 ....................
8  3 ....................

9  30 ....................
10  15 ....................
11  16 ....................
12  18 ....................
13  9 ....................
14  11 ....................
15  14 ....................

**6** Study the information in the table. Complete the sentences below.

| Name | Nationality | Age | Interests | | |
|---|---|---|---|---|---|
| | | | football | music | computers |
| Lisa | British | 30 | 🙂 | 🙂 | 🙂 |
| Paulo | Brazilian | 10 | 😍 | 🙂 | 🙂 |
| Cheng | Chinese | 16 | 🙁 | 🙂 | 🙂 |
| Klara | German | 14 | 🙂 | 🙂 | 😍 |
| Anup | Indian | 27 | 🙂 | 😍 | 🙁 |

1  My name's Lisa. I'm from **the UK**. I'm **thirty**. I like **music** and I'm **into** computers. **I'm not into** football.
2  My name's Paulo. I'm from ......................... I'm ......................... . I ......................... football. I like ......................... . I'm not into ......................... .
3  My name's Cheng. I'm from ......................... . I'm ......................... . I ......................... music. I'm ......................... computers. I ......................... football.
4  My name's Klara. I'm from ......................... . I'm ......................... . I ......................... football. I'm into ......................... and I love ......................... .
5  My name's Anup. I'm from ......................... . I'm ......................... . I ......................... football. I ......................... music. I ......................... computers.

**7** CHALLENGE! Complete the sentences so that they are true for you.

My name's ......................... . I'm from ......................... . I'm ......................... . I love ......................... . I'm into ......................... . I don't like ......................... .

# Welcome B  Are you in a band?

## The verb *be*: affirmative

**1** Complete the sentences with the affirmative form of *be*.

1 I ........'m........ fifteen.
2 We ........................ into hip hop music.
3 Holly ........................ from the UK.
4 They ........................ South African.
5 You ........................ good at sport.
6 It ........................ a great band.
7 Scott ........................ my friend.
8 David and Liam ........................ into football.

**2** Complete the text with the affirmative form of *be*.

Hi. My name is Ethan. I ¹ ........'m........ fifteen and I ² ........................ American. My home ³ ........................ in New York. It ⁴ ........................ a great city! In this photo, I ⁵ ........................ with Olivia and Ellie. They ⁶ ........................ my friends. Olivia ⁷ ........................ at the same school as me, but Ellie ⁸ ........................ at a different school. We ⁹ ........................ in a rock band. We ¹⁰ ........................ really into rock!

## The verb *be*: negative

**3** Choose the correct words to complete the sentences.

1 I isn't / **(I'm not)** from Europe.
2 Caitlin and Jack **isn't** / **aren't** at the same school.
3 We **aren't** / **not** into sport.
4 Tom **isn't** / **am not** fourteen.
5 It **aren't** / **isn't** a great city.
6 You **are not** / **is not** in a band.

**4** Rewrite the sentences using the negative form of *be*.

1 My name is Tara.
   My name isn't Tara.
2 I'm Russian.
   .....................................................
3 My home is in Moscow.
   .....................................................
4 My friends are at a concert.
   .....................................................
5 We're into samba music.
   .....................................................
6 You're in a samba band.
   .....................................................

## The verb *be*: questions and short answers

**5** Put the words in order to make questions.

1 you / into tennis / are / ?
   Are you into tennis?
2 from Glasgow / is / he / ?
   .....................................................
3 at the same / we / school / are / ?
   .....................................................
4 good at / am / music / I / ?
   .....................................................
5 they / into baseball / are / ?
   .....................................................
6 fifteen / you / are / ?
   .....................................................
7 good / Eva / at sport / is / ?
   .....................................................

**6** Match questions 1–6 to short answers a–f.

1 Am I good at tennis? ..c..
2 Are you into football? ........
3 Is Jack sixteen? ........
4 Is Jess from London? ........
5 Are we in the same class? ........
6 Are they American? ........

a No, we aren't. You're in 8A and I'm in 8B.
b No, they aren't.
c ~~Yes, you are. You're great!~~
d No, I'm not. I don't like it.
e Yes, he is.
f No, she isn't. She's from Bristol.

**7** Complete the conversation with the correct form of *be*.

Emily  Hi! I ¹ ......'m...... Emily. What's your name?
Yann   My name ² ................ Yann. Nice to meet you.
Emily  ³ ................ you from the UK?
Yann   No, I ⁴ ................ . I ⁵ ................ from France.
Emily  Ah! You ⁶ ................ French!
Yann   Yes! And you? ⁷ ................ you British?
Emily  No, I ⁸ ................ British. I ⁹ ................ Australian.
Yann   What are you into, Emily?
Emily  I ¹⁰ ................ into music. I ¹¹ ................ in a band with Amy.
Yann   ¹² ................ she your friend?
Emily  No, she ¹³ ................ . She ¹⁴ ................ my sister.
Yann   ¹⁵ ................ you famous in Australia?
Emily  No, we ¹⁶ ................! But, we ¹⁷ ................ good!

**8** **CHALLENGE!** Complete the profile for you. Then write sentences with the correct form of *be*.

Name: ........................  Age: ........................
Nationality: ........................  City: ........................
Likes: ........................
Dislikes: ........................

# Welcome C  Happy families

## V  Family

**1  Complete the table with family words.**

| Male | Female | Both |
|---|---|---|
| dad | [1] _mum_ | [2] |
| [3] | daughter | |
| brother | [4] | |
| cousin | cousin | [5] |
| grandfather | [6] | [7] |
| [8] | niece | |
| [9] | aunt | |
| grandson | [10] | |

## V  Colours

**2  Find nine more colours in the wordsearch.**

| A | T | P | E | L | R | B | A |
|---|---|---|---|---|---|---|---|
| M | T | U | O | G | E | U | S |
| G | B | R | O | W | N | Y | B |
| O | C | P | B | K | L | B | L |
| Y | E | L | L | O | W | H | A |
| Q | T | E | U | C | H | R | C |
| S | V | A | E | P | I | N | K |
| L | G | R | O | J | T | Y | P |
| O | R | A | N | G | E | S | U |
| T | E | W | D | N | K | V | P |
| R | E | D | H | R | I | L | R |
| E | N | S | L | T | F | W | I |

## Possessive adjectives

**3  Choose the correct possessive adjectives.**

1  My sister is into music. **My / Her** favourite music is hip hop.
2  My grandparents love football. It's **our / their** favourite sport.
3  'Is Daisy **your / its** friend?' 'Yes, she's my best friend.'
4  'Is this your dog?' 'Yes, it's **their / our** dog!'
5  This is my uncle and this is **his / her** son, Jake. Jake is my cousin.
6  'Is this your book?' 'No, it isn't **his / my** book.'
7  'I'm in a football team.' 'What's **your / its** name?' 'Newport F.C. – it's a great team!'

**4  Choose the correct words to complete the sentences.**

1  This is **they're / their** computer.
2  **You're / Your** my friends.
3  **They're / Their** in my class.
4  **It's / Its** name is Spot. **Its / It's** a great name for a dog!
5  **You're / Your** books are in my bag.
6  She's **their / they're** mother.

## V  Feelings adjectives

**5  Look at the picture and choose the correct words.**

My brother and I are in a hockey team. My brother is very [1]**happy / tired** because hockey is his favourite sport. He's always very [2]**bored / excited** about our matches. But I'm [3]**happy / bored** because I don't like hockey. People are sometimes [4]**angry / hot** with me because I'm not very good. Then I am [5]**sad / excited**. After a match, my brother is [6]**hot / cold**, [7]**cold / tired** and [8]**angry / thirsty**, but I'm [9]**cold / exited** and [10]**thirsty / hungry**.

My brother

Me

## V  Plural nouns

**6  Complete the sentences with the plural form of the words below.**

■ brother ■ country ■ man ■ person ■ team ■ ~~woman~~

1  The _women_ in my family are my mum, my grandmother and my aunt.
2  ............................ from the UK are British.
3  Lucy is my sister, and Matt and Tom are my ............................ .
4  My favourite ............................ are Belgium, France and Germany.
5  The two football ............................ in my city are Manchester United and Manchester City.
6  The ............................ in the band are Marc, David and my dad!

## this, that, these, those

**7  Complete the sentences with this, that, these and those.**

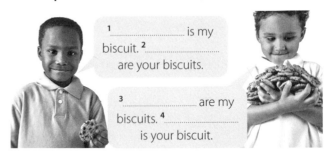

[1] ............................ is my biscuit. [2] ............................ are your biscuits.

[3] ............................ are my biscuits. [4] ............................ is your biscuit.

**8  CHALLENGE!  Find a photo of your family. Write sentences about the photo. Use your answers to the questions to help you.**

■  Who is in the photo?
■  Are your family bored, happy, cold, tired, etc.?

# Welcome D  Friends

## have got

**1** Complete the sentences with the affirmative (✔) or negative (✘) form of *have got*.

1 We _____'ve got_____ a new teacher. ✔
2 I _____ a dog. ✘
3 Henry _____ a sister. ✘
4 You _____ a mobile phone. ✔
5 Lily _____ a brother. ✘
6 You _____ a nice bag. ✔
7 My parents _____ a laptop. ✘
8 I _____ a big house. ✔

**2** Put the words in the correct order to make questions. Then complete the short answers.

1 you / got / a dog / have / ?
   _Have you got a dog?_
   Yes, I _____have_____.
2 a cousin / Bethany / got / has / ?
   _____
   Yes, she _____.
3 have / a cat / they / got / ?
   _____
   No, they _____.
4 I / have / your book / got / ?
   _____
   No, you _____.
5 got / we / have / a new teacher / ?
   _____
   Yes, you _____.
6 you / got / a mobile phone / have / ?
   _____
   No, I _____.
7 Jake / a guitar / has / got / ?
   _____
   No, he _____.

## Ⅴ  Appearance adjectives

**3** Choose the correct adjectives to complete the text.

The man and the woman are **¹straight /(tall.)**They aren't **²old / small**. The man has got **³fair / curly** hair. His hair is **⁴small / short** and **⁵dark / young**. The woman has got **⁶straight / tall** hair. Her hair is **⁷big / fair** and **⁸long / short**. The children are **⁹small / big** and **¹⁰young / old**. They aren't **¹¹big / fair!**

## Object pronouns

**4** Replace the words in bold with object pronouns.

1 We've got a great music club at school. I'm in **the club**. ____it____
2 Mr Johnson and Miss Slade are my favourite teachers. I like **Mr Johnson and Miss Slade** a lot. _____
3 This is Jessie. She's a good singer. I'm in a band with **Jessie**. _____
4 Our grandparents are with **me and my brothers** today. _____
5 That's Sophie! I'm in the baseball team with **Sophie**! _____
6 Jez isn't a nice boy. I don't like **Jez**. _____

**5** Complete the text with object pronouns.

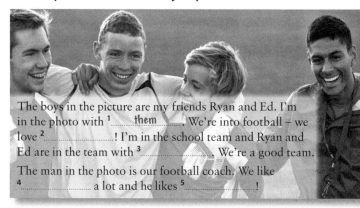

The boys in the picture are my friends Ryan and Ed. I'm in the photo with **¹** ____them____. We're into football – we love **²** _____! I'm in the school team and Ryan and Ed are in the team with **³** _____. We're a good team. The man in the photo is our football coach. We like **⁴** _____ a lot and he likes **⁵** _____!

## a / an and the

**6** Choose the correct words to complete the sentences.

1 I've got **a /(an)**orange bag.
2 I like **a / the** boys in my class.
3 This is **a / an** great band!
4 Have you got **a / an** apple?
5 They've got **a / an** cat. **A / The** cat is black.
6 His dad bought him **a / an** expensive guitar. He plays **a / the** guitar every day.

**7** Choose the correct words to complete the dialogue.

Jo      There's a new girl in the class.
Lucy   Oh! What's **¹(her)/ his** name?
Jo      Ella.
Lucy   **²Has / Have** she got **³short / small**, brown hair?
Jo      No, she **⁴hasn't / haven't**. She **⁵'ve / 's** got **⁶tall / long**, fair hair.
Lucy   Ah, I know her! Is she **⁷tall / old**?
Jo      Yes, she is. She's into baseball. She's really good at **⁸it / him**. She's in the team with **⁹my / me**.
Lucy   **¹⁰Has / Have** she got **¹¹a / the** brother?
Jo      Yes, she has. His name is Mark.
Lucy   I know **¹²him / her**! I'm in a club with **¹³him / it** – music club. He's got **¹⁴small / short**, curly hair.
Jo      That's right! Mark and Ella are nice. I like **¹⁵us / them**.

**8** CHALLENGE!  Describe three family members.

_I've got a sister. Her name is Jen. She's got long, curly hair. She's got big eyes._

## V  Days, months and seasons

**1** Write the days.

1  Sunday
2  M
3  T
4  W
5  T
6  F
7  S

**2** Complete the crossword. Then put the letters in the grey squares in the correct order to write the extra month.

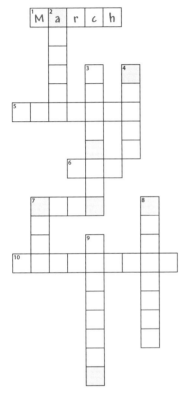

Extra month: _ _ _ _ _ _ _

Across
1  It's got 31 days. It's in spring.
5  It's got 31 days. It's in autumn. Halloween is in this month.
6  It's the fifth month of the year.
7  It's the seventh month of the year.
10  It's the ninth month of the year. It's in autumn.

Down
2  It's got 31 days. It's in summer.
3  It's got 28 or 29 days. It's the second month of the year.
4  It's the fourth month of the year.
7  It's got 30 days. It's the beginning of summer.
8  It's the eleventh month of the year.
9  It's got 31 days. It's in winter. It's Christmas!

**3** Write the seasons.

1  25 December
2  21 April
3  15 August
4  10 October

## V  Numbers 31+

**4** Match the words to the numbers.

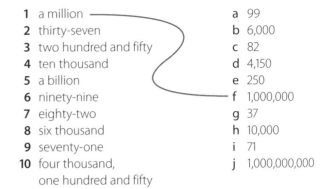

1  a million — f  1,000,000
2  thirty-seven
3  two hundred and fifty
4  ten thousand
5  a billion
6  ninety-nine
7  eighty-two
8  six thousand
9  seventy-one
10  four thousand, one hundred and fifty

a  99
b  6,000
c  82
d  4,150
e  250
f  1,000,000
g  37
h  10,000
i  71
j  1,000,000,000

**5** Write the numbers.

1  35  thirty-five
2  56
3  73
4  98
5  300
6  5,000

## V  The time

**6** Write the times.

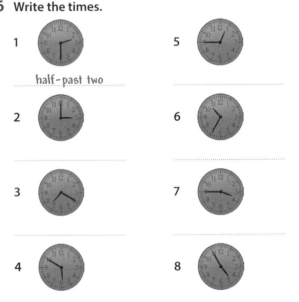

1  half-past two
2
3
4
5
6
7
8

## V  Ordinals and dates

**7** Write the next ordinals.

1  eleventh,  twelfth
2  second,
3  fifteenth,
4  third,
5  first,
6  nineteenth,
7  twenty-third,
8  thirty-first,
9  twelfth,
10  tenth,

**8** Put the dates in the correct order.

1  ...... the fifteenth of March
2  ...... the twenty-fourth of December
3  ...... the twelfth of December
4  ...... the thirtieth of May
5  ..1.. the thirty-first of January

**9** CHALLENGE!  Write five dates that are important in your family. Write why they are important.

# Welcome E The world is a village

**1 Complete the sentences with the words below.**

■ describe ■ have ■ how ■ what ■ what ■ when ■ where ■ who

1 ___How___ old are you?
2 _____ is your favourite sport?
3 _____ are you from?
4 _____ you got a pet?
5 _____ your family.
6 _____ is your favourite singer?
7 _____ is your birthday?
8 _____ is your name?

**2 Match the sentences in exercise 1 to gaps a–g in the dialogue. There is one sentence that you do not need.**

**Presenter** Today we're with Ruby Ali! She's a raga singer. Raga is traditional Indian music
ᵃWhere are you from?

**Ruby** I'm from ¹Sheffield / Bristol. It's a big city in the UK. My grandparents are from India and my family love Indian music!

**Presenter** ᵇ

**Ruby** I'm ²33 / 23.

**Presenter** ᶜ

**Ruby** It's on the ³21ˢᵗ / 20ᵗʰ April. It's in my favourite season, spring.

**Presenter** ᵈ

**Ruby** My mum, Rabinda! She's into music, too. She's in a raga group with me and my ⁴brother / dad – he plays the sitar.

**Presenter** ᵉ

**Ruby** They're great! Well, I've got my mum and dad, and I've got two brothers, Anil and Mirat. Mum is tall. She's got ⁵long / short, black hair. Dad's got short, ⁶grey / brown hair (and he hasn't got a lot of it!). He's tall, too. Anil is short. He's got straight hair. Mirat is tall. Mirat loves sport. He's in his school football team.

**Presenter** ᶠ

**Ruby** I'm not into sport! I don't like it. But I like my brother's team. So … the answer is football!

**Presenter** ᵍ

**Ruby** No, I haven't! I love ⁷cats / dogs, but I haven't got one. Mum and Dad have got three pets. They've got two cats and a dog. Their favourite is the dog. Her name is Mili. She's my favourite, too!

**Presenter** Thanks, Ruby!

**3 🔊 3.02 Listen to the interview and check your answers in exercise 2.**

**4 🔊 3.02 Listen again and choose the correct words to complete Ruby's answers.**

**5 Write the names of the people in the text.**

1 a dog ___Mili___
2 two singers _____
3 a person with straight hair _____
4 a tall student _____
5 a person with short hair _____

**6 Choose the correct words to complete the sentences.**

1 Rubi comes from a big / small city.
2 Her grandparents are Indian / British.
3 Her birthday is in winter / spring.
4 Her mum / dad has got a sitar.
5 Her mum is in a raga group with Anil / her dad.
6 Anil / Mirat is good at sport.

**7 CHALLENGE! Write a description of someone you know. Include this information:**

■ his / her age
■ his / her interests
■ his / her appearance

**1** Study the highlighted words and check the meanings in a dictionary. Then do the languages quiz.

## What do you know about languages?

**1** How many languages are there in the world?
   a  about 1,500,000
   ⓑ about 7,000
   c  about 3,500

**2** What place has got about 2,200 different languages?
   a  Asia
   b  Africa
   c  South America

**3** A quarter of the world's population live in Europe. How many languages are there in Europe?
   a  about 150
   b  about 370
   c  about 230

**4** How many characters has the Russian alphabet got?
   a  42
   b  26
   c  33

АБВГДЕЁ
ЖЗИЙКЛ"
МНОПРСТ
УФХЦЧШ
ЩЪЫЬЭЮ
ЯЄ

**5** What language has got the most speakers?
   a  Mandarin Chinese
   b  English
   c  Spanish

**6** Mandarin Chinese writing uses over 50,000 characters. How many characters do Mandarin speakers use every day?
   a  2,000–3,000
   b  9,000–10,000
   c  6,000–7,000

**7** What country has got the most native English speakers?
   a  the United Kingdom
   b  the USA
   c  Australia

**8** How old is the modern English language?
   a  over 10,000-years-old
   b  over 8,000-years-old
   c  under 7,000-years-old

**9** Esperanto is an artificial language. What number of speakers has it got?
   a  approximately 2,000,000
   b  approximately 9,000
   c  approximately 1,000,000

Answers

1b 2a 3c 4c 5a 6a 7b 8c 9a

**2** Find the words below in the quiz and answer the questions. Use a dictionary to help you.

■ about ■ around ■ over ■ under

**1** What two words mean *approximately*?
   ...... about ...... ......................

**2** Complete the definitions.
   a  ............................ 50 is the same as 50>.
   b  ............................ 50 is the same as <50.

**3** Read the factfile. Then choose the correct words to complete the sentences.

## English language factfile

| |
|---|
| Speakers of English as a native / first language: around 375 million |
| Speakers of English as a foreign language: around 750 million |
| People who use English on the internet: around 72 million |
| Number of people who study English every year: 1 billion+ |

**1** **Over** / **Under** 350 million people speak English as their native language.
**2** **Approximately** / **Over** 750 million people speak English as a foreign language.
**3** **Under** / **About** 72 million people use English on the internet.
**4** **Over** / **About** 1 million people study English every year.

**4** **CHALLENGE!** Write about you, your country and your language. Answer the questions. Use the internet to help you. Use the words in exercise 2.

**1** Where are you from?
   I'm from ...................................................... .
**2** What's your nationality and language?
   My nationality is ..........................................
   and my language is ..................................... .
**3** How many people speak your language?
   ............................................... people speak my language.
**4** How many languages are there in your country?
   There are ......................................................
   languages in my country.

# Progress check  Welcome

Read 1–16 and evaluate your learning. Give yourself a mark from 1 to 3.
How can you improve?

**1** I can't do this.　　**2** I have some problems with this.　　**3** I can do this well.

| A  Hello | Mark (1–3) | How can I improve? |
|---|---|---|
| **1**  Name five nationalities. | | |
| I can identify nationalities. | | |
| **2**  Name five countries. | | |
| I can identify countries. | | |
| **3**  Write the numbers as words.<br>　　a 23　　b 12　　c 18　　d 14　　e 30 | | |
| I can write numbers 1–30. | | |

| B  Are you in a band? | Mark (1–3) | How can I improve? |
|---|---|---|
| **4**  Choose the correct words.<br>　　1 I **am** / **is** / **are** a singer.　　2 We **am** / **is** / **are** in a team. | | |
| I can use the affirmative form of the verb *be*. | | |
| **5**  Complete the sentences with the negative form of *be*.<br>　　1 They ............................ in my class.　　2 I ............................ his sister. | | |
| I can use the negative form of the verb *be*. | | |
| **6**  Write questions and short answers<br>　　1 you / from the USA / ? (✔)　　2 he / good at sport / ? (✘) | | |
| I can ask questions and give short answers using the verb *be*. | | |

| C  Happy families | Mark (1–3) | How can I improve? |
|---|---|---|
| **7**  Write the male form of the words below.<br>　　a grandmother　b aunt　c sister　d wife　e mum | | |
| I can identify members of the family. | | |
| **8**  Write the possessive adjectives of the subject pronouns.<br>　　a you　b she　c we　d they | | |
| I can use possessive adjectives. | | |
| **9**  Name three feelings adjectives. | | |
| I can use feelings adjectives. | | |
| **10**  Write the plural form of the nouns.<br>　　a child　　b man　　c nationality　　d woman | | |
| I can use regular and irregular plural nouns. | | |

| D  Friends | Mark (1–3) | How can I improve? |
|---|---|---|
| **11**  Write sentences with *have got*.<br>　　a he / a guitar / ✔　b they / a dog / ✘　c you / a brother / ? | | |
| I can use *have got*. | | |
| **12**  Write the opposites.<br>　　a young　　b dark　　c small　　d long　　e curly | | |
| I can use appearance adjectives. | | |
| **13**  Name six object pronouns. | | |
| I can use object pronouns. | | |
| **14**  Complete the sentences with *a*, *an* or *the*.<br>　　Max is in ......... football team. It's ......... school team. | | |
| I can use *a*, *an* and *the*. | | |

| E  The world is a village | Mark (1–3) | How can I improve? |
|---|---|---|
| **15**  Write the numbers as words.<br>　　a 31　b 3,621　c 647　d 2,110 | | |
| I can write numbers 31+. | | |
| **16**  Write the dates.<br>　　a Christmas Day .........　b Halloween .........　c New Year's Day ......... | | |
| I can use ordinals and dates. | | |

## Vocabulary Breakfast in space

**V Daily routines**

**1** Match 1–8 to a–h to make sentences about daily routines.

| | | |
|---|---|---|
| 1 | My brother and I start | **a** TV after dinner. |
| 2 | I have | **b** football after school. |
| 3 | Before dinner I do | **c** a book before I sleep. |
| 4 | I watch | **d** school at 9.00. |
| 5 | My friend and I chat | **e** on the phone every day. |
| 6 | On Saturday, I meet | **f** lunch at school at 12.30. |
| 7 | We play | **g** my homework. |
| 8 | I read | **h** friends at the cinema. |

**2** Complete the sentences with the words below.

■ get ■ use ■ ~~get~~ ■ have ■ meet ■ chat ■ do ■ start ■ get

1 On weekdays, I ............*get*............ up at 7.00.
2 I .......................................... breakfast with my family at home.
3 I .......................................... dressed and go to school.
4 They .......................................... school at 9.00.
5 I .......................................... my homework after I .......................................... home.
6 Mum and Dad .......................................... the internet to watch films.
7 My sister and her friends .......................................... on the phone.
8 At weekends, I .......................................... friends.

**3** Complete the text with the phrases below. There is one phrase that you do not need.

■ do homework ■ get dressed ■ get home ■ ~~get up~~
■ go to bed ■ have a shower ■ have breakfast
■ have dinner ■ meet friends ■ start school
■ watch TV

Hi! I'm Jen. I'm a secondary school student, but I'm also a TV actor. My life is fun, but it's not always easy. On a school day, I ¹ ........*get up*........ at 7.00 and ² .......................................... before my brothers use the bathroom! I ³ .......................................... – I wear a school uniform. I ⁴ .......................................... with my family at 7.30. I ⁵ .......................................... at 9.00 and the first lesson is at 9.15. After school, I don't go home. I go to the TV studio and I work from 6.00 to 9.00. I ⁶ .......................................... at the studio with the actors – we all like pizza! I ⁷ .......................................... at 10.30 – I go by taxi. I'm very tired and I ⁸ .......................................... immediately. At the weekend, I ⁹ .......................................... first – it's important to study. Sometimes, I ¹⁰ .......................................... and we go to the cinema or the shops.

**V insight Prepositions of time**

**4** Complete the sentences with prepositions of time.

1 ............*At*............ the weekend, Liam plays football.
2 I watch TV .......................................... I go to bed.
3 .......................................... the evening, I watch films.
4 Jake meets his friends .......................................... Wednesday.
5 .......................................... summer, I like to go camping.
6 School starts .......................................... 9.30.
7 .......................................... Christmas, we meet family and friends.
8 We go on holiday .......................................... August.

**5** Choose the correct daily routine and prepositions of time. Choose '–' if no preposition is necessary.

## Our day

Adam and Hannah ¹(get)/ watch / start up early every day. They ²start / have / get dressed and help their dad on their farm ³before / in / on 7.30! They help on their farm ⁴in / – / before every day. The animals have ⁵breakfast / lunch / dinner before they ⁶get / go / start school. Lessons start ⁷in / on / at 9.00. ⁸On / – / At Monday and Wednesday, Adam and Hannah help on the farm after school finishes ⁹on / in / at the afternoon. The animals are hungry again! They get ¹⁰shower / lunch / home at 5.30. They ¹¹get / have / do homework and ¹²watch / do / have TV – normal things! 'It's great to help on the farm ¹³at / in / on spring and summer,' says Hannah. 'But it's difficult ¹⁴at / in / on December and January. It's very cold!' says Adam.

**6** CHALLENGE! Write four sentences about your daily routine on a school day and four sentences about your daily routine at the weekend.

1 *I get up at seven o'clock on a school day.*
2 ..........................................................................................
3 ..........................................................................................
4 ..........................................................................................
5 ..........................................................................................
6 ..........................................................................................
7 ..........................................................................................
8 ..........................................................................................
9 ..........................................................................................

# Grammar  Bright and early

## Present simple: affirmative

**1** Write sentences with the present simple affirmative.

1 before breakfast / Lisa / have a shower
   *Lisa has a shower before breakfast.*

2 a lot / you / talk / in class

3 like / pizza / Jenny

4 study / English and Spanish / my brother

5 the internet / use / my parents / at work

6 do exercise / every afternoon / Ana

**2** Complete the text with the correct form of the verbs below.

■ do ■ feel ■ go ■ have ■ like ■ ~~play~~ ■ start ■ teach

Ethan and Lucas ¹............*play*............ football for Watford F.C., but they are also students at Harefield Academy in London. Their school ²........................... very special sports lessons.
School ³........................... at 7.30 in the morning with a football lesson. The football teacher is Watford F.C.'s coach. At weekends, he works at Watford F.C., but on school days, he ⁴........................... football at the Academy.
After the football class, the boys ⁵........................... to normal lessons.
At the end of the school day, Lucas ⁶........................... his homework at a homework club at the Academy, but Ethan ⁷........................... studying at home. Ethan and Lucas ⁸........................... very happy at the Academy.

## Present simple: negative

**3** Complete the sentences with the present simple negative form of the verbs below.

■ chat ■ ~~go~~ ■ have ■ meet ■ sleep ■ take ■ use ■ watch

1 Cameron ...............*doesn't go*............... to bed late.
2 My uncle ........................... the internet.
3 I ........................... lunch with my family.
4 We ........................... friends on Sunday.

5 Mum ........................... a lot of photos.
6 They ........................... on the phone.
7 You ........................... TV in the morning.
8 My cat ........................... at night.

**4** Rewrite the sentences using the present simple negative form.

1 I get up early at the weekend.
   *I don't get up early at the weekend.*

2 Dad uses the internet at work.

3 My friends and I meet at the cinema.

4 My cousins live in London.

5 My sister sleeps a lot.

6 I like swimming.

**5** Complete the article with the present simple affirmative and negative form of the verbs in brackets.

Liam, 21, is a ballet dancer at the Royal Opera House. He ¹............*goes*............ (go) there six days a week. He ²........................... (not work) on Sunday.
All the ballet dancers ³........................... (start) their morning with lessons. 'We ⁴........................... (have) classes at lunchtime,' explains Liam. 'I ⁵........................... (not have) lunch before three o'clock in the afternoon!
At six o'clock, Liam ⁶........................... (get) dressed for the Royal Ballet's evening show. About 2,000 people ⁷........................... (watch) a ballet at the Royal Opera House every evening. Liam ⁸........................... (finish) his dance at ten at night. He ⁹........................... (get) home at about eleven. 'It's very difficult,' he says. 'I ¹⁰........................... (not meet) friends in the evening, but my job is amazing!'

**6** CHALLENGE! Write three present simple affirmative sentences and three present simple negative sentences that are true for you. Use the verbs below and your own ideas.

■ do ■ go ■ have ■ study ■ use ■ watch

1 ...........................
2 ...........................
3 ...........................
4 ...........................
5 ...........................
6 ...........................

# Vocabulary and grammar  British schools

## V School subjects

**1** Write the school subjects next to the clues. Use the words below.

- geography ■ history ■ ICT ■ maths
- modern languages ■ ~~physical education~~
- religious education ■ science

1  We do sport! ..physical education...
2  We study lots of things, e.g. animals, electricity and atoms. ......................
3  We use computers. ......................
4  We make calculations with numbers. ......................
5  We study the past. ......................
6  We study religions. ......................
7  We study different places in the world. ......................
8  We learn new languages. ......................

## V Classroom items

**2** Which of these items belong in your school bag (B) and which belong in the classroom (C)? Write B or C.

1  blackboard ..C..          10  poster ........
2  interactive whiteboard ........  11  map ........
3  bin ........               12  exercise book ........
4  ruler ........             13  pupil ........
5  clock ........             14  desk ........
6  pencil case ........       15  pencil sharpener ........
7  rubber ........            16  calculator ........
8  teacher ........           17  chair ........
9  pen ........               18  pencil ........

## Present simple: questions and short answers

**3** Put the words in order to make present simple questions. Then write answers that are true for you.

1  study / do / Spanish / you ?
   Do you study Spanish?
   No, I don't.
2  your dad / start work / does / early ?
   ......................................
   ......................................
3  do / use the internet / you / in class ?
   ......................................
   ......................................
4  your friend / does / like / maths ?
   ......................................
   ......................................
5  PE / your friends / have / on Wednesday / do ?
   ......................................
   ......................................
6  your school / does / finish / at 4.00 ?
   ......................................
   ......................................

## Question words

**4** Complete the present simple questions with the question words below. Then write answers that are true for you.

- how many ■ how old ■ what ■ when ■ ~~where~~ ■ who

1  ........Where........ do you live?
   ......................................
2  ...................... do you start school?
   ......................................
3  ...................... is your history teacher?
   ......................................
4  ...................... is your favourite lesson?
   ......................................
5  ...................... brothers and sisters do you have?
   ......................................
6  ...................... are you?
   ......................................

**5** Complete the dialogue. Use question words and the present simple form of the verbs in brackets.

Libby  Hi! I'm Libby. [1] ......What's...... (be) your name?
Sam    I'm Sam. [2] ...................... (be) your teacher?
Libby  Mrs Potter. I'm in class 8P.
Sam    I'm in class 8W with Mrs West.
Libby  [3] ...................... (have) English now?
Sam    Yes, I do.
Libby  Me too! I love English, because I love reading. [4] ...................... (read) a lot?
Sam    No, I don't. I like watching films.
Libby  There's a film club after school today. It's great.
Sam    That sounds good. [5] ...................... (be) it?
Libby  It's in the hall. [6] ...................... (want) to meet me after school?
Sam    Yes. That sounds great.

**6** CHALLENGE! Imagine there is a new student in your class. What questions would you ask him / her? Write eight questions.

1  ......................................
2  ......................................
3  ......................................
4  ......................................
5  ......................................
6  ......................................
7  ......................................
8  ......................................

## V  Transport

**1** Complete the second sentences so that they have the same meaning as the first sentences.

1 I walk to school.
I go to school on .................... foot .................... .

2 Do you go by bike to school?
Do you .................................................... to school?

3 Dad drives to work.
Dad goes to work .................................................... .

4 We go by plane to the USA in the summer.
We .................................... to the USA in the summer.

5 We don't drive to school because there's a train.
We go to school .................................................... .

6 They go by car to the supermarket.
They .................................... to the supermarket.

7 I haven't got a bike, so I go on foot.
I .................................... to school because I haven't got a bike.

8 Let's ride our bikes to the park!
Let's ....................................to the park.

## Classroom language

**2** Look at the pictures. Are you allowed to do these things in the classroom?

**3** Choose the correct words to complete the sentences.

1 Answer / **Don't answer** the questions. .........
2 **Look** / Don't look at the board. .........
3 Eat / **Don't eat** in class. .........
4 Sit / **Don't sit** down. .........
5 **Work** / Don't work in pairs. .........
6 Use / **Don't use** your mobile phone in class. .........

**4** 🔘 3.03  Listen to the dialogue. Number the phrases in exercise 3 in the order you hear them.

**5** 🔘 3.03  Read phrases a–k. Then listen again and tick the phrases that you hear.

a  Can you say that again, please? .........
b  Look at the board. .........
c  How do you say that in English? .........
d  Don't eat in class! .........
e  Open your books on page 122. .........
f  Don't write in your textbook. .........
g  Don't use your mobile phone in class! .........
h  What does 'diagram' mean? .........
i  Check your answers. .........
j  Sit down, please. .........
k  Sorry, I don't understand. .........

**6** 🔘 3.03  Complete the dialogue with the phrases in exercise 5. Then listen again and check.

Teacher  Good morning. ¹.................................... OK, please ².................................... What does the diagram show?

Clara  Excuse me, Mr Lake. ³....................................

Teacher  Diagram – this is a diagram. It's a picture that helps us understand something.

Clara  Oh, OK. It's a diagram of a human skeleton.

Teacher  Yes, good. OK. ⁴....................................

Clara  ⁵....................................

Teacher  Page 122. Look at the diagram and answer the questions. Yes, Clara?

Clara  ⁶.................................... Where is the diagram?

Teacher  Page 122 – that's the wrong book. Open your textbook. And Clara – please ⁷....................................

Clara  Sorry, Mr Lake.

Teacher  OK. You can work in pairs to answer the questions. Andrew! It's not lunchtime yet. ⁸....................................

**7** **CHALLENGE!**  Write a sentence with classroom language for three of the photos in exercise 2.

1 ....................................................................
....................................................................

2 ....................................................................
....................................................................

3 ....................................................................
....................................................................

# Reading  On the road

1 **Match phrases 1–3 to definitions a–c. Then read the text about a roadie.**

1  a roadie ........
2  go on tour ........
3  a technician ........

a  travel to lots of different places
b  someone who travels with musicians and bands
c  someone who controls special equipment

2 **Read the text again. Choose the correct summary of the text.**

1  how to find work with bands
2  a roadie's life
3  problems for roadies

3 **Answer the questions.**

1  Who is Matt Mason?
   Matt Mason is a roadie.
2  Who is Matt on tour with this summer?
   ........................................................
3  What does he like about his job?
   ........................................................
4  What school subject helps Matt in his job?
   ........................................................
5  Where is Matt tonight?
   ........................................................
6  What does Matt do after a concert?
   ........................................................
7  What doesn't Matt like about his job?
   ........................................................
   ........................................................

4 **Are the sentences true (T) or false (F)? Correct the false ones.**

1  Roadies find jobs on the internet.
2  Matt gets up early in the morning.
3  Matt travels by plane.
4  Roadies go to bed early.
5  Matt sees his family at the weekend.
6  Matt wants to visit famous places.

5 **Match the highlighted words in the text to definitions 1–8.**

1  (verb) to be sad because you don't see a person you like ............. miss
2  (verb) to see a place (or people) ..............
3  (noun) the place in a theatre where actors and musicians perform ..............
4  (adjective) normal ..............
5  (noun) music show or performance ..............
6  (noun) work ..............
7  (verb) to control or to use ..............
8  (adjective) not interesting ..............

# On the road

Matt Mason is a roadie. A roadie helps a band with concerts. He's on tour with Coldplay this summer.

## What do you like about your job?

5 I watch concerts every night! I work with great people. I love it!

## How do people become roadies?

Go to a theatre and help small drama groups.
10 It's a good start. You don't make money, but you learn a lot. It's a good idea to study at school, too. For example, science helps! I use electronics in my work every day. Use the internet to find a job with bands on tour. Check different bands'
15 websites for work.

## What's a typical day for a roadie?

I don't have a typical day. We travel a lot in Europe when we're on tour and the journeys are very long. For example, tonight we've got a concert
20 in Paris and tomorrow night we're in Brussels!

Roadies get up early. We travel to the next theatre in big tour buses. After we arrive, we start work. I'm a lighting technician, so I put the lights on the stage. I work all afternoon. In the evening,
25 I operate the lights at the concert.

After the concert, before we go to bed, the roadies put everything in the tour bus again. This isn't easy because we're all tired! We go to bed very late.

## What don't you like about your job?

30 I miss my family. I chat to them on the phone, but sometimes I don't see them for months. That's difficult. Also, we go to lots of different cities, but we don't visit anything – we only see theatres! I want to see some famous places. The
35 journeys are boring, but I have a great life!

**6** Complete the sentences with the correct form of the words in exercise 5.

1 In the summer, we ......visit...... our family in the USA.
2 On a ..................... day, I get up at 7.30.
3 My aunt ..................... equipment in a science laboratory.
4 This film is very ...................... . I don't like it.
5 I ..................... my brother. He doesn't live at home now because he's at university.
6 The actors are on ...................... It's very exciting!
7 I'm at a ...................... . This is my favourite band. It's great to see them!
8 My dad has a new ...................... . He's a teacher at my sister's school.

**7** CHALLENGE! Imagine you are a roadie. Write an email to your family. Use the plan to help you.

Subject:

Hi .....................................................(add name/s)
How are you?
At the moment, I'm in ..........................................
..................................................(place). I'm on tour with
..................................(name of musician or band).
.......................................................................
.......................................................................
.......................................................................
.......................................................................

(Write about the band or musician, e.g. an opinion about their music.)
My job is great, but sometimes I'm tired.
.......................................................................
.......................................................................
.......................................................................
.......................................................................
.......................................................................

(Describe your daily routine, e.g. when you get up and have breakfast, when you start work, when you have lunch, when you have a break, when you have dinner, when you go to bed.)
.......................................................................
.......................................................................
.......................................................................
.......................................................................
.......................................................................

(Say what you like and don't like about your job.)
I miss you! See you in December!
From ..................................(add your name)

# Writing  A questionnaire

## Capital letters

**1** Add capital letters to the sentences. One of the sentences is correct.

1  I've got science, english and maths today.
2  My birthday is in july. my brother's birthday is in October.
3  Have i got homework today?
4  My friend's name is jessica smith and she is great.
5  My favourite film is *twilight*.
6  I play football on wednesday.
7  Dad's name is David and my mum's name is Claire.
8  My cousin is french.

**2** Match questions 1–5 in the questionnaire to answers A–E below.

> ### Questionnaire
>
> 1  What's your favourite sport? ........
> 2  What's your favourite month of the year? ........
> 3  What's your favourite season? ........
> 4  What's your favourite book? ........
> 5  Who's your favourite cartoon character? ........

**A**  I love *Diary of a Wimpy Kid*, because <u>it</u> <sup>G</sup> very funny and I like the drawings. I read it at night before I go to sleep. I also really like the films

**B**  Spring! I also love summer, because we have a long summer hoilday. I meet my friends swim in the sea and go on holiday with my family. Perfect!

**C**  Tintin! He's an old cartoon caracter, but I think he's great! He's very clever. My parents love him, too! Jake, my brother, has got all the tintin books. Tintin is belgian – that's great!

**D**  I love swiming. I meets my friends Holly and Cameron and we walk to the swimming pool. We are in a swimming team On Saturday, we swim in the morning from nine to twelve o'clock. Sometimes we has a swimming competition in the afternoon.

**E**  It's April, because my birthday is in april. I also like April because I love spring. I usually cycle a lot in spring because the weather is nice.

**3** There are twelve mistakes in the answers to the questionnaire. Find and underline:

1  one more mistake in paragraph A
2  two mistakes in paragraph B
3  three mistakes in paragraph C
4  four mistakes in paragraph D
5  one mistake in paragraph E

**4** Match the mistakes in the answers to the questionnaire to the types of mistake. Write:
S for spelling        P for punctuation
G for grammar      C for capital letters

**5** Correct the mistakes in the answers to the questionnaire.

1  .......~~it~~.............. it's ..........
2  ..................................
3  ..................................
4  ..................................
5  ..................................
6  ..................................
7  ..................................
8  ..................................
9  ..................................
10  ..................................
11  ..................................
12  ..................................

---

### WRITING GUIDE

■ **Task**  Write your answers to the questionnaire in exercise 2.

■ **Ideas**  Answer the questions and make notes.
   Question 1:  Who do you do the sport with? What do you do?
   Question 2:  Why is it a good month? What is special about it? What do you do in that month?
   Question 3:  Why do you like that season? What makes it special? What do you do?
   Question 4:  What do you like about this book? When do you read it?
   Question 5:  Why do you like the character? Why are they special?

■ **Plan**  Use the answers to the questionnaire as a model. Organize your ideas into paragraphs.
   Paragraph 1:  What's your favourite sport?
   Paragraph 2:  What's your favourite month of the year?
   Paragraph 3:  What's your favourite season?
   Paragraph 4:  What's your favourite book?
   Paragraph 5:  Who's your favourite cartoon character?

■ **Write**  Write your answers to the questionnaire. Use your notes and plan to help you.

■ **Check**  Check the following points:
   ■ spelling
   ■ grammar: present simple affirmative and negative
   ■ punctuation
   ■ capital letters

# Progress check Unit 1

| A Breakfast in space | Mark (1–3) | How can I improve? |
|---|---|---|
| 1 Name three things astronauts do on the space station every day. | | |
| I can understand a text about a daily routine. | | |
| 2 Name five things that you do every day. | | |
| I can talk about my daily routine. | | |
| 3 What do you do at the weekend / on Friday / in summer? | | |
| I can use prepositions of time to talk about when I do things. | | |

| B Bright and early | Mark (1–3) | How can I improve? |
|---|---|---|
| 4 Name three things a friend does every day. | | |
| I can use the present simple with *he, she* and *it*. | | |
| 5 When do we use the present simple? | | |
| I can identify when to use the present simple. | | |
| 6 Rewrite the sentences in the negative form.<br>1 They watch films at the weekend.    2 She likes pizza. | | |
| I can use the present simple in affirmative and negative sentences. | | |

| C British schools | Mark (1–3) | How can I improve? |
|---|---|---|
| 7 What's the difference between a day school and a boarding school? | | |
| I can understand a text about British schools. | | |
| 8 Which school subjects use the objects below?<br>a calculator   b Spanish dictionary   c map | | |
| I can identify school subjects. | | |
| 9 Put the words in order to make questions. Write short answers that are true for you.<br>1 study / do / history / you ?<br>2 your friend / like / does / homework ? | | |
| I can use the present simple to ask and answer questions. | | |
| 10 What question words do we use to find out about<br>a things?   b time?   c people?   d numbers? | | |
| I can use question words with the present simple. | | |

| D Journeys to school | Mark (1–3) | How can I improve? |
|---|---|---|
| 11 Rewrite the sentences. Start each new sentence with *I go.*<br>1 I walk to school.    2 I cycle to my friend's house. | | |
| I can talk about transport and journeys. | | |
| 12 Give two affirmative and two negative classroom instructions. | | |
| I can understand classroom instructions. | | |

| E A questionnaire | Mark (1–3) | How can I improve? |
|---|---|---|
| 13 Which of the following needs a capital letter?<br>■ place names ■ months ■ seasons ■ days of the week<br>■ nationalities | | |
| I can use capital letters correctly. | | |
| 14 Answer the questions.<br>1 Who's your favourite actor?   2 What's your favourite song? | | |
| I can complete a questionnaire. | | |
| 15 Write three questions you want to ask a teenager from the USA. | | |
| I can write a questionnaire. | | |

# 2 Time out

## Vocabulary Cycling in the desert

### V Free-time activities

**1 Complete the sentences with the words below.**

■ acting ■ painting ■ playing computer games
■ playing the drums ■ rock climbing ■ ~~swimming~~

1 I'm not really into sport, but I like ..........swimming.......... in the pool with my friends.
2 Kitty is in a rock group. She likes ..........................
and singing.
3 My friends and I are into ..........................,
especially simulation games like *SimCity*.
4 In the holidays, George's family go to Scotland. They like .......................... in the mountains.
5 I'm artistic. I love drawing and .......................... .
6 I enjoy ........................... My favourite subject at school is drama.

**2 Write the free-time activities next to the clues. Use the words below.**

■ cooking ■ dancing ■ ~~drawing~~ ■ painting
■ playing tennis ■ singing ■ skateboarding

1 It's artistic. You use a pencil. ..........drawing..........
2 It's musical. You don't need a musical instrument. ..........................
3 It's something you do with food. ..........................
4 It's a sport. My favourite players are Roger Federer and Andy Murray. ..........................
5 You move to music. ..........................
6 You do this in special parks or in the street. You go fast! ..........................
7 It's artistic. You use paint. ..........................

### V insight Likes and dislikes

**3 Choose the correct words to complete the text.**

Jack ¹enjoys / hates all sports! He's really ²interested / into cycling (he goes everywhere on his bike), and he ³doesn't like / likes playing tennis with his friends at the weekend. Josh ⁴likes / hates sport. He doesn't do a lot of exercise! He's not ⁵enjoy / interested in tennis or football, but he ⁶likes / into skateboarding. Josh is ⁷interested in / enjoys music. He ⁸loves / doesn't playing the drums. He's also ⁹into / interested art and he ¹⁰isn't interested in / loves photography.

**4 Rewrite the sentences. Replace the words in bold with their antonyms.**

1 Jack **enjoys** skateboarding.
Jack doesn't enjoy skateboarding.
2 I **love** dancing.
..........................
3 They **aren't interested in** cooking.
..........................
4 Dad **dislikes** my music.
..........................
5 Kelly **is into** sport.
..........................
6 I **don't enjoy** playing computer games.
..........................
7 We're **interested in** photography.
..........................
8 I **like** playing tennis.
..........................

### V Sports

**5 Complete the table with the sports below. Some sports go in more than one category.**

■ aerobics ■ archery ■ athletics ■ badminton
■ ~~basketball~~ ■ canoeing ■ cricket ■ gymnastics ■ hockey
■ karate ■ rugby ■ running ■ ~~sailing~~ ■ skiing ■ ~~volleyball~~

| Ball sports |
| --- |
| basketball, .........., .........., .........., .......... |
| **Team sports** |
| volleyball, .........., .........., .......... |
| **Individual sports** |
| sailing, .........., .........., .........., .........., .........., .........., .......... |

**6 CHALLENGE!** Look at the free-time activities in the table in exercise 5. Do you like these activities? Write a sentence for eight free-time activities using *love, like, be into, enjoy* or *be interested in* in the affirmative or negative.

1 ..........................
2 ..........................
3 ..........................
4 ..........................
5 ..........................
6 ..........................
7 ..........................
8 ..........................

# Vocabulary and grammar  Healthy living

## Adverbs of frequency

**1** Put the words in order to make sentences.

1 often / go / after / cycling / school / I
I often go cycling after school.

2 don't / often / we / TV / watch

3 Jade / does / aerobics / always / Tuesday / on

4 never / homework / I / do / at the weekend

5 usually / hungry / is / after / training / Tom

6 meets / after / school / usually / Kelly / he

7 sometimes / plays / dad / the guitar / my

8 bored / often / I / on / am / Sunday

**2** Study a triathlete's training schedule. Write answers to the questions below using the correct adverbs of frequency.

|         | Morning | Afternoon |
|---------|---------|-----------|
| Monday    | run   | swim  |
| Tuesday   | run   | gym   |
| Wednesday | run   | cycle |
| Thursday  | swim  | run   |
| Friday    | cycle | cycle |
| Saturday  | run   | gym   |
| Sunday    | relax! |       |

1 How often does she go running in the morning?
(usually / always)
She usually goes running in the morning.

2 How often does she go to the gym on Sunday?
(never / sometimes)

3 How often does she go swimming in the afternoon?
(usually / not often)

4 How often does she go to the gym in the afternoon?
(never / sometimes)

5 How often does she relax on Sunday?
(always / often)

## V Sports collocations: play, go, do

**3** Complete the advert with *play*, *go* or *do*.

Action Camps UK

# Action Camps UK

All our camps have indoor and outdoor sports facilities. You can:

| 1 | play | badminton | 5 | | rugby |
| 2 | | karate | 6 | | running |
| 3 | | cricket | 7 | | basketball |
| 4 | | hockey | 8 | | aerobics |

Westbourne Camp is next to the sea. At this camp you can: 9 ............... canoeing, 10 ............... sailing and 11 ............... volleyball.

Stanford Camp specializes in Olympic sports. Here you can: 12 ............... athletics, 13 ............... archery and 14 ............... gymnastics.

New for this summer – an indoor ski slope, so you can 15 ............... skiing.

**4** Which sport in each group cannot be used with the verbs?

| 1 | do   | volleyball | karate     | archery    |
| 2 | play | badminton  | cricket    | canoeing   |
| 3 | go   | sailing    | hockey     | skiing     |
| 4 | do   | aerobics   | gymnastics | rugby      |
| 5 | go   | running    | canoeing   | basketball |

**5** CHALLENGE! Write sentences that are true for you. Use *play*, *go* or *do* and adverbs of frequency.

1 I / dancing / with / my friends

2 my parents / skiing

3 my best friend / basketball / at school

4 my friends / karate / after school

5 I / swimming / at the weekend

6 My friends and I / volleyball / at the sports centre

# Vocabulary and grammar  Making music

## V  Musical instruments

**1**  Which instrument in each group is the odd one out?

| | | | |
|---|---|---|---|
| **1** saxophone | clarinet | (piano) | trumpet |
| **2** violin | keyboards | cello | guitar |
| **3** piano | drums | keyboards | flute |
| **4** flute | guitar | clarinet | trumpet |

**2**  Write the instruments next to the clues. Use the words in exercise 1.

1  This instrument is similar to a violin. ........*cello*...........
2  This instrument is similar to a clarinet. Jazz musicians play this instrument. .................................
3  This instrument is similar to a piano. It's black and white. .................................
4  People play these instruments with their hands only.
....................................................................
....................................................................
5  People play these instruments with their mouth and hands.
....................................................................
....................................................................

**3**  Replace the words in bold with their antonyms.

It's always very **¹noisy** at our Saturday drama club. We start with the **²usual** activity of warming up our voices – we sing! Our singing is very **³good**. We sing **⁴the same** songs every week. After that we go on stage and we practise acting. We've got **⁵a new** show to practise at the moment. It's **⁶easy** to remember all the words!

## can / can't for ability

**4**  Choose the correct words.

1  He can / (Can he) play the piano?
2  We can **sing** / **to sing**.
3  John **can to** / **can** speak Spanish.
4  You **can't** / **don't can** ride a bike.
5  Can **dance you** / **you dance**?
6  My sister **doesn't can** / **can't** play the guitar.
7  They can **swimming** / **swim**.
8  Mum can't **drive** / **to drive**.

**5**  Study the information and write sentences.

| | Act | Dance | Sing | Cook | Draw |
|---|---|---|---|---|---|
| Abbie | ✔ | ✔ | ✗ | ✗ | ✗ |
| Ryan | ✔ | ✗ | ✔ | ✗ | ✔ |

1  Abbie / act / but / sing
   *Abbie can act, but she can't sing.*
2  Ryan / sing / but / Abbie / sing
   ....................................................................
3  Abbie / Ryan / cook
   ....................................................................
4  Abbie / dance / but / Ryan / dance
   ....................................................................
5  Ryan / draw / but / Abbie / draw
   ....................................................................

**6**  Complete the article with the words below. Add *can / can't* to the verbs.

■ dance ■ drums ■ not play ■ not speak ■ play ■ read
■ sing ■ ~~understand~~ ■ violin ■ watch

An amazing person – قرصيدص الل
incroyable
невероятный
increíble
amazing
形容词

**Mabou Loiseau**

Mabou Loiseau is five-years-old. She
¹ ....*can understand*.... seven languages – French, Creole, English, Spanish, Mandarin, Arabic and Russian! She speaks French, English and Creole at home because these are her parents' languages, but her parents ² .................... the other languages. Mabou has lessons in those languages. She ³ .................... songs in Spanish and she ⁴ .................... stories in Russian.

Mabou is also a musician. She ⁵ .................... six musical instruments. She plays classical instruments like the piano and the ⁶ .................... . She also plays the guitar. She plays a noisy instrument, too – the ⁷ ....................! Her mother ⁸ .................... the drums, but her father can play. In fact, he's her drums teacher!

Lots of little girls enjoy dancing. Mabou loves it! She ⁹ .................... very well. She goes to ballet lessons every week.

She's a very unusual child and I think she's incredible!

**7**  CHALLENGE!  Write about someone you know. Choose a famous person, a friend or a family member. Write about three things they can do and three things they cannot do.

1  ....................................................................
2  ....................................................................
3  ....................................................................
4  ....................................................................
5  ....................................................................
6  ....................................................................

## V Languages

**1** **Match 1–6 to a–f to make sentences.**

1 In Portugal and Brazil, people speak ...f...
2 I work in Egypt now. I speak .........
3 I live in Beijing, so I speak .........
4 In Argentina, Chile and Mexico, people speak .........
5 In New Zealand, people speak .........
6 His mother is from the Netherlands, so he speaks .........

a Arabic.
b Spanish.
c English.
d Dutch.
e Chinese.
f ~~Portuguese.~~

## Adverbs of manner

**2** **Complete the text with adverbs of manner. Change the adjectives below into adverbs.**

■ bad ■ ~~easy~~ ■ good ■ hard ■ quick ■ quiet

Leila Baxter is a journalist and she travels to different countries for her work. 'I learn languages
¹ ......easily......,' she explains. At the moment, she lives in Egypt. 'I can speak Arabic ² ........................ . My mother is Moroccan and we speak Arabic together.'

'My job is exciting. I find out about people's lives and write reports. I write ³ ........................ . A slow journalist isn't very useful! I have one problem, I spell ⁴ ........................! I can't live without my dictionary.

'I work very ⁵ ........................ . That's OK because I love my job, but sometimes I like to sit ⁶ ........................ and read. Everybody needs to relax!'

**3** **Rewrite the sentences using the adverb form of the adjectives in brackets.**

1 My brother sings. (bad)
  My brother sings badly.
2 I speak. (quick)
  ....................................................
3 Do you play your violin? (quiet)
  ....................................................
4 I can't play the keyboards. (good)
  ....................................................
5 Athletes train every day. (hard)
  ....................................................
6 You run. (slow)
  ....................................................
7 Can you learn new dances? (easy)
  ....................................................

## Requests with *can* and *could*

**4** **🔊 3.04 Listen and match the dialogues to pictures A–D.**

Dialogue 1: .........       Dialogue 3: .........
Dialogue 2: .........       Dialogue 4: .........

**5** **Tick the pictures in exercise 4 in which the responses to requests are 'yes'.**

**6** **🔊 3.04 Put the words in the correct order to make requests. Match them to responses a–d. Then listen again and check your answers.**

1 you / me, / please / help / Could ?
  ....................................................
2 kitchen / me / a / get / Can / from / drink / you / the ?
  ....................................................
3 a / Can / get / pizza, / me / please / you ?
  ....................................................
4 you / Could / the / please / window, / open ?
  ....................................................

a Yes, of course. Here you are.
b No, sorry. I can't. It doesn't open.
c Yes, of course. Where's your car?
d No, sorry. I can't. I want to work. You can get a drink.

**7** **CHALLENGE! Choose two pictures and write a dialogue for each one. Use requests and responses.**

**1** What are your favourite free-time activities? Put the activities in order from 1 to 8 (1 = your favourite activity, 8 the activity you don't like).

.......... listening to music
.......... meeting friends
.......... playing a musical instrument
.......... playing computer games
.......... doing sport
.......... reading
.......... using the internet
.......... watching TV

**2** Read the article. Match headings A–E to paragraphs 1–5.

**A** Sport is popular, too
**B** Do computers control teenagers' lives?
**C** A good mix
**D** What other activities do teenagers like?
**E** ~~Parents' worries~~

**3** Read the article again and choose the correct answers.

**1** Many parents
  a don't want their children to use computers.
  (b) think their children are only interested in computers and TV.
  c worry about teenagers making friends on the internet.
  d think computers help teenagers with homework.

**2** What is over 40% of teenagers' favourite activity?
  a using the internet
  b watching TV
  c meeting friends
  d watching films

**3** What do almost 50% of teenagers like?
  a reading
  b sport
  c meeting friends
  d walking

**4** Many teenagers
  a play an instrument.
  b sing.
  c buy music online.
  d listen to music.

**5** Most teenagers
  a don't often do their homework.
  b do lots of activities in their free time.
  c watch TV with their parents.
  d only spend time on their computers.

**6** The writer of the article thinks
  a computers control teenagers' lives.
  b computers can teach teenagers a lot.
  c teenagers have a good mix of using computers and doing other activities.
  d people can't live without computers.

# Free time = screen time?

With computers and TVs in their bedrooms, and the internet on their mobile phones, do today's young people spend all of their free time looking at a screen?

5 **¹ Parents' worries**

A lot of adults worry about their children watching TV and playing computer games. Some think that computer games stop their children doing sports, making new friends 10 or doing homework.

**2**

Computers are part of everyday life. As well as playing computer games, teenagers use computers in their free time to buy 15 music, watch films and go on social-networking sites. However, computers don't control teenagers' lives. In fact, a recent study about European teenagers says that going online isn't the favourite 20 activity of many teenagers – only 22% are really into it. About the same number – 20% – prefer watching TV. However, over 40% of teenagers say their favourite activity is meeting friends.

**4** Study the highlighted words in the article. Then match the highlighted words to the words or phrases below.

1 but ............... *however* ...............
2 in addition to .........................................
3 it's true that .........................................
4 25% .........................................
5 using the internet .........................................
6 for example .........................................

**5** Rewrite the sentences using the words in brackets.

1 My favourite sport is swimming. It's true that I love it! (in fact)
   *My favourite sport is swimming. In fact, I love it!*

2 The children play football and hockey. (as well as)
   .........................................

3 Liam loves art, but he can't paint. (however)
   .........................................

4 He spends 25% of his time playing computer games. (a quarter)
   .........................................

5 I use the internet every evening. (go online)
   .........................................

6 I love modern languages, for example, French. (such as)
   .........................................

25
3
.........................................

Almost half of all European teenagers say sport is their favourite activity. They like to go cycling, go walking, go swimming, or they play team games, such as football.

30
4
.........................................

Reading – books, magazines, blogs – is the favourite activity of a quarter of teenagers. Many teenagers are into music. About 60% love listening to music and about 5% can
35 sing or play an instrument.

5
.........................................

For some teenagers, computers and TV are very important. But most teenagers spend their free time doing different activities.
40 So, their parents don't need to panic!

**6** **CHALLENGE!** Write a paragraph about your free time. Use the phrases in exercise 4 and answer the following questions.

- What is your favourite free-time activity?
- How often do you use your computer?
- What do you use the computer for?
- How often do you watch TV?
- Do your parents worry about what you do in your free time? Why / why not?
- Do you think you spend your free time well? Why / why not?

**1** Complete 1–7 in the letter with the words and phrases below.

- 12 Manchester Drive ■ Dear Charlie ■ Westcliff ■ ~~Essex~~
- 24 October, 2013 ■ SS0 9YH ■ Best wishes ■ Gemma

1 ....................................................

2 ....................................................

Essex

3 ....................................................

4 ....................................................

5 ....................................................

Thank you for your letter. I don't live in a city. I live in a town, so that's different from you! Is it nice in your city? I live with my mum, my dad ᵃ............. my sister, Josie, ᵇ............. I haven't got a pet. You're lucky to have a cat. I love cats!

Your school is very big – 1,300 students is a lot! I go to Belfairs High School, ᶜ............. it's not a very big school – there are 750 students. The students in my class are very friendly. My favourite subject at school is modern languages. I can speak English ᵈ............. Spanish. I also enjoy science and maths. I don't like PE. I'm not very good at team sports! So we are different! It's great that you are in your school football team.

At the weekend, I like meeting my friends. We usually go to the cinema. My favourite films are the Twilight films, too! Sometimes on Sunday I go swimming ᵉ............. cycling with my best friend, Megan. I like doing sport at the weekend, ᶠ............. not team sports at school!

Write again soon!

6 ....................................................

7 ....................................................

## Linking words: *and, but, or*

**2** Complete a–f in the letter in exercise 1 with *and, but* or *or*.

**3** Choose the correct linking word to complete the sentences.

1 I love drawing, **and** / **but** I don't like painting.
2 I've got a dog **and** / **or** a cat.
3 At the weekend, I usually play football **or** / **but** basketball.
4 Do you prefer acting **but** / **or** dancing?
5 I love cycling, **and** / **but** I can't cycle now, because I haven't got a bike.
6 I'm good at languages. I can speak English, Spanish **and** / **but** French.

## WRITING GUIDE

- **Task** Imagine you are Charlie. Write Charlie's first letter to Gemma.

- **Ideas** Which paragraph has the information below?

  1 Gemma's weekend     1 / 2 / 3
  2 Gemma's family       1 / 2 / 3
  3 Gemma's school       1 / 2 / 3

  **What information do you think is in Charlie's first letter to Gemma? Use the information in Gemma's letter to answer the questions.**

  1 Gemma lives in a town. Where does Charlie live?

  ....................................................

  2 What type of pet has Charlie got?

  ....................................................

  3 Does Charlie go to a big school or a small school?

  ....................................................

  4 Gemma's school has 750 students. How many students go to Charlie's school?

  ....................................................

  5 What subjects does Charlie like?

  ....................................................

  6 What sport is Charlie good at?

  ....................................................

  7 What are Charlie's favourite films?

  ....................................................

- **Plan** Use Gemma's letter as a model. Organize your ideas into paragraphs.

  Paragraph 1:  Write about Charlie's town / city, family and pet(s).
  Paragraph 2:  Describe Charlie's school and favourite subjects.
  Paragraph 3:  Describe what Charlie usually does at weekends.

- **Write** Write Charlie's letter to Gemma. Use your notes and plan to help you. Remember to use the linking words *and, but* and *or*.

- **Check** Check the following points:
  - spelling
  - grammar
  - punctuation
  - linking words *and, but* and *or*
  - all the information about Charlie
  - different paragraphs for different topics

# Progress check Unit 2

Read 1–13 and evaluate your learning in Unit 2. Give yourself a mark from 1 to 3. How can you improve?
**1** I can't do this.   **2** I have some problems with this.   **3** I can do this well.

| A Cycling in the desert | Mark (1–3) | How can I improve? |
|---|---|---|
| **1** Name six free-time activities. | | |
| I can understand a text about free-time activities. | | |
| **2** Give three phrases to describe likes and three phrases to describe dislikes. | | |
| I can express my likes and dislikes. | | |

| B Healthy living | Mark (1–3) | How can I improve? |
|---|---|---|
| **3** Name three team sports and three individual sports. | | |
| I can talk about different sports. | | |
| **4** Add *play*, *go* or *do* to the following sports.<br>a rugby   b aerobics   c running | | |
| I can use the correct verb with sport nouns. | | |
| **5** Complete the table with adverbs of frequency.<br>always ............ sometimes ............ | | |
| I can use adverbs of frequency. | | |

| C Making music | Mark (1–3) | How can I improve? |
|---|---|---|
| **6** Write sentences with *can* in the affirmative (✔), negative (✘) or question form (**?**).<br>a Mia / ride a bike ✔   b Adam / dance ✘   c Alice / swim **?** | | |
| I can use *can* / *can't* to talk about ability. | | |
| **7** Write the antonyms for the adjectives.<br>a noisy   b usual   c good   d different   e new   f easy | | |
| I can recognize and use antonyms. | | |

| D Superheroes | Mark (1–3) | How can I improve? |
|---|---|---|
| **8** Do the languages for the countries end in *-ish*, *-ian*, *-ese* or *-ch*?<br>a France   b Egypt   c China   d Poland   e Italy | | |
| I can recognize spelling patterns. | | |
| **9** Change the adjectives into adverbs and write a sentence with each adverb.<br>a bad   b quick   c quiet   d easy   e hard   f good | | |
| I can change adjectives into adverbs of manner. | | |
| **10** Write a request with *can* and a request with *could*. | | |
| I can make and respond to requests. | | |

| E An informal letter | Mark (1–3) | How can I improve? |
|---|---|---|
| **11** Answer the questions about informal letters.<br>1 Where do you put your address and the date?<br>2 How do you start a letter?   3 How do you end a letter? | | |
| I can write a letter correctly. | | |
| **12** Complete the sentences with linking words.<br>1 I love singing ............ dancing.<br>2 I'm not into playing tennis, ............ I like watching it.<br>3 What pet have you got? Is it a cat ............ a dog? | | |
| I can use linking words in a sentence. | | |
| **13** What topics can you include in an informal letter to a penpal? | | |
| I can plan an informal letter. | | |

**Progress check Unit 2   27**

# 3 Home and away

## Vocabulary House of the future

**V** **Inside and outside the home**

**1** Write the places next to the clues. Use the words below.

■ bathroom ■ ~~bedroom~~ ■ garden ■ kitchen ■ living room

1 You sleep in here. ........ bedroom ........
2 You cook in here. ..........................
3 You have a shower in here. ..........................
4 You relax and watch TV in here. ..........................
5 This is outside. ..........................

**2** Put the words below in the correct category.

■ ceiling ■ door ■ ~~floor~~ ■ roof ■ wall ■ window

| Inside | Outside | Inside and outside |
|--------|---------|--------------------|
| floor  |         |                    |
|        |         |                    |
|        |         |                    |

**V** **In the home**

**3** Which item in each group is the odd one out?

1 bedroom
  wardrobe  (bidet)  bedside table  chest of drawers
2 bathroom
  bidet  washbasin  mirror  freezer
3 living room
  fireplace  fridge  armchair  carpet
4 kitchen
  freezer  washing machine  dishwasher  stairs

**V** **insight** Prepositions of place

**4** Look at the picture. Choose the correct prepositions of place to complete the description.

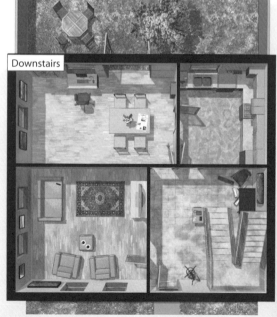

This is my house. I live here with my parents. **¹On / Under / In front of** the house is a small garden. The first room on the left is the living room. **²In front of / Behind / Between** the living room is the dining room. The kitchen is **³next to / behind / on** the dining room. The back garden is in **⁴front of / next to / behind** the kitchen.

My bedroom is upstairs. It's a very small room. There's a big cupboard **⁵on / between / behind** my parents' bedroom and the bathroom.

The bathroom is **⁶next to / opposite / on** my bedroom. **⁷Near / In / On** the bathroom, there is a shower, a toilet and a washbasin.

I love our back garden. We've got a table and chairs outside – they are **⁸near / between / under** a beautiful tree.

**5** Answer the questions about the house in exercise 4.

1 What is opposite the TV? ........ the sofa ........
2 What is on the table in the dining room? ..........................
3 What is under the window in the kitchen? ..........................
4 What is opposite the door in the kitchen? ..........................
5 What is in front of the desk in the small bedroom?

  ..........................
6 What is opposite the bed in the parents' room?

  ..........................
7 What is in front of the bed in the parents' room?

  ..........................
8 What is between the shower and the toilet in the bathroom? ..........................

**6** **CHALLENGE!** Write a description of your bedroom. Include prepositions of place and names of furniture. Use the following questions to help you plan your description.

■ Is your bedroom big or small?
■ What colour are the walls, ceiling and floor?
■ Have you got any posters on the walls?
■ What furniture have you got?
■ Where is all the furniture in your room?
■ What is your favourite thing in your bedroom?
■ What can you see out of the window?

## there is / there are with some / any

**1  Match 1–6 to a–f to make sentences.**

| | | | |
|---|---|---|---|
| 1 | There is | a | any cupboards in this room. |
| 2 | There are | b | any rooms for five people? |
| 3 | There isn't | c | a chair for you. Please sit down. |
| 4 | There aren't | d | a TV in the hotel room? |
| 5 | Is there | e | some good hotels here. |
| 6 | Are there | f | a bath, but there is a shower. |

**2  Complete the sentences with *a, an, some* or *any*.**

1  There's .......**a**....... DVD player in this room.
2  There aren't ..................................... tennis courts.
3  Is there ..................................... park for children to play in?
4  There are ..................................... lovely beaches near here.
5  There isn't ..................................... hotel in this street.
6  Are there ..................................... shops open today?
7  There aren't ..................................... nice cafés near the hotel.
8  Is there ..................................... unusual place to stay?

**3  Study the hotel information and write sentences. Use affirmative, negative and question forms of *there is / there are*. Then write short answers.**

# Ice Hotel Quebec

## Rooms

 36 rooms ✔

- Each room has a bed and some ice shelves!
- 🚻 toilet? ✘
- 🚿 shower? ✘ (There are bathrooms in a different building.)
- 🔥 fireplace ✘
- ☕ café ✔
- 🍽 restaurant ✘
- 🏊 swimming pool ✘

## Activities

- ⛷ skiing ✔
- 🏂 snowboarding ✔
- 🚶 walking ✔

1  café / ?
......................**Is there a café?**..........................**Yes, there is.**......
2  swimming pool / ?
.................................................................................
3  toilets / in the bedrooms / ?
.................................................................................
4  restaurant / ?
.................................................................................
5  shelves / in the bedrooms / ?
.................................................................................
6  activities / ?
.................................................................................
7  fireplace / ?
.................................................................................
8  bed / in each bedroom / ?
.................................................................................

**4  Complete the telephone conversation with *there is / isn't, there are / aren't* and *a, some* or *any*.**

Bella  Hi Amy, it's Bella!
Amy  Hey! How are you? What's your campsite like?
Bella  Not good! [1] ......**There isn't a**...... swimming pool!
Amy  Oh dear. [2] ..................................... beach?
Bella  Yes, there is, but it's far away. [3] .....................................
bus in the morning, but [4] .....................................
bus in the afternoon.
Amy  That's annoying! What's your caravan like?
Bella  It's OK. There are four beds and
[5] ..................................... chairs and a table.
Amy  [6] ..................................... TV?
Bella  No, there isn't!
Amy  [7] ..................................... games?
Bella  No, there aren't! I'm bored!
Amy  [8] ..................................... nice people?
Bella  [9] ..................................... family next to us.
[10] ..................................... boy – the same age as me.
Amy  Oh yes? Is he friendly?
Bella  Yes, he's nice. He likes cycling and
[11] ..................................... bikes we can use.
Amy  Well, maybe your holiday isn't bad after all!

**5  CHALLENGE!  Imagine you are on holiday here. Write an email to your friend. Describe what there is / isn't in the wigwam. Use the words below or your own ideas.**

■ bath ■ bed ■ ceiling ■ chair ■ electricity ■ floor ■ roof
■ rug ■ table ■ window

## V Around town

**1** Look at the map. Answer the questions using the words below.

- bank ~~bus stop~~ café museum restaurant theatre
- leisure centre shopping centre train station

1 What's in front of the shopping centre? __bus stop__
2 What's between the restaurant and the cinema?
  ...................................................
3 What's between the .................... and the
  ...................? a leisure centre
4 What's in front of the theatre? ....................
5 What's behind the theatre? ....................
6 What's next to the museum? ....................
7 What's in the park? ....................
8 What's opposite the police station? ....................

## Possessive 's

**2** Complete the second sentences so that they have in the same meaning as the first sentences. Use possessive 's.

1 I've got a letter for Leo.
  I've got __Leo's letter.__
2 This library ticket belongs to Clara.
  This is ....................
3 This shop sells clothes for men.
  This shop sells ....................
4 This house belongs to my grandmother.
  This is ....................
5 Sian is a friend of my sister.
  Sian is ....................
6 These are the pictures of the children.
  These are ....................

## *whose* and possessive pronouns

**3** Replace the words in bold with possessive pronouns.

A Ruth    Whose is this bag ?
  Jen     I don't know. Adam, is it **¹your bag**?

Adam    No, it isn't **²my bag**. I think it's Sara's bag.
Claire  Yes, it is **³her bag**.

B Sally    Look at this old photo of our town.
  Freddie  Is that Scott's house?
  Sally    No, it isn't **⁴his house**. I think it's Jake and
           Alice's house.
  Harry    Yes, it is **⁵their house**. And look at the photo
           of the school.
  Sally    It's **⁶our school**! It's very different!

C Woman        Excuse me, boys. Whose are those bikes?
  Brad and Kai  We don't know. They aren't **⁷our bikes**.
  Jim          What about the girls in the skatepark? Are
               they **⁸their bikes**?
  Brad         Hey, girls!
  Lisa and Amy  What?
  Brad         Are those **⁹your bikes**?
  Lisa         Yes, they're **¹⁰our bikes**.

**4** Choose the correct words to complete the dialogue.

Mum      This is a great restaurant. Look, here's our food.
Waiter   Hello, everybody! OK, I've got a margarita
         pizza …
Mum      That's **¹my /(mine)/ it's**, thank you.
Waiter   And, a pepperoni pizza …
Mum      Er, that's **²yours / hers / mine**, Dad, right?
Grandad  Yes, that's right.
Mum      It's my dad **³his / he / 's** pizza.
Waiter   OK. Here you are, sir. And two mushroom
         pizzas.
Lily and Grace   They're **⁴ours / theirs / mines**.
Waiter   OK. Here you are girls. So, **⁵whose / who's /
         who** pizza is this? It's a margarita with extra
         ham.
Mum      Jake, it's **⁶his / you / yours**.
Waiter   Enjoy your meal!
Mum      Thank you. Jake, your pizza looks delicious.
Jake     It does. But it's small!
Grandad  Small!? I think the pizzas are very big! I can't
         eat all of **⁷my / mine / theirs**!
Jake     Mum, can I have some of grandad **⁸'s / mine /
         his** pizza?
Mum      I don't know. Dad, is your pizza too big? Can
         Jake have some of **⁹yours / his / ours**?
Grandad  Yes, of course. Good idea!

**5** **CHALLENGE!** Write a paragraph about where you live. Use your answers to the following questions to help you plan your paragraph.

- What is your favourite place in your town / city? Why?
- Is there somewhere you can do sport?
- Where can you go shopping?
- What is your parents' favourite place?
- Is there a park?
- Is there a library? How often do you go there?
- Is there a station? Do you often travel by train?
- What doesn't your town / city have? Is this good or bad? Why?

## V City to country

**1** Write the places next to the clues. Use the words below.

■ city ■ city centre ■ countryside ■ suburb ■ town ■ village

1 It's very big. It has universities, shopping centres, leisure centres, parks, libraries and lots of flats and houses. _____city_____

2 It's big. It often has a shopping centre, a leisure centre and a library. It usually has a station, but not always. _____

3 It's small. It doesn't have a lot of houses. There are usually one or two shops. _____

4 This is a green place. There aren't any towns or cities. _____

5 It's around the outside of a city. A lot of people live here. _____

6 In this part of a city there are usually banks, shopping centres and a station. _____

**2** Complete the text with the places in exercise 1. There is one word that you do not need.

Hi! My name's Alisha and I live in Sydney. It isn't the ¹ _____capital_____ of Australia (that's Canberra), but Sydney is a very big ² _____. Sydney's ³ _____ has got lots of shops, restaurants and museums. And the best thing about it? It's next to the sea! There are also two parks – Hyde Park and the Royal Botanic Gardens. There's also the famous Sydney Opera House!

I live outside the centre in a ⁴ _____ called Manly, but it is part of Sydney. I'm very lucky because Manly has got an amazing beach! I love swimming and surfing.

Thirty kilometres south of Sydney is the Royal National Park and fifty kilometres north are the Blue Mountains. These are both big areas. They're great for walking in. The ⁵ _____ in these places is amazing. My grandparents live near the Royal National Park in a ⁶ _____ called Helensburgh. I travel there by train from Sydney. It's got a library and some shops. I often visit the Park with my grandparents. We enjoy looking at Australian animals. What's my favourite? The koala!

## Asking for and giving directions

**3** 🌐 **3.05** Listen to the dialogue and answer the questions.

1 Where is Ben?
   a Green Street
   b the High Street
   c Summer Street

2 Where does he want to go?
   a the University
   b the Science Museum
   c the Art Museum

**4** 🌐 **3.05** Listen again. Follow the directions and draw the route.

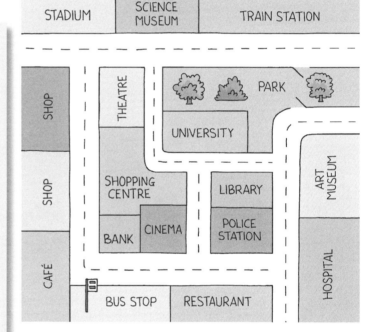

**5** 🌐 **3.05** Read the directions and number them in order to match the route. Then listen again and check.

...... That's Summer Street, it's opposite the restaurant.

...... Go straight up Summer Street to the university.

...... Stay on University Street, go past the park on your right.

...... Turn right down the High Street.

..1.. Cross the road.

...... Take the first road on the left, between the police station and the cinema.

...... The Science Museum is in front of you, next to the stadium.

...... At the end of the street, turn left onto University Street.

**6** **CHALLENGE!** Write a dialogue with directions for a different route to the Science Museum.

**1  Answer the questions.**

1  Do you share a bedroom?
2  Do you live in a house or a flat?
3  Do you want more space in your home?

**2  Match summary sentences A–E to paragraphs 1–4. There is one summary sentence that you do not need.**

A  One family explains their problem.
B  People need more space!
C  Using the cellar isn't a new idea.
D  Rooms under houses are also possible.
E  There are now three more rooms.

**3  Choose the correct options to complete the sentences.**

1  Many people in London want
   a  a new house.
   b  a big family.
   c  to live in a different city.
   d  more space.

2  A cellar is
   a  next to the house.
   b  behind the house.
   c  under the house.
   d  on the house.

3  Who doesn't share a room in the Dunsmore family?
   a  Matt
   b  Ben
   c  Mrs Dunsmore
   d  Sophie

4  Matt wants a place
   a  to listen to music.
   b  to spend time with friends.
   c  to do homework.
   d  to share with his brother.

5  The Dunsmore family's new rooms are
   a  in the garden.
   b  behind the garden.
   c  next to the garden.
   d  under the garden.

6  In Matt's new rooms, he can't
   a  cook meals.
   b  have a shower.
   c  sleep.
   d  study.

# Going down!

**1**

Eight million people live in London and a lot of them want more space to live in. Walk around the suburbs of London and what
5 can you see? Streets and streets of houses and flats. Many buildings have got windows in their roofs because people often create an extra room under the roof. For lots of families, there's a bedroom and sometimes
10 an extra bathroom in the attic of their house.

**2**

But people don't only go up, they also go down. Some old houses in London have a cellar. A cellar isn't usually a very nice room
15 – it's under the house and it can be cold and damp. However, builders can convert cellars into nice, warm rooms. The new room is often a kitchen or dining room. This isn't a very new idea, but having a room under
20 your *garden* is!

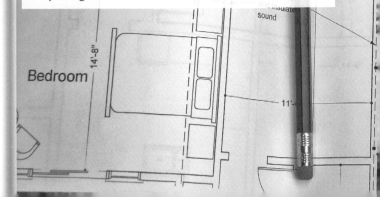

Bedroom  14'-8"

## 3

Underground living is one answer to space problems in London. Mr and Mrs Dunsmore in South London explain. 'Our house has
25 got three bedrooms and we've got three children – Matt (17), Sophie (15) and Ben (10). The boys share a room, but it's very cramped. Matt has got important exams next year, so he needs a peaceful place
30 to study. He doesn't want a 10-year-old with him.'

## 4

Whose idea is it to build under the garden? 'Mine!' smiles Mrs Dunsmore. 'The new
35 rooms are nearly finished. There's a bedroom, a toilet and a small kitchen with a sink, a cooker and a fridge.' And, how does Matt feel? 'I'm happy. It's cool!'

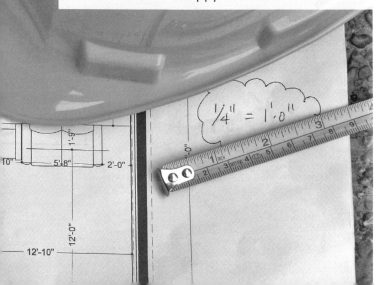

**4** Match the highlighted words in the text to definitions 1–6.

1 (verb) to use something with another person
......*share*......
2 (adjective) wet and cold ........................
3 (adjective) quiet ........................
4 (verb) make ........................
5 (adjective) very small and uncomfortable
........................
6 (verb) change, transform ........................

**5** Complete the sentences with the correct form of the words in exercise 4.

1 I work in the library because it's very ......*peaceful*...... and I don't like noise.
2 There's only one cola in the fridge – let's ........................ it.
3 Our bathroom is very ......................... It makes me feel cold!
4 My aunt is a designer. She ........................ beautiful clothes.
5 This children's robot ........................ into a car!
6 There isn't a lot of space in my bedroom. It's very ........................ .

**6** CHALLENGE! Imagine you and your family live in this underground house. Write a description of the house. Use prepositions of place and furniture words. Use the questions to help you plan your description.

- Where are the rooms?
- What is in the rooms?
- Who sleeps in each room?
- What is your favourite room? Why?

**1** Read the tourist guide. Match the parts of the tourist guide 1–6 to the information A–F.

| | |
|---|---|
| **1** first paragraph | **A** exciting activities |
| **2** first bullet | **B** introduction to the city |
| **3** second bullet | **C** a famous building |
| **4** third bullet | **D** relaxing activities |
| **5** fourth bullet | **E** typical British food |
| **6** final bullet | **F** views of the city |

# Day trip to Brighton

Brighton is a city on the south coast of the UK. It is famous for its past connections to King George IV (1762–1830) and the beautiful and unusual buildings from his time. Today it is home to a lot of artists and musicians. There are two universities in Brighton and it's very popular with young people.

• ¹.................... go to the Royal Pavilion – George IV's holiday home! The outside looks like an Indian palace. Inside you can see the King's dining room, living room and bedrooms. Have a drink and a cake in the Pavilion's café – it's got great views of the Pavilion gardens.

• ².................... walk down to Brighton's famous sea front. Take a ride in Brighton's wheel. Look at the views of the city, the sea and the pier.

• ³.................... find a restaurant on the beach and have some traditional British fish and chips for lunch.

• ⁴.................... visit Brighton Pier! Do you like exciting rides? This is the place for you! The pier has got lots of games and rides for you to enjoy!

• ⁵.................... explore the streets in The Laines. Here you can find interesting shops and there is a lot of street art. There are also a lot of cafes so it's a great place to have a snack and relax at the end of your busy day.

**V**  Sequencers

**2** Complete the tourist guide with the sequencers below. Sometimes more than one answer is possible.

■ after that ■ finally ■ first ■ next ■ then

**3** Underline the imperatives in the bullet points in the tourist guide.

## WRITING GUIDE

■ **Task**  Write a tourist guide for a city you know.

■ **Ideas**  Choose a city. Answer the questions and make notes.

**1** Where is it and what is it famous for?
**2** Are there any interesting buildings to visit?
**3** Where can you go to see views of the city?
**4** Where can you have breakfast, lunch and dinner?
**5** What exciting activities are there?
**6** What relaxing activities are there?

■ **Plan**  Organize your ideas into paragraphs. Use the Day trip to Brighton tourist guide to help you.

Introduction: information about the city
Bullet 1: interesting buildings
Bullet 2: views of the city
Bullet 3: where to eat
Bullet 4: exciting activities
Bullet 5: relaxing activities

■ **Write**  Write the tourist guide. Use your notes and plan to help you. Remember to use sequencers and imperatives.

■ **Check**  Check the following points:

■ spelling
■ grammar
■ punctuation
■ sequencers
■ imperatives
■ different bullet points for different topics

# Progress check Unit 3

Read 1–12 and evaluate your learning in Unit 3. Give yourself a mark from 1 to 3. How can you improve?
1 I can't do this.    2 I have some problems with this.    3 I can do this well.

| A  House of the future | Mark (1–3) | How can I improve? |
|---|---|---|
| 1  Where do you build an Earthship? | | |
| I can understand a text about houses of the future. | | |
| 2  Name a room that has got a dishwasher, a sink and a cooker in it. | | |
| I can talk about rooms and features in the home. | | |
| 3  Where are these things are in your living room? Use prepositions of place. <br> a sofa   b shelves   c armchair   d table | | |
| I can use prepositions of place to describe where things are. | | |

| B  Enjoy the view | Mark (1–3) | How can I improve? |
|---|---|---|
| 4  Give a sentence or question with the following words: <br> a some   b any   c an | | |
| I can use a / an, some and any. | | |
| 5  Write sentences using the correct form of there is / are and a / some or any. <br> a shutters / ?   b TV / ✔   c shelves / ✘ | | |
| I can write sentences using there is / there are with a / some / any. | | |
| 6  Name eight places in a town. | | |
| I can talk about places in a town. | | |

| C  Underground city | Mark (1–3) | How can I improve? |
|---|---|---|
| 7  Rewrite the sentences using 's. <br> 1  It's the bedroom of my brother. <br> 2  They are the toys of the children. | | |
| I can use the possessive 's. | | |
| 8  Replace the words in bold with possessive pronouns. <br> 1  It's **the girl's** bag. <br> 2  This is **me and my family's** house. | | |
| I can use possessive pronouns and whose. | | |

| D  Around town | Mark (1–3) | How can I improve? |
|---|---|---|
| 9  Give an example of the following places. <br> a a city   b a town   c a village | | |
| I can identify places where we live. | | |
| 10  Describe how to get from your school to a shop. | | |
| I can ask for and give directions. | | |

| E  A tourist guide | Mark (1–3) | How can I improve? |
|---|---|---|
| 11  Name four sequencers. | | |
| I can use sequencers in a tourist guide or text. | | |
| 12  Which places can you include in a tourist guide to where you live? | | |
| I can plan a tourist guide. | | |

# 4 The natural world

## Vocabulary It's wild!

### V The natural world

**1 Complete the crossword.**

**Across**
1 People play football on this green plant.
6 Something white or grey in the sky.
7 A beautiful and colourful part of a plant.
8 A desert plant.
9 The general name for a thing that grows in the ground.

**Down**
2 You can find this on a beach. You can build castles with it.
3 Birds live in this.
4 It's white and cold. You can ski on it.
5 A very high hill. You can find these in the Alps and Pyrenees.

### V Animals

**2 Write the animals next to the clues. Use the words below.**

■ butterfly ■ chicken ■ cow ■ eagle ■ elephant ■ giraffe
■ horse ■ monkey ■ pig ■ spider ■ tiger ■ whale

**Wild animals**
1 It can fly. It isn't a bird. It gets its food from flowers.
   _butterfly_
2 It lives in Africa. It's tall. It's brown and yellow.

3 It lives in Asia. It hunts. It's brown, orange and black.

4 It lives in the sea. It's big.
5 It likes sitting in trees, but it isn't a bird. It climbs and jumps from tree to tree.
6 It's got eight legs.
7 It's a bird. It flies a lot and it hunts.

8 It lives in Africa and Asia. It's very big. It's grey.

**Farm animals**
9 It's usually pink.
10 It's a bird. It doesn't fly a lot. It gives us eggs.

11 It eats grass. People ride these animals.
12 It eats grass. It's a big animal. It gives us milk.

### V Animal verbs

**3 Complete the sentences with the verbs below.**

■ bite ■ carry ■ dig ■ follow ■ hunt ■ look for ■ run away

1 Wolves __hunt__ in groups.
2 A chicken can't .................... from a fox.
3 Horses .................... people on their backs.
4 Some spiders .................... people.
5 Rabbits .................... holes to make homes.
6 Young animals usually .................... their mothers.
7 Monkeys .................... food in trees and plants.

**4 Complete the text with the words below.**

■ cactus ■ clouds ■ digs ■ flowers ■ look for
■ mountains ■ sand

The Sonoran Desert is a typical desert with high, rocky
¹ __mountains__ and hot
² .................... on the ground. It also has typical desert plants, such as the
³ ..................... It is dry and very hot here – about 45°C in the summer. But then the ⁴ .................... come and it starts to rain. After the rain, plants grow quickly and
⁵ .................... appear.

*Sonoran desert toad*

The rain is also good news for the Sonoran desert toad. This toad spends a lot of its life underground. When there isn't any water, it ⁶ .................... a hole in the ground and stays there. It only comes out of its hole when there is rain. This means that it sometimes stays underground for years!

What do the toads do when they come out of their holes? They eat! They ⁷ .................... food in the desert – they eat insects, spiders, even scorpions!

**5 CHALLENGE! Research the answers to questions 1–8 on the internet. Write a paragraph about the emperor penguin.**

1 Where do emperor penguins live?
2 How many eggs do females lay each year?
3 Where do females lay their eggs?
4 What do the females do after they lay their eggs?
5 Who carries the egg?
6 Do the males eat in winter?
7 When do the females return?
8 What do the males do next?

## V  Pets

**1** Write the pets next to the clues. Use the words below.

■ budgie ■ cat ■ dog ■ fish ■ guinea pig ■ hamster ■ lizard ■ mouse ■ parrot ■ rabbit ■ snake ■ tortoise

1 They are birds. ......budgie......, ....................

2 This animal isn't very fast! It can hide its head.
...............................

3 These small animals sometimes live in a special home inside people's houses. ...................., ....................

4 These animals live in the garden. Foxes try to eat them. ...................., ....................

5 One goes walking with people, the other can go out when it wants to. ...................., ....................

6 They swim and live in aquariums. ....................

7 In the wild, these animals live in the desert.
...................., ....................

## Present continuous

**2** Complete the telephone conversation with the present continuous form of the verbs in brackets.

Tom  Hi Mia! What ¹...are you doing... (you / do)?
².................... (you / do) your homework?

Mia  I ³.................... (not study). I ⁴....................
(watch) TV.

Tom  But there's a geography exam tomorrow!

Mia  I know, but this programme is about geography.
I ⁵.................... (learn) about the Sundarbans forest.

Tom  That's interesting.

Mia  It's amazing. The forest is the home of the Bengal tiger. There's a tiger on the TV now. It
⁶.................... (follow) a young deer. It
⁷.................... (not make) any noise. Oh no!

Tom  ⁸.................... (the tiger / chase) the deer?

Mia  No. The deer ⁹.................... (not run away). The
tiger ¹⁰.................... (bite) the deer. It's horrible!

Tom  Don't be silly. It's natural!

**3** Study the information about polar bears. Then complete the questions and write answers. Use the present continuous.

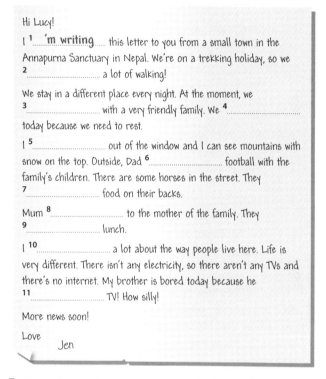

**A polar bear's year**

**Autumn**
• Female polar bears eat a lot. They also dig holes in the snow to sleep in.

**Winter**
• Male polar bears hunt for seals on the ice.
• Females sleep a lot. Cubs (babies) arrive.

**Spring**
• The cubs play together. Females teach their cubs how to hunt.

**Summer**
• Polar bears don't eat a lot. They can't hunt for seals. They need ice to walk on when they hunt and there isn't a lot of ice in summer.

It's January.
1 females / hunt / ?
Are the females hunting?            No, they aren't.

It's August.
2 bears / eat a lot / ?

It's April.
3 cubs / play / ?

It's September.
4 females / eat / ?

**4** Complete the letter with the present continuous form of the verbs below.

■ carry ■ cook ■ do ■ learn ■ look ■ not walk
■ not watch ■ play ■ stay ■ talk ■ write

Hi Lucy!

I ¹ ...'m writing... this letter to you from a small town in the Annapurna Sanctuary in Nepal. We're on a trekking holiday, so we ².................... a lot of walking!

We stay in a different place every night. At the moment, we ³.................... with a very friendly family. We ⁴....................
today because we need to rest.

I ⁵.................... out of the window and I can see mountains with snow on the top. Outside, Dad ⁶.................... football with the family's children. There are some horses in the street. They ⁷.................... food on their backs.

Mum ⁸.................... to the mother of the family. They
⁹.................... lunch.

I ¹⁰.................... a lot about the way people live here. Life is very different. There isn't any electricity, so there aren't any TVs and there's no internet. My brother is bored today because he ¹¹.................... TV! How silly!

More news soon!

Love
    Jen

**5** CHALLENGE!  Imagine you are in Australia on holiday. Write a letter to your friend. Use the following questions to help you plan your letter. Use the words below and your own ideas.

■ What are you and your family doing?
■ Where are you staying?
■ What are you looking at now?
■ What other animals can you see on your holiday?

■ drive / in Australia
■ stay / in caravan
■ meet / people
■ go / the beach
■ watch / animals
■ follow / kangaroo
■ not watch / TV
■ not sleep / in a bed
■ enjoy / the holiday
■ take / photos

## V Describing weather

**1 Match the adjectives to the temperatures below.**

■ cold ■ cool ■ hot ■ warm

1 35°C ...................................   3 10°C ...................................
2 –15°C ...................................   4 18°C ...................................

**2 Write the adjectives for each weather description.**

1 There aren't any clouds. It's hot. ....._sunny_.....
2 There's thunder, it's raining and there's a lot of wind.
   ...................................
3 Everything is white! ...................................
4 It isn't raining or snowing, but the sky isn't blue.
   ...................................
5 The clouds and the trees are moving. ...................................
6 People are carrying umbrellas. It's wet. ...................................

## V Adjective suffix: -y

**3 Rewrite the sentences. Change the words in bold to the form in brackets.**

1 There are some **clouds**. (adjective)
  It's _cloudy_ ...................................
2 It's **snowy** in Prague. (noun)
  There's ...................................
3 There's a lot of **wind** in the desert. (adjective)
  It's ...................................
4 It's **rainy** in the UK. (noun)
  There's ...................................
5 It's **stormy** in California at the moment. (noun)
  There's a ...................................
6 There's the **sun**! (adjective)
  It's ...................................!

## Present simple or present continuous

**4 Tick (✔) the correct sentences. Rewrite the sentences that are incorrect.**

1 I am swimming every Saturday. ...........
2 We're watching a film at the moment. ...........
3 It's snowing every winter in Russia. ...........
4 It's always cold in Antarctica. ...........
5 It rains today in London. ...........
6 Kim and Dan do their homework now. ...........
7 We are starting school at 9.00 every day. ...........
8 Mum visits my aunt this week. ...........

I   _I swim every Saturday._

**5 Write sentences using the present simple or present continuous.**

1 we / go / to / France / every Christmas / .
  _We go to France every Christmas._
2 the lions / sleep / at the moment / .
  ...................................
3 Paul / have / lunch / now / .
  ...................................
4 my mum / work / in a zoo / every Monday and Thursday / .
  ...................................

5 you / do / your homework / now / ?
  ...................................
6 I / not enjoy / this film / .
  ...................................
7 you / have got / a pet / ?
  ...................................
8 Zoe / travel / in India / this month / .
  ...................................

**6 Complete the interview with the present simple or present continuous form of the verbs in brackets.**

**A flood in Manila, the Phillippines**

Presenter  Today we [1] _'re talking_ (talk) about the weather in the Philippines. I'm here with Linda Torres, who lives here. Linda, what's the weather usually like here?

Linda  It's usually warm and sunny, but at the end of summer it's very rainy and there are floods. Often people [2] ................... (not know) when the rain is coming. People [3] ................... (not be) always ready for the bad weather.

Presenter  But there's some good news, isn't there?

Linda  Yes. Now there's a new weather app, for mobile phones. It [4] ................... (tell) people when a storm is coming. Eighty per cent of people in the Philippines [5] ................... (have got) a mobile phone, so the app is very useful.

Presenter  What can you see on the app today?

Linda  Well, the rain [6] ................... (come) now!

Presenter  Where is your family?

Linda  My grandparents [7] ................... (stay) with us at the moment. They [8] ................... (not live) in a safe area – the water [9] ................... (cover) their street every year.

Presenter  What [10] ................... (your grandparents / do) now?

Linda  They [11] ................... (play) with my little brother and sister.

Presenter  And where is your mother?

Linda  She is at the shops. She [12] ................... (buy) some extra food.

**7 CHALLENGE!** Write a short weather report about today. Then write a report about the typical weather for each month in your country. Write two or more sentences for each month.

## V Outdoor activities

**1** Choose the sports that need the equipment.

1 crash pad
   (bouldering)   horse riding   caving
2 water
   surfing   mountain biking   rock climbing
3 helmet
   caving   surfing   diving
4 rope
   zorbing   bungee jumping   bouldering
5 hill
   snowboarding   diving   canoeing

**2** Write the activities next to the clues. Use the words in exercise 1.

1 You go under the ground. It's dark. ........caving........
2 You jump from high places. ..............................
3 You go up small rocks without equipment

   ..............................
4 You are on a bike. You don't ride on the road.

   ..............................
5 You sit on a horse. ..............................
6 You are inside a big ball. You roll down hills.

   ..............................
7 You sit in a special boat. ..............................
8 You do this in the sea. You need a special board.

   ..............................
9 You do this on the snow. ..............................
10 You do this under the water. You can see fish.

   ..............................

**3** Read the profiles and complete the sentences with activities from exercise 1. Give reasons for your choices.

**Harry**   likes: swimming, looking at fish
            dislikes: cycling

1 It's good for Harry to choose ............diving............,
   because he enjoys swimming and looking at fish.
2 It's not good for Harry to choose ..............................,
   because ..............................

**Alisha**   likes: animals, being outdoors
             dislikes: going to the beach, swimming

3 It's good for Alisha to choose ..............................,
   because ..............................
4 It's not good for Alisha to choose ..............................,
   because ..............................

**Nick**   likes: the mountains, winter
           dislikes: cold weather, the dark

5 It's good for Nick to choose ..............................,
   because ..............................
6 It's not good for Nick to choose ..............................,
   because ..............................

## Making suggestions

**4** 🔊 **3.06**  Listen to the dialogue. Which club do Anna and Josh decide to go to?

1  BASKETBALL PRACTICE 4.30pm. CANCELLED Practice starts again next week. ☑

2  TENNIS BOOSTER Come along and improve your game! In the sports hall at 4.30 p.m. ☐

3  MOUNTAIN BIKING Are you ready for adventure. Meet at the school gate at 4.30pm. You must wear a helmet. ☐

4  RUNNING CLUB Get in training for the half marathon! ☐

5  CHESS CLUB All levels, come along and play. Meet in the library at 4 p.m. ☐

**5** 🔊 **3.06**  Listen again. Number the clubs in the order in which Anna and Josh mention them.

**6** Write S (suggestion) or R (response) for the sentences.

a I'd prefer to do something inside. .........
b What about going mountain biking? .........
c That sounds great. .........
d Let's go to running club! .........
e What about chess club? .........

**7** 🔊 **3.06**  Complete the dialogue with the phrases in exercise 6. Then listen and check.

Josh   Oh, look. Basketball practice is cancelled today.
Anna   Oh no! I can call my mum and ask her to come and pick us up.
Josh   No, look, there are lots of other clubs today. Let's do something else.
Anna   Good idea. [1] ..............................
Josh   [2] .............................., but I haven't got my helmet with me.
Anna   OK, then … [3] .............................. Look, they are training for a half-marathon! That's cool!
Josh   [4] .............................. Look out of the window! It's raining!
Anna   Right, inside … Well, [5] .............................. Can you play chess?
Josh   I can, but I'd prefer to do a sport.
Anna   Oh look – there's tennis in the sports hall.
Josh   Fine, I love tennis. Let's go!

**8** **CHALLENGE!** Write a dialogue between two friends choosing a club. Include suggestions and responses.

## Reading Storm chasing

**1** **Read the blog and choose the correct answers.**

1 What is the blog about?
   a the weather in Tornado Alley
   b scientists' reports on tornadoes
   c one man's hobby
2 Storm chasers spend most of their time
   a at home on the internet.
   b in a truck or a car.
   c in a shelter.

**2** **Read the blog again. Match sentences A–F to gaps 1–5 in the blog. There is one sentence that you do not need.**

A He thinks there are some storms 150 km away.
B ~~Basically, I follow storms.~~
C We're going home.
D The storm isn't here.
E The sky is black.
F We can see the tornado.

**3** **Read the text again. Are the sentences true (T) or false (F)? Underline the information in the text that tells you which sentences are true.**

1 This is the writer's first trip as a storm chaser. .........
2 Storm chasers are always scientists. .........
3 Storm chasers watch weather reports on TV to find out where storms are. .........
4 Storm chasers don't always see tornadoes when there is a storm. .........
5 Sometimes storm chasers drive long distances. .........
6 It isn't safe to stay in a truck when a tornado is coming. .........

**4** **Match the highlighted words in the text to definitions 1–7.**

1 (noun) objects people use to calculate and measure something

   _instruments_

2 (noun) small pieces of ice that come from the sky

3 (adjective) angry, bored, frustrated

4 (noun) a safe place

5 (adjective) very big

6 (adjective) covered with water

7 (adjective) amazing; great

---

Subject: **Storm chasing in Tornado Alley, Nebraska USA**

# Storm chasing

### Tornado Alley. Nebraska USA

Welcome to my blog. I'm a storm chaser. What does this mean? [1]Basically, I follow storms. It's exciting! I do it every spring – spring is tornado season! Some storm chasers
5 are scientists. Others, like me, just like the adventure. We do it in our free time.

This month, I'm chasing storms with my friend, Joe. We don't see a tornado with every storm, but we often do!

10 ### Day 1

We're driving through Tornado Alley in the USA. We're starting our trip in Nebraska. We've got a computer, a video camera and instruments that tell us about the weather. Joe
15 is looking at satellite weather reports on the internet. He uses information in the reports to calculate where the storm is starting.

Joe says we've got a long drive in our truck today. [2]..................................................
20 So let's go!

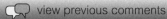 

## Day 2

We're in the middle of an incredible storm! ³

There are a lot of clouds and it's very windy.
25 The wind speed is 160 km per hour! It's raining. Driving is very dangerous at the moment because there's a lot of water on the roads. It's flooded in places. But there aren't any tornadoes!

## Day 3

30 It's not a good day today. After a seven-hour drive, we're near Tulsa, Oklahoma, but there aren't any clouds! ⁴

We're tired and fed up! I'm looking at some 35 satellite information. Joe and I are deciding where to drive tomorrow. There's a possible storm 200 km from here tomorrow. So, another long drive …

## Day 4

40 This is it! The clouds are moving quickly. Now there's lots of hail – huge balls of hail are falling on the truck. It's really noisy and there's ice everywhere! ⁵

But we're driving away from it. It's too 45 dangerous! We need to get out of our truck and find a shelter to stay in.

It's the end of the storm! But what a day! Fantastic! Time to sleep …

**5** Complete the sentences with the words in exercise 4.

**1** It's raining a lot. We need to find a .....*shelter*...... .

**2** We're driving a ..................... car. There are seven of us and all our bags!

**3** A pilot uses lots of ..................... to fly a plane.

**4** The ..................... is making holes in the grass.

**5** The children are ....................., because it's rainy and they can't play outside.

**6** The new film in the cinema is ..................... . Go and see it!

**7** The bathroom is ..................... after my brother's bath.

**6** CHALLENGE!  Study the advert. Would you like to go on a tornado tour? Write two or more reasons why you want to go and two or more reasons why you don't want to go.

**Tornado tours – a holiday with a difference!**

Try a new type of holiday – storm chasing!

* travel with professional storm chasers
* see amazing tornadoes
* learn about the weather
* visit a new place every day
* discover Tornado Alley – see mountains, grasslands and deserts!

I want to go on a Tornado tour because …

I don't want to go on a Tornado tour because …

# Writing Describing a photo

## Expressing uncertainty

**1** Complete the sentences with expressions of uncertainty. Use *I think*, *probably* and *perhaps*. Sometimes more than one answer is possible.

  **1** ............................ they are friends because they are playing a game together.
  **2** They are ............................ brother and sister because they've got the same eyes and hair colour.
  **3** The baby is crying. ............................ it is hungry.
  **4** ............................ they work at the zoo.
  **5** It's ............................ very cold because it's snowing.
  **6** The old lady is happy. ............................ the letter is from her grandchild.
  **7** The children are ............................ swimming in the water because it is warm.
  **8** It's ............................ the boy's birthday because he's got a lot of presents.

**2** Look at photo A and answer the questions. Use the words below and your own ideas.

  ▪ penguins ▪ beach ▪ scientists ▪ snow ▪ push ▪ clouds ▪ boat ▪ water ▪ cold ▪ jackets

What is …
**1** in the foreground? .........................................
**2** in the background? .........................................
**3** in the middle? .........................................
**4** on the left? .........................................
**5** on the right? .........................................

**3** Complete the description below. Use your answers in exercise 2 to help you.

> This is a photo of ¹............ . There are ²............ penguins in the photo: one is in the ³............ of the photo and the other is on the ⁴............ . Perhaps they are in the Antarctic, because a lot of penguins live there.
>
> There are three people in the ⁵............ of the photo. I think it's probably cold because the people are wearing big jackets. The person on the ⁶............ is pushing a boat into the water. In the background, behind the people, there are some ⁷............ . There are some clouds in the sky, too.
>
> The penguins are standing on the beach and watching the people. The penguins are probably feeling scared.

**4** Look at photo B. Answer the questions. Use the words in brackets.

  **1** What are the people doing?
    (I think)
    ...................................................................
  **2** Where are they?
    (perhaps)
    ...................................................................
  **3** What do you think the people are saying or thinking?
    (perhaps)
    ...................................................................
  **4** What are the animals doing?
    (I think)
    ...................................................................

### WRITING GUIDE

■ **Task**  Choose photo B or a photo from unit 4. Write a description of the photo.

■ **Ideas**  Answer the questions and make notes.
  **1** Where do you think it is?
  **2** What's the weather like?
  **3** How many people and animals can you see?
  **4** What do you think the people and animals are doing or thinking?
  **5** What is in the foreground, the background and the centre?
  **6** What is in the middle, on the left and on the right?

■ **Plan**  Follow the instructions. Use the description in exercise 3 to help you.
  **1** Start your description with the subject of the photo. *This is a photo of …*
  **2** Describe what the weather is like.
  **3** Describe what is in the photo and where the things are in the photo. *In the foreground, there are …*
  **4** Describe what you think the people and animals are doing or thinking. *I think they are probably …*

■ **Write**  Write your description. Use your notes and plan to help you. Remember to use expressions of uncertainty and vocabulary to describe where things are in the photo.

■ **Check**  Check the following points:
  ▪ spelling
  ▪ grammar
  ▪ punctuation
  ▪ expressions of uncertainty: *I think*, *probably* and *perhaps*
  ▪ vocabulary to describe where things are in the photo

# Progress check Unit 4

Read 1–15 and evaluate your learning in Unit 2. Give yourself a mark from 1 to 3. How can you improve?

**1** I can't do this.    **2** I have some problems with this.    **3** I can do this well.

| A  It's wild! | Mark (1–3) | How can I improve? |
|---|---|---|
| **1** Name two geographical features you find in the:<br>a  grasslands   b  desert   c  forest. |  |  |
| I can identify different geographical features. |  |  |
| **2** Name six different animals. |  |  |
| I can name different animals. |  |  |
| **3** Complete the sentences with an animal verb.<br>1  A cat ............................... from a dog.<br>2  A rabbit ............................... a hole. |  |  |
| I can use animal verbs. |  |  |
| **4** Give one strategy for learning a new word. |  |  |
| I can use strategies to learn and remember new vocabulary. |  |  |

| B  What are you watching? | Mark (1–3) | How can I improve? |
|---|---|---|
| **5** Write the names of two pets that live inside the house and two that live outside. |  |  |
| I can talk about different types of pets. |  |  |
| **6** Complete the sentences so they are true for you.<br>1  At the moment, I'm ............................... .<br>2  At the moment, my friend ............................... . |  |  |
| I can use the present continuous to talk about things happening at the moment. |  |  |

| C  What's the weather like? | Mark (1–3) | How can I improve? |
|---|---|---|
| **7** Use adjectives to describe the temperature and the weather in summer and winter. |  |  |
| I can describe the weather. |  |  |
| **8** Change the nouns into adjectives.<br>a  snow   b  wind   c  rain |  |  |
| I can use the adjective suffix -y to change nouns into adjectives. |  |  |
| **9** What's the difference between these sentences?<br>a  I cycle to school every day.   b  I am cycling to school now. |  |  |
| I can use the present simple and the present continuous in the correct situations. |  |  |

| D  Get active | Mark (1–3) | How can I improve? |
|---|---|---|
| **10** Name five activities. Where can you do them? |  |  |
| I can name different activities. |  |  |
| **11** Which activities do you use the following things for?<br>a  a rope   b  a hill   c  a boulder   d  a helmet |  |  |
| I can talk about different activities. |  |  |
| **12** Give three ways of making a suggestion to go swimming. |  |  |
| I can make suggestions. |  |  |
| **13** Give two positive and one negative response(s) to a suggestion. |  |  |
| I can respond to suggestions. |  |  |

| E  Describing a photo | Mark (1–3) | How can I improve? |
|---|---|---|
| **14** Give two words that you can use to express uncertainty. |  |  |
| I can express uncertainty. |  |  |
| **15** Give three phrases to describe where things are in a photo. |  |  |
| I can describe photos. |  |  |

# 5 Food, glorious food

## Vocabulary Food matters

### V Food

**1 Match the food items 1–12 to definitions a–l.**

1 apple ...f...
2 bread ........
3 carrot ........
4 chocolate ........
5 coffee ........
6 cucumber ........

7 mushroom ........
8 nuts ........
9 orange ........
10 cheese ........
11 tomato ........
12 lettuce ........

a It's brown or white. It's a healthy carbohydrate.
b It's a dairy product. You can have it in a sandwich.
c They're usually brown and hard. They grow on trees.
d It's a vegetable. It's brown or white. It grows in forests and in dark places.
e It's usually red. It's on a lot of pizzas.
f ~~It's a fruit. It's red or green.~~
g It's high in sugar and fat. It's delicious!
h It's a drink. It's brown. You can put milk and sugar in it.
i It's a vegetable. It's long and orange. It grows underground.
j It's a vegetable. It's long and green.
k It's a vegetable. It's green. You can eat the leaves.
l It's a fruit. Its name is also its colour.

**2 Complete the crossword.**

### Across

2 These small snacks are made with lots of sugar.
3 This fruit is orange inside and it's got a stone in the middle.
4 This is a carbohydrate. It's white or brown and people eat it with Indian and Chinese food.
7 This is a dairy food that's high in fat. It's a liquid, but it's not milk.
8 These are made from potatoes. They're high in fat, but they're a tasty snack.
10 This is white. It's in sweets and cakes.
11 These vegetables grow under the ground. They're carbohydrates.
13 This is a type of fish. It's pink.
15 This is a piece of meat from a cow.
16 People eat these small, round fruits. They also make juice and wine from them.

### Down

1 These are summer fruits. They're red.
2 We eat the leaves of this green vegetable.
5 Tomatoes are the main ingredient in this red sauce.
6 This goes with salt. It's brown.
9 This carbohydrate is Italian, but you can buy it in any country.
11 These are small round and green vegetables.
12 This goes with pepper. It's white.
14 When we cut these vegetables, they make us cry!

### V insight Compound nouns

**3 Choose the correct words to make compound nouns.**

1 tomato cream / (sauce)
2 ham cake / sandwich
3 mushroom pizza / cake
4 ice sauce / cream
5 chocolate cake / salad
6 fruit salad / oil
7 olive cream / oil
8 orange juice / oil

**4 CHALLENGE!** Write eight sentences about food. Use the following questions to help you.

■ What foods do / don't you like?
■ What foods do you often eat during the day?
■ What do you eat on special days, for example, your birthday?
■ What do you eat when you meet friends?

...................................................................
...................................................................
...................................................................
...................................................................
...................................................................
...................................................................
...................................................................
...................................................................

# Grammar  School food with a difference

## Countable and uncountable nouns

**1  Write C (Countable) or UC (Uncountable).**

1  milk _UC_
2  apple ...............
3  bread ...............
4  carrot ...............
5  food ...............
6  tomato sauce ...............
7  egg ...............
8  orange juice ...............
9  coffee ...............
10  orange ...............

**2  Match 1–8 to a–h to make sentences.**

1  There are some
2  There isn't
3  There is a
4  There aren't
5  Is there
6  Are there any
7  There is some
8  Is there an

a  rice in the cupboard.
b  any pizzas for lunch today.
c  eggs?
d  any food in the fridge.
e  orange in your bag?
f  potatoes in the shop.
g  any meat?
h  farm at our school.

**3  Complete the text with *some* or *any*.**

Jo  Let's make [1] _some_ food for lunch. What about pasta?

Andy  That sounds good. Have we got [2] ............... sauce?

Jo  No, we haven't got [3] ............... sauce. We need to make it.

Andy  Are there [4] ............... tomatoes?

Jo  Yes, there are [5] ............... tomatoes. And there's an onion. Is there [6] ............... olive oil in the cupboard?

Andy  Yes, there is. Well, that's a good start. We've got [7] ............... tomatoes, an onion and [8] ............... oil. Are there [9] ............... mushrooms?

Jo  No, there aren't [10] ............... mushrooms.

Andy  Never mind. Let's get cooking!

## much, many, a lot of

**4  Write sentences with *much*, *many* or *a lot of*.**

1  have got / you / sweets / in your bag (**?**)
   _Have you got many sweets in your bag?_

2  I / have got / pasta / for dinner (**✘**)
   .........................................................

3  how / potatoes / do / you / want (**?**)
   .........................................................

4  we / have got / food (**✔**)
   .........................................................

5  how / fruit / is / there (**?**)
   .........................................................

6  the shop / have got / sweets (**✔**)
   .........................................................

7  Kia / have got / vegetables / for her lunch (**✘**)
   .........................................................

**5  Choose the correct words to complete the text.**

### Teenagers and food

How [1] (much)/ many **food do you eat? Do you eat the right food? Check out your diet!**

Healthy carbohydrates — Fruit and vegetables — Protein — Food with high sugar and fat levels — Dairy products

How [2]much / many **vegetables do you eat?**

You can eat [3]much / a lot of fruit and vegetables every day: five pieces (or more) are good for you.

**Which foods are healthy carbohydrates?**

Bread, pasta, rice and potatoes are healthy carbohydrates. They give us energy. But be careful. It's easy to add [4]many / a lot of fat to these healthy foods – don't!

How [5]much / many **protein do you eat every day?**

You need protein every day, but you don't need [6]many / much of it. Fish is very good – it doesn't have [7]much / many fat. Nuts have [8]many / a lot of fat, but it's good fat.

How [9]much / many **dairy products do you have every day?**

You need about two to four portions of dairy food every day. There are [10]much / a lot of low-fat dairy products – choose these.

**What about sweets, crisps and cake?**

We all know that [11]a lot of / many sugar and fat is bad for us. But how [12]much / many cake is OK? The answer is don't eat it every day and have small amounts when you do.

**6  Complete the text with *some*, *any*, *much*, *many* or *a lot of*.**

Hi! I'm Lucy and I'm a vegan. I don't eat food that comes from animals. So I don't drink [1] ...._any_.... milk or eat [2] ............... eggs or yoghurt. Of course, I don't eat [3] ............... meat or fish.
How [4] ............... protein is there in my diet? I have [5] ............... protein, because I eat nuts.
I think my diet is healthy. I eat [6] ............... fruit and vegetables every day. How [7] ............... vegetables do I eat? A lot! I love them!
I have [8] ............... olive oil (not a lot) every day. It's important to have [9] ............... fat every day and olive oil is a good fat.
I don't eat [10] ............... food that is high in sugar, but I usually have [11] ............... cake with my family at the weekend. Vegan cake, of course!

**7  CHALLENGE!  Write a short paragraph about your diet. Include information about how much protein, fruit, fat and sugar you eat.**

# Vocabulary and grammar Traditional food

## V On the dinner table

**1** Write the dinner table objects next to the clues. Use the words below.

■ bowl ■ cup ■ fork ■ glass ■ knife ■ mug ■ plate ■ ~~spoon~~

1 You use a ......spoon...... to eat ice cream.
2 You put cold drinks in a ............................... .
3 You put hot drinks in these things. A ........................... is small and a ........................... is big.
4 You put your meal on a ........................... .
5 You put puddings like yoghurt and ice cream in a ........................... .
6 You use these to eat. The ........................... goes in your mouth. The ........................... cuts your food.

## V Food quantities

**2** Tick the correct phrases. Rewrite the phrases that are incorrect. Replace the words in bold. Sometimes more than one answer is possible.

1 a **loaf** of bread ........................... ✔
2 a **bottle** of water ...........................
3 a **carton** of pasta ...........................
4 a **jar** of cake ...........................
5 a **can** of crisps ...........................
6 a **tin** of tomatoes ...........................
7 a **slice** of coffee ...........................
8 a **packet** of orange juice ...........................
9 a **kilo** of onions ...........................
10 a **litre** of milk ...........................

### a little / a few

**3** Choose the correct words.

1 I usually have a little /(few) chips with my fish.
2 Can you add a little / few milk to my coffee, please?
3 Dad always has a little / few sugar in his coffee.
4 It's OK to have a little / few sweets.
5 Do you want a little / few olive oil on your salad?
6 A little / few people in my class like custard.
7 A little / few chocolate on ice cream is delicious.
8 I've got a little / few packets of crisps for the party.

**4** Rewrite the sentences so they have a similar meaning. Use the words *a little* or *a few*.

1 I haven't got much money today.
I / have got / money / today
**I've got a little money today.**

2 There aren't many tomatoes.
there are / tomatoes
...........................

3 There isn't much milk in the fridge.
there's / milk / in the fridge
...........................

4 I haven't got a lot of oranges.
I / have got / oranges
...........................

5 There isn't a lot of bread.
there's / bread
...........................

6 I haven't got much pasta.
I / have got / pasta
...........................

**5** Complete the text messages with the words below.

■ carton ■ ~~few~~ ■ forks ■ glasses ■ litre ■ little ■ loaf ■ packets ■ knife

| ◀ MESSAGES |
|---|
| A Hi! Have you got any food for the picnic? |
| B I've got a ¹..........few.......... sandwiches and three ²........................... of crisps. |
| A OK. I've got a ³........................... of bread and a ⁴........................... cheese. Any drinks? |
| B I've got a big ⁵........................... of orange juice and a ⁶........................... of water. |
| A We need a ⁷........................... to cut the cheese. |
| B OK. I've got one. Do we need any ⁸...........................? |
| A No. We can eat with our fingers. |
| B I've got some ⁹........................... for the drinks. |
| A Great. See you soon. |

**6** **CHALLENGE!** Imagine you are planning a party with your friend. Write the text messages you send to each other. Include food quantities and *a few / a little*.

...........................
...........................
...........................
...........................
...........................
...........................
...........................
...........................

**V** Opinion adjectives

**1** Complete the sentences with the words below.

- boring ■ delicious ■ disgusting ■ exciting ~~exciting~~ ■ interesting
- lovely ■ scary ■ strange

1 Some people really like caving and zorbing. They think they're ......exciting...... activities.
2 I love chocolate. It tastes ........................... .
3 Mike is unusual, but not in a good way. I think he's
........................... .
4 I don't like geography. I think it's ........................... .
5 I'm into history. I think it's really ........................... to learn about the past.
6 I don't like spinach. It smells bad and it tastes horrible. It's ...........................!
7 I don't want to try bungee jumping. It's ........................... and dangerous!
8 Look at my new bag. I think it's ........................... .

**2** Complete the sentences so that they are true for you. Use the adjectives in exercise 1.

1 School holidays are ........................... .
2 Ice cream is ........................... .
3 Mountain biking is ........................... .
4 Walking in the countryside is ........................... .
5 Watching TV is ........................... .
6 British food is ........................... .

### Ordering food

**3** Complete the menu with the words below. Then write one more item in each category in the menu.

- Desserts ■ Drinks ■ Main courses ■ Starters

**The Corner Café**

1 ...........................
- ◆ Green salad
- ◆ Vegetable soup
- ◆ Garlic bread
- ◆ ...........................

2 ...........................
- ◆ Pizza with ham and mushrooms
- ◆ Indian chicken curry and rice
- ◆ Pasta with garlic and tomato sauce
- ◆ ...........................

3 ...........................
- ◆ Fruit juice: apple or orange
- ◆ Cola
- ◆ Hot drinks: tea, coffee, hot chocolate
- ◆ ...........................

4 ...........................
- ◆ Ice cream: strawberry or chocolate
- ◆ Traditional English trifle
- ◆ Fruit salad
- ◆ ...........................

**4** ⊙ 3.07  Listen to the dialogue. What doesn't Lisa eat?

**5** ⊙ 3.07  Listen again. Complete the waiter's notes.

ticket 52
52

Starters: ¹ ..........................., ² ...........................
Main course: ³ ..........................., ⁴ ...........................
Drinks: ⁵ ..........................., ⁶ ...........................
Dessert: ⁷ ...........................

**6** Study the sentences. Write W (waiter), L (Lisa) or J (Joe) next to the phrases they use.

a Are you ready to order? ...........................
b I'd like some pea and ham soup. ...........................
c Would you like a starter? ...........................
d No, I'm fine, thanks. ...........................
e Would you like anything to drink? ...........................
f Can I have a sparkling water, please? ...........................

**7** ⊙ 3.07  Complete the dialogue with the phrases in exercise 6. Then listen and check.

| Waiter | Hello. ¹ ........................... |
| Joe | Yes, thank you. |
| Waiter | ² ........................... |
| Lisa | Yes, please. I'd like a green salad, please. |
| Waiter | OK. And what would you like for your starter? |
| Joe | ³ ........................... |
| Waiter | What would you like for your main course? |
| Lisa | Can I have pasta with pesto and tomato sauce, please? |
| Joe | And I'd like the chicken curry and rice. |
| Waiter | ⁴ ........................... |
| Joe | I'd like a glass of apple juice. |
| Lisa | ⁵ ........................... |
| Waiter | Of course. Do you want to order dessert now? |
| Lisa | Hmmm. I love trifle! Can I have some trifle, please? |
| Joe | ⁶ ........................... |
| Waiter | OK. Thank you. |

**8** **CHALLENGE!** Write a dialogue between a waiter and two people who are at the restaurant. Use the items you added to the menu in exercise 3.

# Reading London restaurants

**1** Scan the text. Match photos 1–3 with the restaurants. Write the name of the restaurant.

Photo 1: ................................................

Photo 2: ................................................

Photo 3: ................................................

**2** Read the text again. Choose the correct answers.

1 Circus is good for people who
   a want to watch something fun.
   b like unusual food.
   c want to work in a circus.

2 Circus is
   a a quiet place for a meal.
   b fun, but the food is bad.
   c a great evening out and has great food, too.

3 LMNT is
   a in a museum.
   b a very old restaurant.
   c full of interesting things to see.

4 At LMNT you can eat
   a snakes and lions.
   b food from Europe.
   c food from Egypt.

5 At Archipelago you can
   a try unusual meat.
   b buy traditional art.
   c eat meals made with unusual plants.

6 A vegetarian can't eat much at
   a Circus.
   b LMNT.
   c Archipelago.

**3** Choose the best restaurant for each statement.

1 'I like dancing after I eat.'

   ................................................

2 'I like fish – it's the only food I eat.'

   ................................................

3 'I want to eat something really different.'

   ................................................

4 'It's my grandmother's birthday. I want to take her out for lunch. She loves Italian food.'

   ................................................

5 'I don't like art. It's so boring.'

   ................................................

6 'I want to watch something while I eat.'

   ................................................

# London restaurants

Do you like unusual eating experiences? Here are three original restaurants in the UK's lively capital!

## Circus

Imagine this – there's a waiter standing at your table.
5 Normal? Not really! This waiter is standing on his hands!
Later a waitress brings you your food ... it's on her head.
It's very entertaining!

While you're eating, you can enjoy the show. The waiters
are all circus acrobats. Sometimes, after eating, people
10 get up and dance! It's always really lively.

Delicious meat, fish and vegetarian options are available.

## LMNT

A restaurant full of surprises! Step inside and you are in
a new, but ancient world.

15 There is Egyptian art everywhere! Snakes and lions
decorate the walls, along with Egyptian hieroglyphs.
King Tutankhamen watches you while you eat.

There's a simple menu with food from countries such as
Britain, France and Italy, and there's usually something
20 tasty for vegetarians too.

## Archipelago

Step inside this restaurant and there isn't much that
makes you think of London. Next to the tables there
are some tropical plants from rainforests. Plus there's
25 some unusual international art to admire. But the real
difference is the food!

What do you usually have for a starter? A salad? Would
you like to try a few caterpillars? In this restaurant,
you can! And for your main course – what about some
30 crocodile? Then finish your meal with a dessert of
scorpions!

The menu is totally original, but perhaps it's not the
place for vegetarians!

**4** Replace the highlighted words in the text with the words in bold in the sentences below.

1 I love your food. It's always **delicious**. ........*tasty*........

2 We are never bored at music club. It's always **busy and exciting**. ..................

3 Lucy is an amazing artist. All her pictures are **really new and different**. ..................

4 Caitlin's likes **basic** clothes. She always wears a black jacket and trousers. ..................

5 This building is **very old**. It's about 300-years-old.

..................

6 That film is great. It's really **fun to watch**. ..................

**5** Complete the sentences with the words in exercise 4.

1 I want something ........*simple*........ for lunch –
perhaps a salad or some soup.

2 I love that TV show. It's really ..................

3 My parents often go to museums because they like
.................. Roman art.

4 Tim wants to write a book. He's got a very
.................. idea for a story.

5 Try this pudding! It's ..................

6 I love Rome. It's a .................. city.

**6** **CHALLENGE!** Write a short text about a restaurant you know or your school canteen. Include the words in exercise 4. Use the following questions to help you plan your text.

- What does the restaurant look like?
- What type of food does it serve?
- Why do you / don't you like it?

# Writing  A description of a festival

**1** **Read the email from Jian to Shimi. Answer the questions.**

  **1** Do you think Jian knows Shimi? Why / why not?

  **2** Is an email to a friend formal or informal ?

---

**Happy New Year!**

Hi Shimi!

Thanks for your email.

Happy New Year! We're celebrating Chinese New Year at the moment. We celebrate in the first month of spring. It's a very important festival for Chinese people, because we think about new beginnings at the start of a new year.

Before the celebrations start we clean our houses. This is a tradition – we are cleaning away all the bad things.

On New Year's Eve, the evening before the New Year, we have a special meal with our family. We eat traditional food. We usually have fireworks at midnight. We say that the fireworks chase away bad spirits. We also wear red clothes. Red means fire, so we say that our red clothes also help chase away evil spirits.

When we wake up on New Year's Day, we find a red envelope in our beds. It's got money and sweets in it – it's a present from our parents and grandparents.

We also have a lantern festival. There are many lights and lanterns. It's beautiful. We often have a dragon dance, too. It's my favourite part of the festival!

I love Chinese New Year, because I like all the traditions and I like being with my family.

Write to me about one of your festivals.

Take care

Jian

---

**2** **Read the email again. Answer the questions.**

  **1** What is the festival?

  **2** When do people celebrate this festival?

  **3** Why do people celebrate this festival?

  **4** What do people do at this festival?

  **5** What kind of food do people eat?

  **6** What clothes do people wear?

  **7** What is Jian's favourite part?

## Linking words of addition: *too, also*

**3** **Cross out the word in the wrong position.**

  **1** I ~~too~~ visit my cousins too.

  **2** I also like also buying the presents.

  **3** The children in my family also are also very excited!

  **4** We too are busy too.

  **5** My mum also sings also.

  **6** My family give too cards too.

**4** **Rewrite the sentences in bold. Use the linking words in brackets.**

  **1** My parents give me my Christmas presents after breakfast. **I also give them presents.**

    .................................................................................. (too)

  **2** We send Easter cards. **We eat chocolate eggs too!**

    .................................................................................. (also)

  **3** Grandad is always happy when we dance. **We are happy too.**

    .................................................................................. (also)

  **4** We make decorations. **We buy them too.**

    .................................................................................. (also)

  **5** The boys send the girls Valentine's cards. **The girls also send the boys cards.**

    .................................................................................. (too)

---

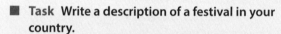

**WRITING GUIDE**

■ **Task** **Write a description of a festival in your country.**

■ **Ideas** **Choose a festival you like. Answer the questions and make notes.**

  **1** What festival do you want to describe?

  **2** When do people celebrate this festival?

  **3** Why do people celebrate this festival?

  **4** What do people do at this festival?

  **5** What kind of food do people eat?

  **6** Why do you like it?

■ **Plan** **Organize your ideas into an email. Use Jian's email to help you.**

  ■ Begin your email with *Hello!, Hi!* or *Dear …*

  ■ Include an opening sentence: *How are you? / Thanks for your email. / I hope you are well.*

  ■ Introduce the festival and say why people celebrate it.

  ■ Describe the festival and write about what happens.

  ■ Finish with *Take care / Lots of love / Best wishes.*

■ **Write** **Write your email. Use your notes and plan to help you. Remember to use the linking words *too* and *also*.**

■ **Check** **Check the following points:**

  ■ spelling

  ■ grammar

  ■ punctuation

  ■ informal language

  ■ linking words *too* and *also*

  ■ your description of the festival

# Progress check  Unit 5

| A  Food matters | Mark (1–3) | How can I improve? |
|---|---|---|
| **1** Give an example of the following types of food:<br>a  a dairy product    b  a vegetable<br>c  a fruit    d  a healthy carbohydrate | | |
| I can talk about different types of food. | | |
| **2** Give three examples of a compound noun. | | |
| I can use compound nouns. | | |
| **3** Why is it a good idea to make a word web? | | |
| I can make a word web to help me record vocabulary. | | |
| **4** What is a fruitarian? | | |
| I can understand text about unusual diets. | | |

| B  School food with a difference | Mark (1–3) | How can I improve? |
|---|---|---|
| **5** Are the following nouns countable or uncountable?<br>a  fruit    b  apple    c  food    d  egg | | |
| I can identify countable and uncountable nouns. | | |
| **6** Complete the sentences with *some* or *any*.<br>There are ............... potatoes, but there isn't ............... meat. | | |
| I can use *some* and *any* with countable and uncountable nouns. | | |
| **7** Complete the sentences with *much*, *many* and *a lot of*.<br>1  Dad eats ............... fruit every day.<br>2  How ............... sandwiches would you like?<br>3  The shop hasn't got ............... vegetables today. | | |
| I can use *much*, *many* and *a lot of* with countable and uncountable nouns. | | |

| C  Traditional food | Mark (1–3) | How can I improve? |
|---|---|---|
| **8** Name three traditional foods from the UK. | | |
| I can understand a text about traditional food. | | |
| **9** Name three things you use when you have your main course. | | |
| I can identify objects on the dinner table. | | |
| **10** Complete the food quantities.<br>a ............... crisps  b ............... milk  c ............... apples | | |
| I can talk about food using quantities. | | |
| **11** Complete the sentences with *a little* and *a few*.<br>Can I have ............... yoghurt and ............... peaches, please? | | |
| I can use *a little* and *a few* with countable and uncountable nouns. | | |

| D  Delicious or disgusting? | Mark (1–3) | How can I improve? |
|---|---|---|
| **12** Give adjectives to describe the following:<br>a  snakes    b  ice cream    c  hip hop music | | |
| I can use opinion adjectives. | | |
| **13** Give two phrases for ordering food. | | |
| I can order food in a restaurant. | | |

| E  A description of a festival | Mark (1–3) | How can I improve? |
|---|---|---|
| **14** Choose the correct words.<br>1  I like chocolate and I like ice cream, **too** / also.<br>2  Rob sings. He **also** / too plays the guitar. | | |
| I can use linking words of addition. | | |
| **15** Write three sentences about a festival in your country. | | |
| I can write about a festival. | | |

# Material world

## Vocabulary  Nearly new

### V  Clothes and accessories

**1  Label the pictures with the words below.**

■ boots ■ cardigan ■ ~~coat~~ ■ dress ■ hat ■ jacket ■ jumper
■ necklace ■ rucksack ■ sandals ■ scarf ■ shirt ■ shorts
■ skirt ■ socks ■ tights ■ trainers ■ trousers

| | | |
|---|---|---|
| 1 | coat | 10 |
| 2 | | 11 |
| 3 | | 12 |
| 4 | | 13 |
| 5 | | 14 |
| 6 | | 15 |
| 7 | | 16 |
| 8 | | 17 |
| 9 | | 18 |

### V  Shops

**2  Match activities 1–7 to shops a–g.**

1 buy trainers and clothes for exercise    **a** bookshop
2 talk about the cost of text messages    **b** chemist's
3 talk to someone about your health    **c** clothes shop
4 send a letter or parcel    **d** market
5 find something to read    **e** phone shop
6 buy jeans, tops and jumpers    **f** post office
7 go shopping outside    **g** sports shop

**3  Complete the text with the words below.**

■ greengrocer's ■ sandwich shop ■ ~~fishmonger's~~
■ baker's ■ department store ■ newsagent's ■ butcher's

In a small village near Oxford, a British family walks to
their local shops. First, they stop at the ¹ <u>fishmonger's</u>
to buy some fish. Next, the mother goes with her son
to buy some vegetables at the ² _____. They
walk past the ³ _____ because they don't want
any meat today. The father and their daughters buy
some bread at the ⁴ _____. The parents like to
read the Saturday newspapers, so they go to the
⁵ _____.

Next, the family decides to go to Oxford. They're hungry,
but they don't want to go to a restaurant. So, they go
into a ⁶ _____ to buy something for lunch. Next,
they go to the ⁷ _____ with lots of different shops
in it. So this place is good for everyone.

### V | insight  Negative prefixes

**4  Choose the correct adjective in brackets and make it
negative. Then complete the sentences.**

1 I don't like maths tests. My answers are often
_____*incorrect*_____. (tolerant / fair / correct)
2 My friend goes to a different school now, so I feel
_____. (happy / fair / expensive)
3 Kelly isn't nice. She doesn't talk to other people. She's
really _____. (important / friendly / lucky)
4 I've got three exams today. I'm very _____!
(fashionable / lucky / friendly)
5 My dad likes _____ meetings. He likes
wearing jeans. (formal / complete / important)
6 Josh can't play basketball today, so our team is
_____. (complete / kind / fair)
7 He's very _____. He doesn't like anything.
(complete / tolerant / formal)
8 Jasmine doesn't share her sweets with her brother.
She's _____. (kind / important / patient)

**5  CHALLENGE!  Write a short text about shopping. Use
your answers to the following questions to help you
plan your text.**

■ How often do you go to the shops?
■ What are your favourite shops? Why?
■ Do you buy lots of things, or do you just look at things?
■ Do you prefer to buy things on the internet? Why /
why not?

# Grammar Cyber Monday

## Comparative adjectives

**1** Read the clues below. Then label the people in the photo.

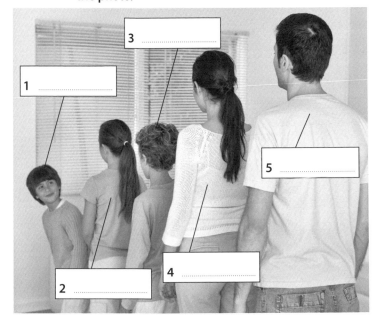

Adam ■ Helen ■ Jacob ■ Jane ■ Tom

1 Jane is taller than Tom, but shorter than Adam.
2 Helen is taller than Jacob but shorter than Tom.
3 Tom is shorter than Jane but taller than Helen.

**2** Write the comparative forms of the adjectives. Which comparative adjective in each group has got a different spelling rule?

1 convenient *more convenient*    busy (*busier*)
tolerant *more tolerant*
2 quick ................    cheap ................
big ................
3 noisy ................    good ................
busy ................
4 easy ................    unusual ................
interesting ................
5 bad ................    far ................
wet ................
6 safe ................    big ................
large ................

**3** Write comparative sentences.

1 Tina / thin / her sister
*Tina is thinner than her sister.*
2 my shoes / small / your shoes
................
3 shopping online / convenient / going to the shops
................
4 your rucksack / good / mine
................
5 George / busy / Helen
................
6 Nik's clothes / unusual / Gemma's clothes
................

**4** Complete the sentences with the comparative form of the adjectives below.

■ bad ■ big ■ fashionable ■ ~~quick~~ ■ quiet

1 Dan drives ..........*quicker*.......... than Maria. He loves driving fast.
2 I can't put all these books in my bag. Can you put them in your bag? It's ................ than mine.
3 My brother's really good at maths. I'm not! I always get ................ marks in maths exams than him.
4 I prefer studying in the library because there isn't a lot of noise. It's ................ than studying at school.
5 I think Polly's got a lot of money. Her clothes are always ................ than mine.

**5** Choose the correct adjective in brackets. Then complete the text with the comparative forms of the adjectives.

# Fair Trade

Most of us like buying new clothes. Do we like [1] *more expensive* (expensive / small) clothing, or do we prefer inexpensive clothes? The answer is obvious! We love cheap clothes and we can have them, because they are made in countries like China and India. It probably isn't [2] ................ (good / interesting) to make clothes in these countries, but it is definitely [3] ................ (cheap / thin).

The cost of making clothes in these countries is approximately 25% [4] ................ (exciting / low) than in Europe or the USA. That's often because workers don't get much money. Some people want this to change. They think its [5] ................ (busy / important) to pay workers a fair price than to have cheap clothes. This is called Fair Trade and it helps workers have [6] ................ (good / friendly) lives.

Fair Trade products such as coffee, chocolate and sugar are popular and a lot of supermarkets have got them on their shelves. Fair Trade clothes are [7] ................ (long / difficult) to find. However some designers are now [8] ................ (interested / big) in Fair Trade, and important fashion events have Fair Trade shows. These days, it's [9] ................ (far / easy) to find Fair Trade than some years ago. So, next time you're shopping, have a [10] ................ (good / popular) look at the clothes.

**6** CHALLENGE! Compare two of your items of clothing. Write five comparative sentences. Use the comparative form of the adjectives below and your own ideas.

■ big ■ cheap ■ fashionable ■ good ■ long ■ short ■ small ■ thin

*I've got a black coat and a blue jacket. My coat is longer than my jacket.*

## V Shopping

**1 Complete the crossword.**

Across

3 When you shop in the USA, you use these to buy things.
6 Someone who buys something is this.
8 People often use this when they shop online. It's safer than using a bank card.
10 Young and old people can usually get this on the price of a train and bus tickets.

Down

1 This is something you buy.
2 When something is 50% cheaper, it is this.
4 Men carry their money in this.
5 Shops often have these in January and July. The shops sell things at a cheaper price than usual.
7 This is something you buy for a very good price.
9 People have problems with this when they spend more money than they've got.

**2 Choose the correct words to complete the sentences.**

1 A (wallet) / sale is a good place to keep your consumers / dollars.
2 I sometimes go to sales / credit cards if there is a big discount / half price.
3 Online stores know what wallets / consumers buy, because the store collects information about their purchases / bargains.
4 I don't use a credit card / dollars, because I don't want to have problems with discounts / debt.
5 This jacket is a sale / bargain – it's half price / a debt!

## Superlative adjectives

**3 Complete the sentences with the superlative form of the adjectives in brackets.**

1 My cousin always buys ..... the latest ..... (late) fashion.
2 Saturday is .......... (busy) day to go shopping.
3 .......... (bad) problem for a lot of consumers is debt.
4 .......... (important) thing in my bag is my wallet.
5 .......... (cheap) items are not always .......... (good).
6 The department store is .......... (far) shop from my house.

**4 Write your opinions. Use the superlative form of the adjectives.**

1 popular / sport / in my class / is …
The most popular sport in my class is football.
2 unusual / thing / I / have got / is …
..........
3 good / shop in our town / is …
..........
4 bad / TV programme / is …
..........
5 easy / subject at school / is …
..........

**5 Complete the text with the superlative form of the adjectives below.**

big ■ convenient ■ expensive ■ good ■ ~~short~~ ■ unusual

There's a new type of shop in town – the pop-up. They don't stay in one place for a long time. The [1] ..... shortest ..... amount of time these shops stay open is about a day, but sometimes it's longer. These shops are really different – they're probably the [2] .......... shops in town!

Not all pop-ups offer discounts. You can buy clothes from the [3] .......... designers in the world at some pop-ups. So, be careful – don't get into debt!

In Shoreditch, London, there's a large collection of pop-ups – it's the [4] .......... pop-up mall in the world.

Going shopping at pop-ups isn't the [5] .......... way of going shopping, because you don't always find what you want. But for people who like original ideas, it's the [6] .......... way to shop!

**6 CHALLENGE! Think of five items of clothing or gadgets that you really like. Describe why you like them. Use one or more superlatives for each item.**

I love my mobile phone. It's the most useful thing I have, because I use Facebook all the time.

## V Gadgets

**1** Complete the sentences with the words below.

■ camera ■ ~~DVD player~~ ■ e-reader ■ games console
■ laptop ■ MP3 player ■ tablet

1 My parents use a __DVD player__ to watch films, but I prefer to watch films online or on my phone.
2 Mum takes her .................................. with her on the train to work. She doesn't use a tablet or a laptop. She reads about three books every week!
3 After school, my friends often come round and we play games on the .................................. . I've got five controls, so we can all play at the same time.
4 Sam's Smartphone is great for taking photos, but his .................................. is better.
5 My .................................. is better than my laptop. I can do all the same things with it, plus I can take photos because it's got a camera. I can't make phone calls with it though!
6 Dads doesn't like my tablet or smartphone. He prefers his .................................. . It's heavier, but easiet to use.
7 My .................................. is always in my bag. I use it to listen to music on my way to school. I don't take my phone or tablet to school.

## V Clothes verbs

**2** Complete the sentences with the verbs below.

■ undo ■ zip up ■ take out ■ do up ■ hang up ■ ~~try on~~
■ take back ■ look for ■ put away ■ unzip ■ put on
■ take off

1 Where's the changing room? I want to ...........__try__............ ........__on__........ these trousers before I buy them.
2 I always .................................. clothes to the shop if there's something wrong with them.
3 I can't reach the zip. Can you .................................. it for me.
4 'Dad, where are my trainers?' 'I don't know! Why don't you .................................. them in your bedroom?'
5 It's cold. Why don't you .................................. your coat?
6 I can't .................................. my necklace. Can you help me?
7 I always .................................. my school uniform before breakfast.
8 When you .................................. your clothes, can you put them in the washing machine, please?
9 Your room is so untidy. Please .................................. .................................. your clothes in your chest of drawers.
10 I've got a bigger wardrobe. It's got more space in it to .................................. my clothes.
11 Can you .................................. my hat and scarf from the drawer, please?
12 'Mum, can you .................................. my dress at the back, please?'

## Buying clothes

**3** 🔊 **3.08** Listen to the dialogues. Are the sentences true (T) or false (F)? Correct the false ones.

1 The boy tries on some yellow trainers.
2 The trainers are too small.
3 The boy buys the trainers in a smaller size.
4 The girl likes the pink jacket.
5 The pink jacket is in the sale.
6 She buys a cheaper jacket instead.

**4** 🔊 **3.08** Study the sentences. Write C (customer) or S (sales assistant). Listen again and tick the phrases that you hear.

1 Could I see the pink one, please? ..........
2 What size are you? ..........
3 Oh, well, never mind then. ..........
4 Do they come in different colours? ..........
5 How much do they cost? ..........
6 Do you need any help? ..........
7 Have you got a smaller size? ..........
8 They're too small. ..........
9 Thanks, I'll take them. ..........
10 The changing rooms are over there. ..........

**5** Read the dialogues and choose the best responses.

1 Assistant  Hello. Can I help you?
  Customer  a Oh well. Never mind then.
              b Yes, please. I'm looking for a hat.
              c Great. I'll take it.
2 Customer  They're cool. Can I try them on?
  Assistant  a Well, we've got these ones here.
              b They're at the back of the shop.
              c Of course, the changing room is over there.
3 Customer  How much is this shirt?
  Assistant  a They are £32.
              b It's £17.50. It's in the sale.
              c Size 36.
4 Customer  Do they come in different colours?
  Assistant  a No, I'm afraid not.
              b The pink one is lovely.
              c Can I try the green ones on, please?

**6** **CHALLENGE!** Write a dialogue between a customer and a sales assistant.

**1** What do you think the title *The teen pound* means?
Read the text and choose the correct answer.

   **1** A new type of money for teenagers.

   **2** The money people give to teenagers.

   **3** The money teenagers have and how they spend it.

**2** Match headings A–F to paragraphs 1–4. There are
two headings that you do not need.

   **A** How do businesses attract teenagers?

   **B** Do teenagers have problems with debt?

   **C** Do teenagers spend more time shopping than
studying?

   **D** What do teenagers spend their money on?

   **E** Why do people like free things?

   **F** Where does the money come from?

**3** Are the sentences true (T) or false (F)? Correct the
false sentences.

   **1** Big businesses are interested in teenager consumers.

   **2** Girls spend more money on their looks than boys.

   **3** Boys usually buy the most expensive computer
games.

   **4** Girls and boys are into spending money on
socializing.

   **5** All British teenagers work at the weekends.

   **6** Companies advertise by giving away free gifts to
teenagers.

   **7** A lot of teenagers have credit cards.

   **8** A lot of teenagers have parents who work in a bank.

**4** Match the highlighted words in the text to
definitions 1–9.

   **1** (verb) to keep money so it can be used later

                     *save*

   **2** (verb) communicate

   **3** (noun) an amount of money to buy what you want

   **4** (noun) famous names or labels that are linked to
certain products

   **5** (noun) where your money is kept in a bank

   **6** (verb) ask someone to an event or to do something
with you

   **7** (noun) products you put on your face

   **8** (noun) a group of people in business who sell things

   **9** (verb) to use something more than you need to

# The teen £pound

Like teenagers everywhere, British teenagers like
to spend money on things they want and the
things big companies want to sell them!

1

⁵ Girls are usually more interested in their
appearance than boys, so they often buy clothes
and make-up, such as lipstick and mascara.
Boys usually spend their money on home
entertainment (such as the most popular
¹⁰ computer game) and gadgets. All teens spend
money on their social lives. This isn't only the
money they use on activities like going to the
cinema. It's also the money they spend on the
latest smartphones, so they can keep in touch
¹⁵ with friends. It's probably cheaper than
going out and it's important to know what
everybody's doing!

**2**

Teenagers can have many different ways of
20 getting money. Some teenagers' parents give
them an allowance, often every week or month.
Their family sometimes give them money
on their birthdays or on special occasions
like Christmas. Some British teens also have
25 weekend jobs in cafés or shops. Banks encourage
teenagers to open an account and save money,
and many teenagers do.

**3**

Big brand names spend millions on advertising
30 to teenagers. Many companies give away things
for 'free', such as texts, downloads, drinks,
food, or even clothes. Others invite teenagers to
follow them on a social-networking site.

**4**

35 Not really. Most teenagers use cash. They're too
young to have a credit card (and when they are
the right age, they often don't want one). So
teenagers don't have problems with debt like
some adults. But, like most people, teenagers
40 can sometimes waste money on things they
don't really need or spend too much. However,
when that happens, they usually go to The Bank
of Mum and Dad – they ask their parents for
more money!

**5 Complete the sentences with the correct form of the words in exercise 4.**

1 My sister doesn't use much ......make-up...... . She prefers to look natural.
2 Let's ........................ everybody in our class to the party!
3 I've got a bank ........................ because I don't want to keep all my money at home.
4 Jason's parents give him an ........................ of £10 a week.
5 I want a new bike, so I need to ........................ some money. I'm not spending money on things I don't need at the moment.
6 Mum works for a small ........................ that makes and sells accessories.
7 Alex doesn't spend his money in a clever way. He ........................ all his money on gadgets and games that he doesn't need.
8 My cousin lives in the USA, so we ........................ by email.
9 Famous ........................ usually cost a lot of money. I don't buy them because most of the money pays for the name, not the product.

**6 Answer the questions.**

1 Do you think teenagers spend too much money on unimportant things? Why / why not?

2 What do teenagers in your country spend most of their money on?

3 What type of adverts do you like and dislike? Why?

4 Do you think adverts are useful? Why / why not?

**7 CHALLENGE!** Write a paragraph about your attitude to money and advertising. Use your answers in exercise 6 to help you plan your paragraph.

**1 Read the review. Answer the questions.**

1 What is the gadget?

2 What are its main features?

3 How much is it?

4 Does the reviewer like the gadget? Why / why not?

Review:
Dancing Feet
– shoes with music!

The latest computer and clothing combination from Tech-chic is the new Dancing Feet shoe collection. The shoes cost around £100. Inside the shoes is an MP3 player that you control with your feet!

Dancing Feet shoes have got some ¹........................ features – you can't find them in any other shoe. Your actions – walking, running, dancing – send different signals to your earpiece. Tap your toe in a certain way and you can search for a new tune. Click your heels together and you can make the music louder! What's more, these shoes are ²........................ – you *want* to wear them! They're also ³........................, because you can wear them inside and outside – and they're fine in the rain!

But, could they be ⁴........................? Do you want to dance all day? They're probably much more expensive than any other shoes you've got. And do you need them when you've got a ⁵........................ MP3 player already?

Do you live for technology? Dancing Feet shoes are perfect! But do you want to save some money? Then put on your ⁶........................ old shoes, put your MP3 player in your pocket and keep dancing!

**V  Positive and negative adjectives**

**2 Use a dictionary to check the meaning of the adjectives below. Are they positive or negative?**

1 favourite ........................

2 irritating ........................

3 practical ........................

4 reliable ........................

5 stylish ........................

6 unique ........................

**3 Complete the review with adjectives from exercise 2.**

**4 Study the highlighted words in the review. Answer the questions.**

1 Do you think the words are nouns, verbs, adjectives or adverbs?

2 What do you think the words mean?

**5 Use a dictionary to check your ideas. Write the new words in your vocabulary notebook with an example sentence.**

### WRITING GUIDE

■ **Task**  Write a review of a gadget.

■ **Ideas**  Choose a gadget. Answer the questions and make notes.

1 How much does it cost?

2 What are its main features?

3 What are its good points?

4 What are its bad points?

5 What is your opinion of it?

6 What positive and negative adjectives can you use to describe it?

■ **Plan**  Plan your paragraphs. Use the review in exercise 1 to help you.

Paragraph 1:  Describe the gadget. Include the price and main features.

Paragraph 2:  good points

Paragraph 3:  bad points

Paragraph 4:  conclusion and your opinion

■ **Write**  Write your review. Use your notes and plan to help you. Remember to include positive and negative adjectives. Use your dictionary to help with any new words you need.

■ **Check**  Check the following points:

▪ spelling

▪ grammar

▪ punctuation

▪ positive and negative adjectives

▪ different paragraphs for different topics

# Progress check  Unit 6

Read 1–12 and evaluate your learning in Unit 6. Give yourself a mark from 1 to 3. How can you improve?
**1** I can't do this.    **2** I have some problems with this.    **3** I can do this well.

| A  Nearly new | Mark (1–3) | How can I improve? |
|---|---|---|
| **1** Name three items of clothing you wear in winter and three items you wear in summer. | | |
| I can describe clothes and accessories. | | |
| **2** Name the shops where you can buy the following things.  **a** cakes   **b** meat   **c** vegetables   **d** fish | | |
| I can talk about different shops. | | |
| **3** Add negative prefixes to the adjectives.  **a** fair   **b** accurate   **c** important   **d** correct | | |
| I can use negative prefixes. | | |

| B  Cyber Monday | Mark (1–3) | How can I improve? |
|---|---|---|
| **4** Write the comparative form of the adjectives.  **a** cheap   **b** big   **c** busy   **d** exciting   **e** good | | |
| I can form comparative adjectives and use the comparative in sentences. | | |
| **5** Compare the two objects using the comparative form of the adjectives.  **1** your dress / pretty / my skirt   **2** football / popular / rugby | | |
| I can compare things. | | |

| C  Black Friday | Mark (1–3) | How can I improve? |
|---|---|---|
| **6** Choose the correct words.  **1** There's a **discount** / **debt** on this jacket.  **2** I don't have a **credit card** / **bargain** because I'm too young.  **3** Two T-shirts for the price of one. That's a **sale** / **bargain**! | | |
| I can use shopping vocabulary. | | |
| **7** Write superlative sentences.  **1** Ryan / good / guitar player  **2** this jacket / smart / in the shop  **3** you / listen to / unusual / music | | |
| I can form superlative adjectives and use the superlative in sentences. | | |

| D  Can't live without it | Mark (1–3) | How can I improve? |
|---|---|---|
| **8** Smartphones do the same job as a lot of other gadgets. Write four gadgets it replaces. | | |
| I can talk about different gadgets. | | |
| **9** Name the opposite actions.  **a** put on   **b** do up   **c** put away   **d** zip up | | |
| I can use verbs to describe actions with clothes. | | |
| **10** Give responses to these questions.  **1** Can I try them on, please?  **2** Have you got them in a bigger size? | | |
| I can use phrases for buying clothes. | | |

| E  A review of a gadget | Mark (1–3) | How can I improve? |
|---|---|---|
| **11** Name three positive and three negative adjectives for describing something. | | |
| I can use a variety of adjectives to express my opinion. | | |
| **12** Name three good things and three bad things about your mobile phone. | | |
| I can write a review. | | |

### V Parts of the body

**1** Write parts of the body for each group.

■ ankle ■ chest ■ elbow ■ face ■ finger ■ ~~hip~~ ■ knee ■ neck ■ shoulder ■ stomach ■ toe ■ wrist

1 Head

.................................... , ....................................

2 Arm or hand

.................................... , .................................... ,

.................................... ,

3 Leg or foot

.......... hip .......... , .................................... ,

.................................... ,

4 Centre of the body

.................................... ,

**2** Choose the correct words to complete the sentences.

1 I'm hungry. My (stomach) / chest is making a lot of noise!

2 You need long hips / **fingers** to play the piano.

3 I think you look really nice when your hair is away from your **face** / knee.

4 I always know what the time is, because I wear a watch on my leg / **wrist**.

5 Often trousers are too short for me, because I've got very long arms / **legs**.

6 My fingers / **ankles** are warm in these boots.

7 It's difficult for my grandad to walk, because he's got a bad face / **hip**.

8 You don't touch the ball with your leg / **hand** when you play football.

9 In winter, I always wear a hat on my hand / **head** and a scarf around my **neck** / hip when I go outside.

10 When I go skateboarding, I always wear special pads on my **elbows** / chest and face / **knees**.

11 I play tennis a lot and one of my toes / **arms** is stronger than the other.

12 My sister doesn't like wearing sandals, because she doesn't like her wrist / **toes**.

### V insight noun suffixes -er / -or

**3** Choose the correct spelling of the nouns.

| verb | noun |
|------|------|
| 1 swim | (swimmer) / swimer |
| 2 skate | skatter / skater |
| 3 play | player / playier |
| 4 compete | competer / competitor |
| 5 visit | visitter / visitor |
| 6 drive | driveer / driver |
| 7 fight | fighter / fightter |
| 8 jog | jogger / jogor |

**4** Complete the radio interview with the words below. Use the noun form of the verbs.

■ direct ■ run ■ legs ■ report ■ shoulders ■ ~~skate~~ ■ stomach ■ swim

Q Today I'm with Sara, a personal trainer. What do you do in your job?

A People come to me and I suggest sports and exercises that are good for them.

Q What type of people do you help?

A All sorts! This morning, for example, there's a woman who comes to see me. She does a lot of ice-skating competitions – she's a great ¹ **skater** . I give her exercises to make her ² .................................... stronger, so she does a lot of running and cycling with me.

Q Do you help any other sportsmen or women?

A Yes, there's a ³ .................................... – he goes to the pool every morning, but he comes to see me to do exercises for the top of his body, especially his arms and ⁴ .................................... .

Q Who else do you see?

A I work with a film ⁵ .................................... . She makes films for TV. She doesn't need special exercises, but she wants to be healthy.

Q So, how about me? I'm a ⁶ .................................... for this radio programme. I work about 40 hours a week. I'm always busy, but I don't do much exercise! What can I do?

A What about being a ⁷ ....................................? Jogging in the park every weekend is a great way of losing weight and staying healthy.

Q Maybe that's a good idea – I need to make my ⁸ .................................... a bit smaller!

**5** CHALLENGE! Write a physical description of the people below. Use words for parts of the body.

1 Footballers **have usually got strong legs and strong chests and shoulders.**

2 Firefighters ....................................

3 Piano players ....................................

4 Runners ....................................

5 Skaters ....................................

6 Sprinters ....................................

7 Swimmers ....................................

8 Throwers ....................................

# Vocabulary and grammar  Keep it clean!

## V Housework

**1** Match verbs 1–8 to nouns a–h.

| | | | |
|---|---|---|---|
| 1 | do | **a** | the table |
| 2 | help | **b** | your bedroom |
| 3 | hoover | **c** | the bed |
| 4 | lay / clear | **d** | the ironing |
| 5 | load / unload | **e** | the car |
| 6 | make | **f** | with the cooking |
| 7 | tidy | **g** | the floor |
| 8 | wash | **h** | the washing machine |

**2** Write the jobs next to the clues.

- do the shopping ■ do the washing up
- hang out / bring in the washing
- load the dishwasher ■ ~~take out the rubbish~~
- walk the dog

1 put things you don't want outside for someone to collect ......take out the rubbish......

2 buy some food .......................................

3 put plates, knifes, forks, etc. into a machine for washing .......................................

4 clean plates, bowls, knives, forks, etc. by hand
.......................................

5 give your dog some exercise .......................................

6 put clothes in the garden and bring them back inside again .......................................

## *have to* and *should*

**3** Choose the correct words to complete the sentences.

1 We **have to** / (**don't have to**) help with the cooking because Dad wants to take us to a restaurant.

2 Alice isn't very healthy at the moment. She **should** / **shouldn't** do some more exercise.

3 Sometimes Mum **has to** / **doesn't have to** work at the weekends because she's a doctor in the hospital.

4 We **don't have to** / **shouldn't** wear a uniform at our school. We can wear anything we like.

5 You **have to** / **should** take exams before you go to university.

6 Mark **doesn't have to** / **shouldn't** leave dirty plates in his bedroom. It's disgusting!

**4** Write sentences that are true for you. Use *have to* / *don't have to*.

1 do / homework / every evening
I don't have to do homework every evening.

2 wash / the car / on Saturday
.......................................

3 load and unload / the dishwasher / in the morning
.......................................

4 study / French
.......................................

5 get up / early / on Sunday
.......................................

6 walk / to school
.......................................

7 help / my parents / at home
.......................................

**5** Write some advice for the problems. Use *should / shouldn't* and the verbs in brackets.

1 I've got a science exam next week. I'm worried about it. (study)
You should study every day this week.

2 I'm really hungry, but my parents aren't here to make me dinner. (prepare)
.......................................

3 There's a party at Jake's house on Saturday night, but it's my mum's birthday too and she wants to go to a restaurant with the family. (go)
.......................................

4 I think Sarah looks terrible today. Her new clothes are horrible. (tell)
.......................................

5 There's a new mobile phone and I want it, but it's very expensive and I haven't got a lot of money. (buy)
.......................................

**6** Complete the conversation with the phrases below.

- don't have to do ■ have to go ■ ~~have to make~~
- have to tidy ■ should do ■ should read
- should try to sleep ■ should clear ■ shouldn't be
- shouldn't get up

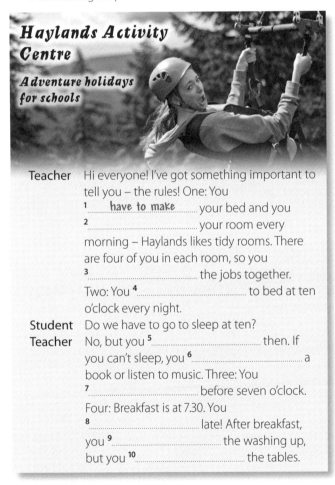

**Haylands Activity Centre**
*Adventure holidays for schools*

Teacher  Hi everyone! I've got something important to tell you – the rules! One: You ¹ **have to make** your bed and you ² .......................... your room every morning – Haylands likes tidy rooms. There are four of you in each room, so you ³ .......................... the jobs together. Two: You ⁴ .......................... to bed at ten o'clock every night.

Student  Do we have to go to sleep at ten?

Teacher  No, but you ⁵ .......................... then. If you can't sleep, you ⁶ .......................... a book or listen to music. Three: You ⁷ .......................... before seven o'clock. Four: Breakfast is at 7.30. You ⁸ .......................... late! After breakfast, you ⁹ .......................... the washing up, but you ¹⁰ .......................... the tables.

**7** CHALLENGE!  Think about what you do at home and answer the questions for you.

- Write two things that you have to do and two things you don't have to do at home.
- What two things should you do to help more?
- What shouldn't you do?

# Vocabulary and grammar  The first Thanksgiving

## V Opposite adjectives

**1** Match the opposite adjectives to the words below.

- dangerous ■ ill ■ happy ■ hard-working ■ rich

1 well ≠ ............................
2 poor ≠ ............................
3 sad ≠ ............................
4 lazy ≠ ............................
5 safe ≠ ............................

**2** Choose the correct adjectives to complete the sentences.

1 It's **happy** / (**dangerous**) to drive when you are tired.
2 Some families are very **poor** / **lazy**. They haven't got much money and the children have to work.
3 I am usually **ill** / **happy** when I'm with my friends, because we have a lot of fun.
4 Teachers are **safe** / **hard-working**, because they have to prepare lessons, mark homework and teach.
5 I don't feel very **rich** / **well**, so I'm going to bed.

**3** Write sentences with the adjectives in brackets.

1 My brother is richer than me. .................... (rich)
2 ................................................ (lazy)
3 ................................................ (ill)
4 ................................................ (safe)
5 ................................................ (sad)

## Past simple: be

**4** Complete the conversation with *was*, *were*, *wasn't* or *weren't*.

the Titanic

A lifeboat from the Titanic

Amy   **1** ___Were___ you at home last night?
Jim   No, I **2**................. My brother and I
      **3**................. at the cinema. Why?
Amy   There was a great programme about the *Titanic* on TV. Countess Lucy Noël Martha
      **4**................. a very rich woman with a lot of money. The man, Thomas William Jones, was the opposite to her. He **5**................. rich at all, but quite poor. He **6**................. a worker on the ship. But they **7**................. both in the same lifeboat. Lucy and Thomas **8**................. very different, but for the rest of their lives, they **9**................. friends.
Jim   It sounds really interesting.
Amy   Yes, it **10**.................

## Past simple: can

**5** Study the factfile. Are the sentences true (T) or false (F)? Correct the false ones.

> ### Transatlantic crossings!
>
> **1838:** *Great Western*, one of the world's first steamships, crosses the Atlantic. It can carry 200 people.
>
> **1901:** Marconi sends the first radio signal across the Atlantic
>
> **1926:** Telephone engineers make a telephone call between the UK and the USA.
>
> **1939:** One of the first passenger aeroplanes flies from the USA to Europe.
>
> **1962:** A satellite sends the first television image from the USA to Europe.

1 In 1930, Europeans could make telephone calls to the USA.
2 In 1900, people couldn't travel across the Atlantic by ship.
3 Before 1901, people couldn't send radio signals across the Atlantic.
4 People couldn't fly to the USA before the 1930s.
5 After 1962, Europeans could watch TV images from the USA.
6 People could communicate quickly across the Atlantic before 1900.

**6** Choose the correct words to complete the text.

> Schools **1was** / (**were**)/ **wasn't** very different in the 19th century to today. Of course, they **2couldn't** / **wasn't** / **weren't** full of computers like they are today. Probably the most important 'gadget' for a 19th century school child **3was** / **were** / **wasn't** a slate – a blackboard the children **4were** / **weren't** / **could** write on.
>
> It **5was** / **could** / **were** impossible for some children to go to school. Why? Money. Poor families **6weren't** / **couldn't** / **wasn't** send their children to school. Instead these poor children **7weren't** / **were** / **could** workers in factories, farms or rich people's houses.
>
> But, it **8could** / **wasn't** / **couldn't** all bad for poor children. Some of them **9could** / **was** / **were** go to 'Dame schools'. These **10were** / **wasn't** / **was** schools in people's houses. There was usually one teacher, often a woman. It **11couldn't** / **were** / **wasn't** easy for the teacher – her house **12wasn't** / **couldn't** / **was** full of noisy children! She **13was** / **couldn't** / **wasn't** teach them a lot of things, maybe only the alphabet and some numbers.
>
> Life **14couldn't** / **could** / **was** different for rich children. Some children **15was** / **were** / **wasn't** at boarding school. Others **16could** / **wasn't** / **were** have their lessons at home with a tutor.

**7** **CHALLENGE!** Think back to 2010. What could you do, or not do? Use the ideas below or your own ideas.

- dance ■ play ■ read ■ ride a bike ■ swim ■ write

## V  Health

**1** **Choose the correct words to complete the sentences.**

1 Dan can't walk at the moment because he's got a painkiller / (broken leg)

2 I always **burn** / **sneeze** when there's a dog or cat near to me.

3 I sometimes feel **dizzy** / **an injection** when I am somewhere high up.

4 Mum says she's got a **headache** / **burn** because my music is very loud.

5 I can't speak today because I've got a **sore throat** / **medicine**. Perhaps I need some **plasters** / **antibiotics**.

6 I need some **medicine** / **bandage** because my **cough** / **antibiotics** is really bad – I can't sleep at night.

7 Babies and children have lots of **burns** / **injections** to protect them for the rest of their lives.

8 That's a bad **cold** / **burn**. You should put a **bandage** / **painkiller** on it.

9 Dad's got **the flu** / **a cut** from a knife, so I'm looking for **a plaster** / **an injection** for him.

10 A **sneeze** / **The flu** is similar to a **cold** / **plaster**, but it's much worse. You usually have to take **painkillers** / **burns**.

**2** **Complete the advice with the words below.**

■ antibiotics ■ bandage ■ injection ■ medicine
■ painkiller ■ plaster

1 'I've got a headache.' 'You should take a
      _painkiller_ .'

2 'I've got a small cut on my finger.' 'Here, put this
      ............................... on it.'

3 'I often travel to countries outside of Europe.' 'You should have an ............................... before you go.'

4 I've got a virus. I can't take antibiotics, so I've got some ............................... from the chemist's to help me feel better.

5 'I've got a chest infection.' 'You should see the doctor and get some ...............................'

6 'My knee hurts when I run.' 'Why don't you put a ............................... on it?'

## V  Health problems

**3** **Put the words in the correct category below.**

■ a broken arm ■ a bruise ■ a blocked nose
■ a nosebleed ■ a stomach ache ■ a temperature
■ a sprained ankle ■ hay fever ■ ill ■ shivery ■ sick
■ toothache ■ unwell ■ weak

1 feel

   ............................................
   ............................................

2 have got
   _a broken arm_
   ............................................
   ............................................

**4** **Complete the sentences with the words below and a suitable verb.**

■ hayfever ■ nosebleed ■ shivery ■ temperature ■ weak

1 My head is very hot. I think I ....._'ve got_..... a
   _temperature_ .

2 I'm not stong today. I don't want to move a lot.
   I ............................... .

3 Dad is sneezing a lot today. I think he ...............................
   ............................... because of those flowers.

4 Sit down! You ............................... a ............................... . There's blood on your face.

5 'I ...............................' 'You should put on a warm jumper.'

## Talking about illness

**5** 🔊 **3.09  Listen to the conversation. What does Dylan think is the problem with Helen?**

1 She feels sick.
2 She's got the flu.
3 She doesn't like antibiotics.

**6** 🔊 **3.09  Listen again and order Dylan's questions and suggestions in the correct order.**

......... Have you got a fever?
......... Do you feel sick?
......... I think you should go home and go to bed.
......... Are you OK?
......... I think you should see a doctor.
......... What's the problem?

**7** 🔊 **3.09  Listen again and complete Helen's responses.**

1 Are you OK?
   No, I'm not. I ............................... .

2 What's the problem?
   I've got a ...............................
   and ............................... a really sore throat.

3 Do you feel sick?
   No, ............................... .

4 Have you got a fever?
   I ............................... .

5 I think you should go home and go to bed.
   Yes, ............................... .

**8** **CHALLENGE!  Imagine that you are Helen's mother or father. You are worried about her. Write a conversation between you and Helen.**

**1** Before you read, use your dictionary to find the meaning of these words. Then write the words, a translation and an example sentence in your vocabulary books.

1 skin ..........................................................................
2 blood ......................................................................
3 tooth / teeth .......................................................
4 operation .............................................................
5 barber ...................................................................
6 blacksmith ..........................................................
7 plague ...................................................................
8 swellings ..............................................................

**2** Read the text. Match summary sentences A–F to paragraphs 1–4. There are two sentences that you do not need.

A Operations were very basic and dangerous.
B We can use some ideas from the past.
C Doctors weren't interested in doing operations.
D A few treatments were sensible.
E Medieval medicine was dangerous and didn't often work.
F Doctors wore special clothes.

**3** Complete the sentences with information from the text. Use your own words if possible.

1 Doctors were ...........*expensive*..........., so a lot of people couldn't go to them.
2 If someone wasn't well, they could put .................................................. on their skin.
3 People often died after operations because there weren't any ....................................... .
4 There were some bad ideas for treating plague, such as ....................................... .
5 Doctors today sometimes use ideas from medieval times, such as leeches and ............................... .

**4** Match the highlighted words in the text to definitions 1–10. There are two definitions that you do not need.

1 (adjective) terrible, awful
..................................*horrific*..................................

2 (noun) links
..........................................................................

3 (adjective) not good, with no use
..........................................................................

4 (adjective) without many options
..........................................................................

5 (noun) jobs
..........................................................................

6 (adjective) normal
..........................................................................

7 (noun) amount of money
..........................................................................

8 (verb) like or be attracted to
..........................................................................

9 (noun) issues
..........................................................................

10 (adjective) silly, ridiculous, stupid
..........................................................................

# Medieval medicine

**1** Medical knowledge in Europe in medieval times (476–1453) was very limited. There were doctors in medieval times, although they were usually only for rich people and they weren't very good. Most
5 people couldn't pay a doctor's fees. For poor people, there was the wise woman. These women could make medicines from plants and animals! Most medicines were useless and some were so dangerous that people could die. Here are some doctors and
10 wise women's treatments:

⊕ For general illness: Make cuts on your body, or put a leech on your skin, so that the 'bad' blood comes out.

⊕ Toothache: Burn a candle near the bad tooth, or
15 touch a dead man's tooth.

⊕ Fever: Eat spiders.

⊕ Skin problems: Put wolf skin on the bad areas.

*Small creatures called leeches were put on people's skin to take out 'bad' blood.*

**2** Operations were horrific. There were no painkillers. Death was common – there were often
20 infections, because there were no antibiotics. There were no special doctors to do these tasks. Instead barbers and blacksmiths could do operations, because they could use their knives and tools. So the blacksmith's or the barber's was the place to go
25 with a bad tooth, or worse ...

But not all medieval medicine was dangerous. Most of these treatments for plague are nonsense, but some aren't bad – going to bed and keeping clean, for example, seem sensible!

30 ⊕ Go to bed.

⊕ Wash the body with vinegar.

⊕ Cut open the swellings.

⊕ Don't eat food that smells bad, such as fish, meat or cheese. Eat bread, fruit and vegetables.

35 ⊕ Clean the road outside the ill person's house.

*A plague doctor. There were flowers and herbs inside the mask to protect the doctor from bad smells.*

4 Modern medicine is obviously very different, but there are connections to the past. Today scientists study plants that can help us when we are ill. Some of those plants were favourites in 40 medieval times. And, some modern treatments even use leeches. They are especially helpful after certain operations. However, perhaps that's the most we can learn from medieval medicine. Anyone fancy a spider sandwich? Maybe not!

5 Complete the sentences with the words in exercise 4.

1 'I can't play football today because it's cold.' 'That's ........nonsense........! You should put a jumper on and then you can play.'

2 I need to pay for my music lessons. They're expensive – the ................................. are very high.

3 Do you ................................. going swimming this afternoon?

4 The activities at the sports centre were ................................. – there was only tennis and aerobics.

5 I can't sing or play a musical instrument. I'm ................................. at music.

6 My uncle is a film director. He's got ................................. with a lot of famous people.

7 A lot of people have a cold in winter. Colds are very

.................................

8 The first people on the boat from England to America were very ill. For them, the journey was

.................................

6 **CHALLENGE!** Study the information in the table about Islamic medicine in medieval times. Complete the table with information from the text about European medicine in medieval times. Then write sentences comparing the two.

| | Islamic medicine | European medicine |
|---|---|---|
| Who do doctors treat? | doctors treat everybody – rich and poor | |
| What do doctors make medicines from? | plants | |
| Are there special doctors who do operations? | Yes. Islamic doctors understand how the human body works. | |
| Are operations successful? | They often are. Doctors understand how to make people sleep while they have an operation. | |
| Do people suffer with infections? | Not always. Doctors use alcohol to clean cuts and stop infections during operations. | |

In medieval times:
Islamic doctors treat everybody, but European doctors only treat rich people.

# Writing  A letter of advice

## Making suggestions and giving advice

**1**  Put the words in order to make suggestions and give advice.

1  talk / you / to / why / your / don't / sister / ?

......................................................................

2  arrange / could / you / a / meeting / your / with / teacher

......................................................................

3  ask / can / your mother / to help / perhaps / you / ?

......................................................................

4  try / to talk / should / to / you / him

......................................................................

5  shouldn't / unkind / be / you / her / to

......................................................................

**2**  Read Ruth's letter and tick the problems below.

> *Dear Katy*
>
> *My friend, Alisha, always gets good marks, but I think she's having some problems now. This year, our school work is more difficult than last year. My friend is worried about her exams and she doesn't think she can get good marks. This is nonsense! She's really clever! But now she is copying other people's work from the internet, because she thinks it's better than her work. This is wrong. Our teachers are always telling us that we have to do our own work. We shouldn't copy.*
>
> *I don't want Alisha to get into trouble. I also want her to understand that she can get good marks without copying. What can I do?*
>
> *Best wishes*
>
> *Ruth*

☐ Alisha isn't doing her own work.
☐ Alisha doesn't like Ruth.
☐ Alisha doesn't usually do well in exams.
☐ Ruth wants to copy Alisha.
☐ Alisha doesn't think she can do her school work well this year.
☐ Ruth doesn't want the teachers to know what Alisha is doing.

**3**  Complete the reply with the words below.

■ could ■ perhaps ■ shouldn't copy ■ should say
■ why don't you talk

> Dear Ruth
>
> This is a difficult situation. Of course you don't want Alisha to get into trouble and you also don't want her to feel so worried about her exams. ¹................................ to her about your schoolwork this year? You ²................................ tell her you think it's very difficult and ask her if she has the same problem.
> Alisha ³................................ other people's work. It's wrong. This is difficult, but you ⁴................................ this to her. Everybody has to do their own work when they do homework or exams. ⁵................................ you can suggest she talks to a teacher. A kind teacher could help Alisha.
>
> Best wishes
>
> Katy

■ **Task**  Read the letter from Max. Write a letter of advice.

> It's my birthday next month and I want to have a big party with my friends. I want to have the party at home – a lot of people at school have parties in their homes. Their parents go out for the evening and it's great to use their house for a party. But my parents don't want to go out if I have a party! They want to stay! They don't want my friends to break things in the house, but my friends aren't bad people. We just want to have some fun, without my parents watching us!
>
> Help me!!!
>
> Best wishes
>
> Max

■ **Ideas**  Follow the instructions to brainstorm ideas.

1  What is Max's problem? Write this at the top of your page.
2  Set a time limit of two minutes and write all your advice for the problem. Write notes, or one or two words. Don't use full sentences.
3  After two minutes, stop and choose your best ideas.

■ **Plan**  Follow the instructions to plan your letter of advice. Use the letter in exercise 3 to help you.

1  Start your letter with *Dear* and end with *Best wishes*.
2  Start with a sentence that shows you understand the problem.
3  Write your suggestions in order of importance.
4  Finish with a sympathetic sentence.

■ **Write**  Write your letter of advice to Max. Use your notes and plan to help you. Remember to include language for making suggestions and giving advice.

■ **Check**  Check the following points:

■ spelling
■ grammar
■ punctuation
■ phrases for making suggestions and giving advice
■ *should / shouldn't* for advice and *have to / don't have to* for obligation

# Progress check  Unit 7

Read 1–14 and evaluate your learning in Unit 7. Give yourself a mark from 1 to 3. How can you improve?

1 I can't do this.　　　2 I have some problems with this.　　　3 I can do this well.

| A  Different shapes | Mark (1–3) | How can I improve? |
|---|---|---|
| **1** Name two parts of the body that are below the hips, two that are below the shoulders, and two that are above the shoulders. | | |
| I can identify parts of the body. | | |
| **2** Change the verbs to -er / -or nouns.<br>　　a jog　b design　c compete　d direct　e visit | | |
| I can change verbs to -er / -or nouns. | | |

| B  Keep it clean! | Mark (1–3) | How can I improve? |
|---|---|---|
| **3** Name five jobs you do at home. | | |
| I can describe housework. | | |
| **4** Name two things you have to do in the week and two things you don't have to do at the weekend. | | |
| I can talk about obligation using *have to* and *don't have to*. | | |
| **5** Write sentences with *should* or *shouldn't*.<br>　　1 I don't feel well today, but I've got a swimming lesson.<br>　　2 I'm worried about my maths exam. | | |
| I can use *should* and *shouldn't* to talk about good and bad ideas. | | |

| C  The first Thanksgiving | Mark (1–3) | How can I improve? |
|---|---|---|
| **6** List three problems in Constance Hopkins's diary. | | |
| I can understand a text about European settlers in the USA in 1620. | | |
| **7** Write opposite adjectives.<br>　　a dangerous　b well　c hard-working　d poor | | |
| I can use antonyms of adjectives. | | |
| **8** Write past simple sentences.<br>　　1 I / be / tired　2 they / be / on a boat　3 it / not be / cold | | |
| I can use the past simple form of *be*. | | |
| **9** Change the sentences to the past simple.<br>　　1 Billy can swim.　　　　　　2 We can't sing very well. | | |
| I can use *can* in past simple sentences. | | |

| D  What's wrong? | Mark (1–3) | How can I improve? |
|---|---|---|
| **10** Name a treatment for the problems.<br>　　a headache　b burn　c cough | | |
| I can use vocabulary about health problems and treatments. | | |
| **11** Complete the collocations.<br>　　a a ................. leg　b ................. dizzy　c ................. a fever | | |
| I can use illness collocations. | | |
| **12** Write sentences describing health problems. Then give advice.<br>　　1 I / a sore throat　2 I / well　3 I / sleep | | |
| I can talk about illness and give advice. | | |

| E  A letter of advice | Mark (1–3) | How can I improve? |
|---|---|---|
| **13** Write some advice for the problem: I am unhappy when my mum is at work in the evenings. | | |
| I can make suggestions and give advice. | | |
| **14** Write a letter of advice for the problem: My friend wants me to go out all the time and it's difficult to do my homework. | | |
| I can write a letter of advice. | | |

# 8 Life story

## Vocabulary Life's ups and downs

### V Life stages

**1** Complete the sentences with the life stages below.

■ be born ■ die ■ fall in love ■ get a job ■ get divorced
■ ~~get married~~ ■ go to university ■ have a baby ■ retire

1 'Do you want to ...**get married**.... when you're older?'
   'No, I don't want a husband.'
2 It's sad when husbands and wives ........................... It
   can be very sad for their children.
3 My aunt's baby could ........................... today!
4 Claire wants to ........................... and be a mother.
5 You have to ........................... if you want to be a doctor.
6 Characters in books and films ........................... with
   each other quickly. It's not realistic!
7 Tom wants to ........................... . He wants some money.
8 My grandfather doesn't want to ........................... . He
   loves his job!
9 It's very sad when people ........................... .

### V Jobs

**2** Choose the correct jobs to complete the sentences.

1 You need a (builder)/ factory worker / lawyer to build
   or repair a house.
2 My dog is unwell, so I need to take it to the **vet** /
   doctor / nurse.
3 An **engineer** / architect / accountant helps
   businesses with their money.
4 My aunt is a **scientist** / nurse / engineer. She studies
   the chemicals in plants.
5 An **architect** / electrician / engineer is putting some
   new lights in our house.
6 'I want to be a **scientist** / builder / teacher.'
   'Do you want to work in primary or secondary schools?'
7 Andy is interested in designing machines, so he
   wants to be an **engineer** / waiter / architect one day.
8 Dad is a **plumber** / electrician / lawyer, so he put the
   bath, sink, shower and toilet in our house.

### V insight Adjective suffixes: -ful and -al

**3** Change the nouns to adjectives. Use suffixes -ful or -al.

1 music ......**musical**......
2 wonder ...........................
3 nature ...........................
4 success ...........................
5 beauty ...........................
6 profession ...........................
7 peace ...........................
8 politics ...........................

**4** Choose the correct adjectives to complete the
sentences.

1 Grace can sing and play the piano. She's very
   beautiful /(musical)/ peaceful.
2 *Avatar* was a very **natural** / musical / successful film.
   It made almost 3,000 million dollars!
3 I think Paris is a very **political** / beautiful / musical
   city. The buildings are very attractive.

4 Mum's car isn't very **powerful** / natural / beautiful. It
   can't go up hills very fast.
5 'I've got a place at university!'
   'That's **political** / peaceful / wonderful! Well done!'
6 I don't like zoos. Animals should live in their
   **successful** / natural / powerful environments.

**5** Complete the text with the words below.

■ a baby ■ ~~born~~ ■ lawyer ■ married ■ peaceful
■ political ■ university ■ successful

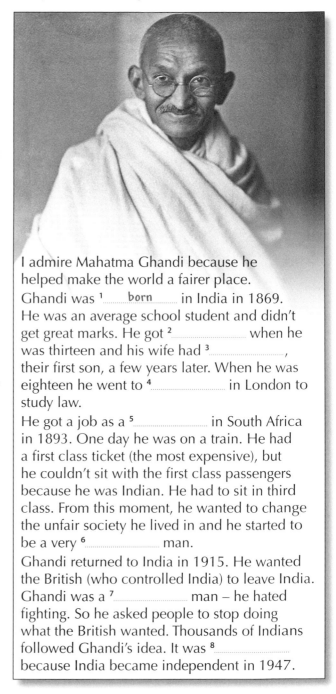

I admire Mahatma Ghandi because he
helped make the world a fairer place.
Ghandi was [1] ....**born**.... in India in 1869.
He was an average school student and didn't
get great marks. He got [2] ........................... when he
was thirteen and his wife had [3] ...........................,
their first son, a few years later. When he was
eighteen he went to [4] ........................... in London to
study law.
He got a job as a [5] ........................... in South Africa
in 1893. One day he was on a train. He had
a first class ticket (the most expensive), but
he couldn't sit with the first class passengers
because he was Indian. He had to sit in third
class. From this moment, he wanted to change
the unfair society he lived in and he started to
be a very [6] ........................... man.
Ghandi returned to India in 1915. He wanted
the British (who controlled India) to leave India.
Ghandi was a [7] ........................... man – he hated
fighting. So he asked people to stop doing
what the British wanted. Thousands of Indians
followed Ghandi's idea. It was [8] ...........................
because India became independent in 1947.

**6** **CHALLENGE!** Choose someone you admire and
write a timeline of life events for them. Use the
internet to find the dates for their life events.

# Grammar  The human story

## V  Past time expressions

**1  Imagine that today's date is Wednesday 21st January 2014. Match times and dates 1–6 to time expressions a–f.**

1  21st November 2013 ....e..
2  July 2004 .........
3  17th / 18th January 2014 .........
4  6.15 p.m., Tuesday 20th January 2014 .........
5  January 2013 .........
6  Monday 19th January 2014 .........

a  a decade ago
b  last weekend
c  last year
d  the day before yesterday
e  ~~two months ago~~
f  yesterday evening

**2  Replace the words in bold with past time expressions. Use the words in brackets to help you.**

1  From 1810 to 1830, life was hard for the workers. (early)
   In the early 1800s

2  From 1900 to 2000, there was a lot of political change. (20th)

3  I was very unhappy **before**. (past)

4  My mum was at school **between 1980 and 1989**. (80s)

5  **From 1995 to 1999** mobile telephones were very popular. (late)

6  I was a big fan of cartoons **between the ages of three and seven**! (little)

## Past simple affirmative: regular verbs

**3  Complete the groups with the past simple form of the verbs below.**

■ carry ■ chat ■ decide ■ play ■ retire ■ stop ■ try ■ walk

1  Most regular verbs .........................................
2  Verbs ending in -e .........................................
3  Verbs ending in consonant -y .........................................
4  Verbs ending in a short vowel and a consonant
   .........................................

**4  Complete the sentences with the past simple affirmative form of the verbs below.**

■ dance ■ disappear ■ reply ■ survive ■ ~~travel~~

1  Last year my friends and I ....travelled.... around Europe by train.
2  We can't find our cat. It ......................... yesterday.
3  Jennie ......................... to my email on Monday.
4  There was a terrible fire, but everyone in the building was lucky – they all ......................... .
5  The party was great. We ......................... all night!

## Past simple affirmative: irregular verbs

**5  Correct the mistakes in bold in the sentences.**

1  I **haved** a bad cold. ....have....
2  The train **leaft** at 3.30. .........................
3  They **goed** to drama club with me. .........................
4  Dad **weared** a uniform to work. .........................
5  I **singed** in a band. .........................
6  My grandparents **comed** to stay. .........................

**6  Put the verbs in brackets in 1–5 into the past simple. Then match 1–5 to sentence endings a–e.**

1  We ......................... (see)
2  My mum ......................... (write)
3  In the noughties, many people ......................... (think)
4  DVDs ......................... (become)
5  When my mum was little, my grandmother
   ......................... (make)

a  clothes for her.
b  her first email in 1995.
c  a new play at the theatre last weekend.
d  popular in the late 1990s.
e  that mobile phones with cameras were very expensive.

**7  Complete the text with the past simple affirmative form of the correct verbs in brackets.**

Perhaps the most important event in human history in recent years is the invention of the internet. In the mid 1960s, some computers [1] ....used.... (stop / use) telephone lines to communicate. Computer engineers [2] ......................... (want / talk) better communication and so they [3] ......................... (start / study) to study new ways of linking computers. In 1969, ARPANET, an early version of the internet, [4] ......................... (connect / say) the computers of four American universities.

In 1971, Ray Tomlinson [5] ......................... (write / hear) a computer programme for sending emails.

At the end of the 1970s, computers [6] ......................... (close / arrive) in the shops and by the early 1980s, computers [7] ......................... (become / appear) in some schools for students to use. They were still very expensive and most weren't linked.

A big change [8] ......................... (use / come) in 1989 when Tim Berners-Lee [9] ......................... (think / find) of the World Wide Web – a system that every computer could use to communicate.

In the 1990s, sending emails and surfing the net [10] ......................... (become / want) part of everyday life.

**8  CHALLENGE!  Ask someone from an older generation when they first used computers and what they thought of them. For example, find out if computers were:**

■ Easy to use?        ■ Exciting?
■ Cheap to buy?       ■ Something you used every day?

**Write a short paragraph.**

# Vocabulary and grammar  Great writers

## V  Types of writing

**1  Complete the sentences with the words below.**

■ article ■ fiction ■ non-fiction ■ ~~novel~~ ■ play ■ poem
■ script ■ short story

1  I always take a really long ............**novel**............ with me on holiday because I love reading stories.
2  I prefer stories to facts so I like reading ............................ .
3  My favourite poet is Sylvia Plath. She wrote a very famous but sad ............................ called *Daddy*.
4  The film director was angry because the actors forgot the words in the ............................ .
5  I love reading ............................ because I want to learn about real things.
6  We saw a fantastic ............................ last night. It was Shakepeare's *Romeo and Juliet* at the theatre.
7  I read a great ............................ last weekend. It didn't take long to read because it was only five pages long.
8  There was a really interesting ............................ about life in the 1800s in my history magazine.

**2  Write examples for each type of writing.**

1  short story *The Hound of the Baskervilles by Arthur Conan Doyle*
2  article ............................
3  fiction ............................
4  non-fiction ............................
5  novel ............................
6  play ............................
7  poem ............................
8  script ............................

## Past simple: negative

**3  Rewrite the past simple affirmative sentences to make them negative.**

1  I jogged around the park this morning.
   *I didn't jog around the park this morning.*
2  You studied a lot last weekend.
   ............................
3  Jennie visited Edinburgh last summer.
   ............................
4  You made the beds on Saturday.
   ............................
5  The children wrote these poems.
   ............................

## Past simple: questions and short answers

**4  Put the words in the correct order to make questions.**

1  did / what / you / last summer / see / in Madrid / ?
   *What did you see in Madrid last summer?*
2  wear / grandma / in the 1960s / did / mini-skirts / ?
   ............................
3  to school / you / did / cycle / yesterday / ?
   ............................
4  you / who / visit / in the holidays / ?
   ............................

5  arrive / did / Kelly / when / ?
   ............................
6  buy / where / that coat / did / you / ?
   ............................

**5  Choose the correct short answers.**

1  Did Shakespeare write poems?
   (Yes, he did.) / King Lear. He wrote poems and plays.
2  What famous characters did Agatha Christie create?
   Yes, she did. / Hercule Poirot and Miss Marple.
3  Did you and your friends enjoy the play last night?
   No, we didn't. / Yes, we did. It was a great play.
4  Did you see Franz Kafka's house in Prague?
   No, I didn't. / Yes, I did. I didn't have time.
5  Where did the Brontë sisters live ?
   They lived in Yorkshire. / No, they didn't.
6  What novels did you study last term?
   Yes, we did. / We read Wuthering Heights.

**6  Choose the correct words to complete the conversation about Marie Colvin.**

James  Mum, look at this newspaper [1](article / script) about Marie Colvin, the American war journalist. I [2]knowed / didn't know anything about her before I [3]read / listened this. She was amazing.

Mum  She was. I think she was one of the best journalists in the world. She died a few years ago.

James  That's right. She died in 2012. [4]You did / Did you know about her when she was alive?

Mum  Yes, [5]I did / she did. I often read her news reports and she wrote articles in *The Sunday Times*. Her articles were great. She [6]not write / didn't write a lot of details about the politics or the fighting. She wrote about the terrible things that happened to ordinary people in war.

James  This article says that in 1999 she helped save some people's lives in East Timor.

Mum  What [7]do she / did she do?

James  1,500 women and children were in danger. Soldiers wanted to kill them. There were some journalists there, too. Most of the journalists didn't [8]wanted / want to stay, so they left. Marie [9]doesn't / didn't leave. She stayed and reported the story. In the end, the soldiers [10]not kill / didn't kill anyone, because the world knew about the problem, thanks to Marie.

Mum  It was awful when she lost her eye. When [11]it / did it happen?

James  In 2001. She was in Sri Lanka. A bomb exploded near her and part of it hit her in the face.

Mum  It [12]didn't stop / stopped her working! She's someone I really admire.

James  Me too.

**7  CHALLENGE!  Write a short paragraph about Marie Colvin. Use the information in exercise 6. Research her life on the internet to find out more about her.**

**V** **insight** Collocations with *take*

**1** **Choose the correct words to complete the sentences.**

1 Take **part** /(care)when you go out today. The weather is awful.
2 Why don't you take **control / place** of the drama club? Everybody listens to you.
3 You're working too hard. You should take a **break / test**.
4 Can you take **care / a photo** of us in front of this building, please?
5 I studied all weekend and now I'm ready to take **a test / control**.
6 Where does the party take **place / turns**?
7 Would you like to take **control / part** in a competition?
8 We hate doing the washing up, so we take **turns / care**. I do it one day and my brother does it the next.

**2** **Complete the text with collocations with *take*.**

My brother, Sam, is learning to drive at the moment. Mum and Dad are teaching him. They take ¹ .....turns..... – Dad teaches Sam one week, Mum does it the next week. It's funny to listen to them in the car. Mum always says, 'Sam! There's a car. Take ² ..................... – don't hit it!' Dad doesn't let Sam decide what to do. He shouts, 'Drive slowly! Turn! Stop! Start!' Dad should let Sam take ³ ..................... – I'm sure Sam knows when to stop and start! As for me, I don't take ⁴ ..................... in this family drama. I just sit in the back of the car and smile! At the end of each lesson, Sam and Mum or Dad all need to take ⁵ ..................... – they are all so angry with each other!

Sam can take ⁶ ..................... soon. It takes ⁷ ..................... in the centre of our town. If he passes, he can drive without Mum and Dad in the car! On that day, I want to take ⁸ ..................... of him next to the car. It would be a nice picture!

### Talking about your weekend

**3** 🔊 **3.10** **Listen to the conversation. Tick the things Eden did last weekend.**

☐ went to a birthday party
☐ saw someone get married
☐ stayed at her grandparents' house
☐ went to a concert
☐ danced
☐ listened to a band
☐ had a baby

**4** 🔊 **3.10** **Complete the sentences with one word only. Then listen again and check your answers.**

1 ..................... you have a good weekend?
2 It ..................... fantastic.
3 That ..................... fun.
4 ..................... was the wedding?
5 It was a .....................!
6 Oh no! ..................... ?

**5** 🔊 **3.10** **Choose the correct questions. Then listen again and check your answers.**

1 Did you have a good weekend? / How about your weekend? Yes, I did. It was fantastic.
2 How was the wedding? / Where was the wedding? It was nice.
3 What about your weekend? / Was there some good music? No! It was a disaster!
4 Why? / How? The band was terrible!
5 How was the party? / Really? Yes, the singer was awful.

**6** **Choose the best responses.**

1 Did you have a good time?
   a That sounds good.　　b No! It was a disaster!
2 I lost my bag!
   a Wow! Lucky you!　　b Bad luck!
3 Really?
   a Yes, I was surprised.　　b How was your weekend?
4 I went to see my favourite team play basketball.
   a Poor you!　　b How brilliant!
5 I was really ill.
   a That was a shame.　　b What about your weekend?

**7** **Complete the dialogue with suitable phrases.**

Holly　Hi! Elliot. Did ¹ ..................... weekend?
Elliot　No, ² ......................
Holly　³ .....................? Why?
Elliot　There was a football match between our school team and Westbridge High on Sunday. On the way, there was a problem with my dad's car. So we had to stop.
Holly　⁴ .....................!
Elliot　I decided to walk to the match. But, I was late, so I started to run. Then I fell and I really hurt my ankle.
Holly　⁵ .....................! Are you OK now?
Elliot　Yes, I'm OK now, but I got to the match late so I couldn't play. Our team lost 5–2! And you? ⁶ .....................?
Holly　⁷ ....................., thanks. I stayed at Grace's house.
Elliot　That ⁸ ......................
Holly　Yes, it was fun.

**8** **CHALLENGE!** **Write a dialogue between the singer and his friend at the wedding weekend. Use the phrases in exercises 4, 5 and 6 to help you plan your dialogue.**

**1  Answer the questions.**

1  Do you like reading stories? What type?

.............................................................

.............................................................

2  Who is your favourite author? Why?

.............................................................

.............................................................

3  What stories did you enjoy reading or watching when you were a child?

.............................................................

.............................................................

**2  Match paragraph headings A–F to paragraphs 1–4. There are two headings you do not need.**

A  Was chocolate his favourite food?

B  Dahl's life in his stories.

C  Dahl's stories on the screen and stage.

D  A world-famous writer.

E  Dahl becomes a millionaire!

F  What is it that readers like?

**3  Read the text again. Are the sentences true (T) or false (F)? Correct the false ones.**

1  Dahl wrote his first novels before 1970.

2  *Matilda* and *The Witches* are plays, not films.

3  Dahls' novels are quite serious.

4  Dahl didn't start writing children's stories before he had his own children.

5  Dahl had a teacher called Mrs Trunchball.

6  Dahl tested chocolate bars when he was a boy.

**4  Answer the questions.**

1  What were the titles of the first children's novels Dahl wrote? .................................

2  What Dahl films could people see for the first time in the noughties? .......................

3  When did Roald Dahl die? .................

4  What can visitors to London go to see if they are Dahl fans? ...................................

5  Did Dahl enjoy his life at boarding school? Why / why not? .......................................

**5  Match the highlighted words in the text to definitions 1–12.**

1  (verb) pleases, makes someone or something happy
   ............ delight ............

2  (noun) versions, different forms .......................

3  (adjective) around the world .......................

4  (adjective) frightened .......................

5  (noun) the years when people are children

   .......................

6  (noun) things you watch at a theatre .......................

7  (adjective) unkind, evil .......................

8  (adjective) liked by a lot of people .......................

9  (verb) find out about .......................

10  (noun) opinions and thoughts .......................

11  (noun) something you remember from the past

   .......................

12  (noun) people in a story .......................

# The world of Roald Dahl

**1**

Is there a child who doesn't know the stories of Roald Dahl? His work delights millions of us in our childhood. He wrote his first children's
5  stories, *James and the Giant Peach* and *Charlie and the Chocolate Factory* in the 1960s, but the characters are just as popular today as they
10  were in the past.
As well as reading the books, children today often discover Dahl's characters through
15  plays and films.

**2**

Recent films of Dahl's books include *Fantastic Mr Fox* (2009) and *Charlie and the Chocolate Factory* (2005). The scripts weren't written by
20  Dahl – he died in 1990 – but that didn't stop the fans watching! *Charlie and the Chocolate Factory* was very popular – the film made almost 500 million dollars worldwide! Other film adaptations include *Matilda* (1996) and
25  *The Witches* (1990). Now there are also popular musical versions of these two stories. Lists of things to do in London usually suggest a trip to the theatre to see these shows.

C

30 Millions of people love Dahl's work years after he wrote the stories. Why? Perhaps it's because the characters make us laugh and they can make us scared. Dahl knew what children liked, but how? He began to write books for children
35 after his own children were born. He couldn't do it before then, he said.

D

Dahl sometimes used people and events from his childhood in his stories. He went to
40 boarding school, which he hated. Some of the teachers were unkind. The cruel teacher in *Matilda* – Mrs Trunchball – was like some of Dahl's teachers. But Dahl had good memories, too. Sometimes, Cadbury – a British chocolate
45 maker – sent a small box to every boy at Dahl's school. Inside the box were new chocolate bars! The boys ate them and sent comments to Cadbury. A dream job! Can you guess which story this memory found its way into?!

6 **Complete the sentences with the words in exercise 5.**

1 For most of my ........childhood........ I lived in the USA. We came to the UK when I was eleven.
2 Are there any good ........................... on at the theatre at the moment?
3 My sister hates spiders. She always feels ........................... when she sees one.
4 Some people hurt animals. It's very ........................... to do this.
5 Nelson Mandela is famous ........................... . Everybody knows who he is.
6 My favourite novel is *Alice in Wonderland* and I like the film ........................... with Johnny Depp.
7 My baby cousin ........................... everyone in the family because he's always happy and smiling.
8 What's your favourite ........................... from last summer?
9 My teacher wrote a lot of ........................... on my short story. They were very helpful.
10 I don't like the ........................... in this film. They're all unkind.
11 We ........................... a lot about Dahl's life on the internet.
12 Going to the theatre is very ........................... in my country.

7 **Write the infinitive form of the underlined irregular verbs in the text. Add these verbs to your irregular verb page in your vocabulary book.**

1 wrote ........write........
2 made ...........................
3 knew ...........................
4 began ...........................
5 ate ...........................
6 sent ...........................
7 found ...........................

8 **CHALLENGE! Write a paragraph about your favourite Roald Dahl story, or a story by another writer. Describe the most important characters and write what happens in the story.**

# Writing  A narrative

## Narrative adverbs

**1** **Choose the correct narrative adverbs.**

1 I didn't know anybody in my new class **soon / at first**.
2 Pippa opened the door and **immediately / at last** she saw who it was – Grandad was there!
3 It was a horrible journey, but **at last / immediately**, after five hours, we arrived home.
4 We made some dinner and **at first / soon** everybody sat at the table to eat.
5 **At first / Suddenly** there was a very loud noise and we all looked up.

**2** **Complete the text with the narrative adverbs below.**

■ at first ■ at last ■ immediately ■ soon ■ suddenly

## My evening at the TV studios

A week ago, my friends Miranda and Josh got three tickets to see my favourite TV talent competition at a TV studio. They asked me to go with them. I said yes ¹......................, of course!

On the day of the show, I went to meet my friends outside the TV centre. ²...................... I couldn't find them because there were a lot of people, but then I saw them. We had to wait for someone to check our tickets. But we didn't wait very long – ³...................... we went into the studio!

There were lots of interesting things to see like the film crew, and all the lights and cameras. We waited more than half an hour for the show to start, but ⁴...................... the presenters came into the studio. Everybody cheered!

We watched ten different singers. Each one sang and then the judges talked about their act. Then it was time to find out who was the winner. ⁵...................... Miranda shouted, 'Look! We're on TV!' And there we were! All three of us were on the large TV screens inside the studio. We went crazy!

Zoe

**3** **Answer the questions about the text in exercise 2.**

1 Where did Zoe, Miranda and Josh go?

2 Where did they meet?

3 What did they see at the studio?

4 Who did they watch at the studio?

5 What happened at the end?

**4** **Complete the sentences to make them more interesting. Use the words and punctuation below.**

■ because ■ soon ■ stormy ■ Why? ■ wonderful

1 Caitlin and I went to the concert, ...................... it was Caitlin's birthday.
2 The band was amazing. The singer sang some ...................... songs.
3 My brother helped me and I ...................... felt better.
4 The weather was ......................, so we stayed inside.
5 I went to the theatre. ...................... Because my favourite actor was in a play there!

---

### WRITING GUIDE

■ **Task**  Write a narrative about a memorable day.

■ **Ideas**  Choose one of the following ideas or think of an idea of your own. Make notes about the day. Think about the verbs you want to use. Are they irregular? Look up the irregular past simple forms.

  ■ a family event
  ■ your birthday last year
  ■ the day you met your best friend
  ■ an day you spent with friends in the summer

■ **Plan**  Use the narrative in exercise 2 as a model. Organize your ideas into paragraphs.

  Paragraph 1:  Introduction: what did you do?
  Paragraph 2:  at the start of the day
  Paragraph 3:  later in the day
  Paragraph 4:  how you feel about the day

  **Look at the notes you made.**

  ■ Can you make your writing more interesting?
  ■ Can you join the ideas together using connectors (*but, also, too*, etc.)?
  ■ What interesting adjectives and narrative adverbs can you use?
  ■ Can you include questions and exclamations?

■ **Write**  Write your narrative. Use your notes and plan to help you. Remember to use the past simple and narrative adverbs.

■ **Check**  Check the following points:

  ■ spelling
  ■ grammar
  ■ punctuation
  ■ past simple regular and irregular forms
  ■ use of narrative adverbs
  ■ use of interesting adjectives
  ■ different paragraphs for different topics

# Progress check Unit 8

Read 1–15 and evaluate your learning in Unit 8. Give yourself a mark from 1 to 3. How can you improve?
**1** I can't do this.　　**2** I have some problems with this.　　**3** I can do this well.

| A  Life's ups and downs | Mark (1–3) | How can I improve? |
|---|---|---|
| **1** Name two life stages for children and two for adults. | | |
| I can talk about life stages. | | |
| **2** Name five different jobs. | | |
| I can identify types of jobs. | | |
| **3** Change the nouns into adjectives.<br>　a nature　b wonder　c power　d beauty | | |
| I can use adjective suffixes -ful and -al. | | |

| B  The human story | Mark (1–3) | How can I improve? |
|---|---|---|
| **4** Imagine it is Wednesday 13th July. Write about the dates using time expressions.<br>　1 Tuesday 12th June　2 May　3 January　4 1900–1999 | | |
| I can use past time expressions. | | |
| **5** Change the sentences to the past simple.<br>　a I like you.　b He watches TV.　c We play football. | | |
| I can use past simple affirmative regular verbs. | | |
| **6** Write past simple sentences.<br>　1 Jess / go / to New York　2 they / sing / together | | |
| I can use past simple affirmative irregular verbs. | | |

| C  Great writers | Mark (1–3) | How can I improve? |
|---|---|---|
| **7** What did Mary Shelley and Emily Dickinson write? | | |
| I can understand a text about great writers. | | |
| **8** Name three types of fiction and one type of non-fiction. | | |
| I can identify different types of writing. | | |
| **9** Write past simple negative sentences.<br>　1 we / not see / the film　2 I / not study / German | | |
| I can use the past simple negative. | | |
| **10** Write questions.<br>　1 who / write / *Jane Eyre* / ?　2 what / dress / you / buy / ? | | |
| I can ask questions using the past simple. | | |
| **11** Complete the short past simple answers.<br>　a No, I ............................ .　b Yes, we ............................ . | | |
| I can use past simple short answers. | | |

| D  Moments to remember | Mark (1–3) | How can I improve? |
|---|---|---|
| **12** Write five collocations with *take*. | | |
| I can make collocations with *take*. | | |
| **13** Write phrases for the situation:<br>　a ask about someone's weekend　b respond to the question<br>　c express interest　d express sympathy | | |
| I can talk about a weekend in the past. | | |

| E  A narrative | Mark (1–3) | How can I improve? |
|---|---|---|
| **14** Write five narrative adverbs. | | |
| I can use narrative adverbs. | | |
| **15** Write a short paragraph about a memorable day. | | |
| I can write a narrative. | | |

# 9 Changes

## Vocabulary  A new model

**1  Match the sentence halves.**

1  Twenty years ago, Dad had long hair ....f....
2  I was a bit overweight, so .........
3  My sister's got lots of freckles .........
4  I was blonde when I was little .........
5  Jake is medium height – .........
6  I'm not fat or thin – .........
7  Naturally, my sister's got brown hair, .........
8  We went on holiday to Spain and .........

a  I started to exercise more.
b  I'm medium weight.
c  but now I've got brown hair.
d  but now she's got dyed hair – it's black.
e  we all came back tanned.
f  but now he's bald.
g  on her nose.
h  he's about 175cm tall.

**2  Which word in each group is the odd one out?**

1  medium height  overweight  medium weight  thin
2  dyed  blonde  tanned  bald
3  moustache  beard  bald  glasses
4  thin  freckles  medium weight  overweight

**V  insight**  *like*

**3  Study the information about brother and sister, Andy and Jen. Then complete the sentences using the correct forms of *be like*, *look like* or *like*.**

|  | Andy | Jen |
|---|---|---|
| Personality | friendly<br>lazy | friendly<br>hard-working |
| Appearance | tall<br>thin<br>blonde, curly hair<br>freckles | short<br>medium weight<br>dark, curly hair<br>tanned |
| Hobbies | sport – playing and watching football, playing tennis and basketball, cycling<br>art – painting | music – singing, acting and dancing<br>art – painting<br>cycling<br>not into sport |

1  In some ways, they ......are like...... each other in personality. For example, they are both friendly.
2  But in other ways they ................ each other: Andy is lazy and Jen is hard-working.
3  Andy ................ Jen. He's tall and she's short, he's thin and she's medium weight.
4  Andy and Jen ................ art, especially painting.
5  Jen ................ football, but Andy ................ it.

## Materials

**V  Materials**

**4  Write the materials next to the clues. Use the words below.**

■ clay ■ leather ■ marble ■ metal ■ plastic ■ wood

1  It's found in the ground. We use it to make plates and bowls. ......clay......
2  Michelangelo, the famous Italian sculptor, used this to make his statues. ................
3  Knives, forks and spoons are made from this. ................
4  This is made from chemicals. It can be soft or hard. It is used for children's toys, bags, cups and computers. ................
5  Shoes and boots are usually made from this. It comes from animals. ................
6  This is a natural material. We get it from trees. People make furniture with it. ................

**5  Choose the correct words to complete the text.**

Look through the ¹**glass**/ **marble** window of any clothes shop and you will see a model which ²**likes**/ **looks like** a person wearing the latest fashions. It's a mannequin of course and some mannequins are very realistic. They have hair and their faces have eyes, noses and mouths – some even have ³**freckles**/ **blonde**. Other mannequins don't have details on their faces and they are often ⁴**bald**/ **medium**, with no hair at all.

Today mannequins are usually made of fibreglass – a mixture of glass and plastic. But in the mid-1800s, they were often made of ⁵**stone**/ **wax** – which was a problem when they got hot under lights because they changed shape and melted! They didn't ⁶**like**/ **look like** people then!

**6  CHALLENGE!  Write a short description of the sculpture and the models in it. Use the questions to help you plan your description.**

■  What material do you think the sculpture is made of?
■  Who are the models and what are they doing?
■  Do you like the models? Why / why not?

## going to: plans

**1** Complete the sentences with the affirmative (✔) and negative (✘) forms of *going to* and the verbs below.

■ buy ■ go ■ play ■ ~~start~~ ■ tidy ■ write

1 Leah ___is going to start___ her new job as a teacher next week. (✔)
2 We ................................ to the cinema at the weekend. It's closed. (✘)
3 I ................................ any more clothes. I've got too many things to wear! (✘)
4 'You ................................ your bedroom today!' 'OK, Mum!' (✔)
5 Maddie and Alisha ................................ a play together. (✔)
6 Rob ................................ football at the weekend because he's got a broken ankle. (✘)

**2** Complete the text with the correct form of *going to* and the verbs in brackets.

Next summer holiday, I ¹ ___'m going to do___ (do) something useful with my time. I ² ................................ (not spend) lots of time watching TV. I ³ ................................ (walk) some dogs! I ⁴ ................................ (not get) any money – I ⁵ ................................ (work) as a volunteer! I ⁶ ................................ (not work) alone. My friends Ben and Vikki ⁷ ................................ (join) me. My older brother, Jordan ⁸ ................................ (organize) everything. The four of us ⁹ ................................ (help) some old or ill people in our town. It's sometimes difficult for these people to walk their dogs, so we ¹⁰ ................................ (do) it for them!

**3** Write sentences with affirmative or negative forms of *going to* so that they are true for you.

1 this weekend / I / go to the cinema
___This weekend I'm not going to go to the cinema.___
2 my parents / go to work / tomorrow
................................
3 I / watch TV / later
................................
4 my friends / come to my house / after school
................................
5 I / cycle home / later
................................
6 my family and I / travel to the UK / in the summer
................................

**4** Put the words in the correct order to make questions.

1 see / you / am / I / going / tomorrow / to / ?
___Am I going to see you tomorrow?___
2 you / going / to / your / grandfather / visit / are / ?
................................
3 on holiday / we / are / going / go / to / where / ?
................................
4 what / you / going / watch / film / are / to / ?
................................
5 travel / how / you / to / to / Italy / going / are / ?
................................

**5** Choose the correct options to complete the dialogue.

Mrs Jones  Hello, Ryan! How are you? How are your mother and your brother, Alex?
Ryan  Hi, Mrs Jones. We're all very well. Mum's really happy! She ¹ ___'s going to get___ married on Saturday!
Mrs Jones  That's wonderful! So, who ² ................................ ?
Ryan  A really nice man called David. I like him.
Mrs Jones  So, your life ³ ................................ !
Ryan  Yes, it is!
Mrs Jones  ⁴ ................................ house?
Ryan  Yes, we are. After the wedding, Mum and David ⁵ ................................ on holiday for a week. Alex and I ⁶ ................................ with our grandparents. Then we ⁷ ................................ to a bigger house. It's got three bedrooms. I ⁸ ................................ a bedroom with Alex anymore!

1 a are going to get
  b get
  ⓒ 's going to get
2 a is she going to marry?
  b she is going to marry?
  c she going to marry?
3 a are going to change
  b is going changing
  c is going to change
4 a You are going to move
  b Going you to move
  c Are you going to move
5 a are going to go
  b is going to go
  c isn't going to go
6 a am going to stay
  b are going to stay
  c going to stay
7 a aren't go to move
  b 're going to move
  c going us to move
8 a isn't going to share
  b am I going to share
  c 'm not going to share

**6** **CHALLENGE!** Imagine you are one of the characters in the family in exercise 5. Write an email to a friend about what is going to happen in your life.

# Vocabulary and grammar  A new year

**1** Complete the table with the noun forms of the verbs.

|  | -ion | -ment |
| --- | --- | --- |
| **1** achieve | – | achievement |
| **2** amuse |  |  |
| **3** attract |  |  |
| **4** celebrate |  |  |
| **5** decorate |  |  |
| **6** disappoint |  |  |
| **7** donate |  |  |
| **8** educate |  |  |
| **9** enjoy |  |  |
| **10** entertain |  |  |
| **11** govern |  |  |
| **12** inform |  |  |
| **13** pay |  |  |
| **14** predict |  |  |

**2** Choose the correct verbs and complete the sentences with the noun form of the verbs.

1 My grandad had a bad ......education...... (educate / donate). He didn't learn a lot at school.

2 Are you enjoying the circus, everybody?  And now for your ........................ (amuse / pay), the clowns are here for you to see!

3 The ........................ (govern / enjoy) is going to spend more money on schools!

4 Do you want to help us pay for the zoo animals? You can make a ........................ (predict / donate) of £2 a month.

5 Why don't you use the internet to help you with your homework? There's a lot of ........................ (inform / decorate) there.

6 Mum makes a ........................ (pay / attract) of £10 a month for my mobile phone.

## will

**3** Write predictions about your future with *will* or *won't*.

1 I / pass my school exams
   I will pass my school exams.

2 I / travel / around Europe

3 I / buy a house

4 I / get a good job

5 I / get married

6 I / have children

**4** Tick the correct sentences. Rewrite the sentences that are incorrect.

1 We will always be happy in this house. ☐
2 Cara will to pass her exams. ☐
3 You won't enjoy the film. It's boring. ☐
4 Mum and Dad will be happy with my results. ☐
5 I am won't see you for a long time. ☐
6 The weather to be will awful tomorrow! ☐

**5** Choose the correct words to complete the text.

For ¹governments / predictions around the world, trying to predict the future is important. They need to make plans. What are the ²education / predictions for the world over the next few years? By 2030, people say there ³will / won't be many more people on Earth: up to 8 billion. Will some people be hungry? Probably. Or perhaps we ⁴will / won't grow enough food for everyone – a great ⁵achievement / entertainment!

What about energy? Scientists ⁶find / will find ways of making electricity more efficiently. We ⁷won't / didn't use gas or oil. Probably all of us ⁸won't / will travel by electric cars.

Will the world of work change? Perhaps there ⁹won't be / are many office workers in the future – people ¹⁰will work / worked from home more.

**6** **CHALLENGE!**  What do you think will happen to the world in 2030? Write a short paragraph with your predictions. Include ideas about:

■ entertainment
■ travel
■ houses and homes

## V Phrasal verbs

**1   Choose the correct words to complete the dialogue.**

Flo   Hey, Oli! Look, there's a notice about a young enterprise business competition!

Oli   What does it say?

Flo   'Calling all students! Can you ¹come up with / give up a business idea? ²Look for / Put together your business plan and give it to Mr Collins by June 30ᵗʰ. The school will ³look for / go ahead some good business people to help you.'

Oli   We should do it. What about that idea you had about helping people sell things online?

Flo   Yes. I know lots of people who haven't got time to take photos and put them online. So they ⁴find out / give up and don't sell anything! We can take the photos, write a description of the items, sell them on a website and monitor the sales. Perhaps we should ask for 5% of the sales price?

Oli   Sounds good. Why don't we ⁵come up with / set up a Facebook page?

Flo   Great idea. I think we should ⁶go ahead / give up with your idea!

**2   Match the definitions to the phrasal verbs in exercise 1.**

a   create ........set up.........
b   prepare ...........................
c   search ...........................
d   start to do ...........................
e   stop trying ...........................
f   think of ...........................

## V On the phone: phrasal verbs

**3   Complete the sentences with the verbs below.**

■ call ■ cut ■ get ■ hang ■ hold ■ look ■ pick ■ put

1   'Tom, can you say bye and ..........hang.......... up, please? I need to make a call.' 'OK, Mum.'

2   How annoying! I was on the phone to Holly and I pressed the wrong button. I ...................... her off!

3   I need to ...................... up the school's phone number. I don't know it.

4   'Jess! Can you ...................... up the phone, please? It's ringing.' 'OK!'

5   'Did you ...................... through to Jack?' 'Yes, but he's watching a film. He asked me to ...................... back.'

6   'Can you ...................... me through to Mrs Butler, please?' 'Yes. Can you ...................... on, please?'

## Talking on the phone

**4   ◉ 3.11   Listen to the telephone conversation. Are the sentences true (T) or false (F)? Correct the false ones.**

1   Megan speaks to Dan's dad.
2   Dan is on his bike.
3   There's a course at the Arts Centre this afternoon.
4   Megan wants to study painting.
5   Megan is going to call the Arts Centre today.

**5   ◉ 3.11   Listen again and complete the informal phrases.**

| Informal | Formal |
|---|---|
| Who's calling, please? | Who's calling, please? |
| ¹...................... Megan. | This is Megan Yates. |
| ²...................... I speak to … | ...................... ...................... through to … |
| I'm ³......................, he's not here … | ...................... Mr Matthews isn't there. |
| ⁴...................... to leave a message? | ...................... a message? |
| I'll ⁵...................... him you called. | ...................... the message. |

**6   ◉ 3.12   Complete Megan's formal conversation with the phrases below. Then listen and check.**

■ Can I take ■ Could you put me ■ I'll give him
■ I'm afraid ■ This is ■ Who's calling

Receptionist   Hello, East-West Arts Centre. Can I help you?

Megan   Hello. ¹...................... through to Jed Matthews in the sculpture studio, please?

Receptionist   Yes, of course. ²......................, please?

Megan   ³...................... Megan Yates.

Receptionist   Just a moment, Ms Yates. ⁴...................... Mr Matthews isn't there. ⁵...................... a message?

Megan   Yes, please. Could you ask him to call me on 0782 224 224 to give me some information about the course, please?

Receptionist   0782 224 224. Yes, no problem. ⁶...................... the message.

Megan   Thank you. Goodbye.

Receptionist   Goodbye.

**7   Complete the table in exercise 5 with the formal phrases in exercise 6.**

**8   CHALLENGE!   Write a phone conversation between Mr Matthews and Megan's mum. Use phrasal verbs and the phrases in exercise 5.**

**1** Read the text. Match headings A–H to paragraphs
1–6. There are two headings that you do not need.

**A** Who can take part?
**B** What can my project be about?
**C** Are you going to apply?
**D** What will I get in the end?
**E** What will happen next?
**F** How many people do the programme every year?
**G** Why should I do it?
**H** When did the programme start?

**2** Read the text again. Choose the correct options.

1 The people organizing the Youth in Action
  programme are
    a the European Commission.
    b people from the UK.
    c adult supervisors.

2 The programme hopes to
    a save the environment.
    b make films.
    c get young people working together.

3 An important idea behind the programme is that
    a it will help people who are poor.
    b anybody can take part.
    c improve young people's health.

4 You have to have a youth worker on your team if you
    a only have three other members.
    b are younger than 18.
    c are over 30.

5 The money for the project
    a comes from the European Commission.
    b is provided by your team.
    c comes from future employers.

6 The Youthpass
    a is part of your report.
    b gets you a place at a university.
    c describes the skills you used on the project.

**3** Choose the best summary sentences for the
paragraphs.

Introduction
  a The European Commission runs a programme to help
    young Europeans work together.
  b There's a programme to get young people to come
    up with interesting projects.

Paragraph 1
  a There are lots of topics the projects can be about.
  b You can only do things connected with art and sport.

Paragraph 2
  a I think the programme is interesting, because you can
    learn how to be European.
  b The programme gives young people a chance to
    learn new skills.

# YOUTH IN ACTION

Do you want to meet people from other countries?

Are you energetic and creative?

Do you like new experiences?

**Yes?** Read on! Perhaps the Youth in Action
programme is for you!

The European Commission runs the Youth in Action
programme to encourage young people to be active
citizens. Its aim is to build good links between young
people across Europe. It's about young people taking
5 control of their futures. YOU have to come up with a
project idea. YOU will work with an adult supervisor,
but YOU are in charge!

**1** ...................................................................

It's your choice! Past project themes include:

10 • the environment – making useful things from
     old materials
   • nature – looking after animals in danger
   • the arts – making films about different
     cultures
15 • sport – using team sports to get to know
     different people.

**2** ...................................................................

Good question! You've got school work and exams.
You're busy! Will the Youth in Action programme

20 mean more work? Yes, but … this is non-formal learning, not schoolwork. It takes place outside of school. You will learn important skills such as:

- putting together a project
- working with people from different backgrounds
25
- setting up a team
- planning your finances.

### 3

Everybody! One of the programme's goals is inclusion. It wants all types of young people to
30 take part and that includes people from different cultures, or those with health problems, or people who can't usually join in activities because they haven't got enough money.

### 4

35 Yes? Great! Get together with a group of four or more people aged between 18 and 30. You can apply if you are under 18, but you'll need a youth worker on your team – someone who normally works with young people as a volunteer or as part
40 of their job. Next, meet and discuss your hopes for the project. Put together a plan. Then apply via the European Commission website!

### 5

After you apply, you'll need to wait about three
45 months. Next you'll find out if the Commission thinks you can go ahead. You'll get a grant from the Commission, so you'll have the money to run your project. You'll agree dates for the project and you'll have to do the project in this time. When the project
50 is finished, you'll send a report to the Commission.

### 6

A Youthpass. This document will give details of everything you did. It's the kind of information that universities are interested in (and future employers
55 when you go to job interviews). But, most important of all, you'll have a great experience and memories to last a lifetime!

**Paragraph 3**
a The programme is open to all young people.
b The programme is only open to people with problems.

**Paragraph 4**
a People who want to apply have to work in a team and plan the project together.
b You need a 30-year-old youth worker.

**Paragraph 5**
a It takes about three months to get the money.
b The European Commission checks the projects at different stages.

**Paragraph 6**
a You can show your Youthpass when you want to get a job.
b At the end, you get a Youthpass which gives details about your achievements.

**4 Match the highlighted words in the text to definitions 1–8.**

1 (verb) to ask for something in a formal way, usually by writing or completing a form ............ apply ............
2 (noun) people's history, family, education, experience
   ..................................................
3 (noun) people who give you a job ..................................................
4 (verb) to give support ..................................................
5 (noun) the fact of being part of something
   ..................................................
6 (verb) to organize and be in control of something
   ..................................................
7 (noun) money that somebody gives to you by an organization or government ..................................................
8 (noun) the money you have ..................................................

**5 Complete the sentences with the correct form of the words in exercise 4.**

1 I am terrible at looking after my ............ finances ............ . I never have money to spend on things I need!
2 We come from different .................................., but we are really good friends.
3 I'm going to .................................. for a job at the sports centre this summer.
4 'I want to join the drama club. Who did I need to speak to?' 'Miss Baker. She .................................. the club.'
5 .................................. like to know what your skills are before they give you a job.
6 My brother is going to get a .................................. to pay for his engineering course.
7 Our sports club thinks .................................. is very important – everybody can join in.
8 I'm going to .................................. Liz to write more stories. I think she will be an amazing writer one day.

**6 CHALLENGE! Write an email to a friend to tell them about the Youth in Action programme. Summarize what the programme is about, who organizes it and what you have to do to take part in it. Use your answers to exercise 3 to help you plan your email.**

# Writing  An informal email

**V  Informal language for emails**

**1**  Match informal sentences a–h to gaps 1–6 in the email. There are two sentences that you do not need.

a  How do you feel about it …
b  I can't wait!
c  It sounds fantastic!
d  It's terrible!
e  I was really sorry to hear …
f  P.S. Good luck in your music exam!
g  When is your exam?
h  Write again soon.

---

Subject: Summer holidays!

Hi Ashley!

Thanks for your last email.
**1**

that you didn't pass your music exam on Monday.
**2**

now? It's good that you can take the exam again next week.

I went to an amazing concert last month with Mum and Dad. My brother Cameron plays the piano and he was in the concert in a huge theatre. The music was wonderful and we were all really proud of Cameron. I'm sure you'll be like him one day.

It's good to hear about your summer holiday plans. **3**

How long are you going to stay in Prague? Prague is beautiful. I hope you like old buildings, because there are a lot to see! The cafés are great too. It's fantastic just walking around the streets. It's really good that you're going to the mountains in the Czech Republic, too! What a great place to explore. Will you go mountain biking and climbing?

I'm excited about my holidays too. We're going to go to Spain in July! We're going to fly to Malaga, then we're going to stay in Seville.
**4**

After that we're going to go to Granada and visit the Alhambra. I'm really excited about that. It's like a palace from a storybook! I'll take lots of photos.

I'm going to be really busy in August, because I've got a job at a restaurant near the beach where we live. So, I won't be on the beach a lot this year, but I'll meet lots of people, so I think I'll have a great time!
**5**

Lots of love

Lucy
**6**

---

**2**  Read the email again and answer the questions.

1  What did Ashley do on Monday?
2  What did Lucy do last month?
3  What is Ashley going to do next week?
4  Where is Ashley going to go in the summer?
5  What do you think Ashley will see and do on holiday?
6  Where is Lucy going to go on holiday?
7  What is she going to do there?
8  Where is she going to work after her holiday?

## WRITING GUIDE

■  **Task**  Imagine you are Ashley. Write Ashley's informal email to Lucy about his plans for the summer.

■  **Ideas**  Make notes about Ashley's plans for the summer and use your answers to exercise 2 to help you. Think of things you can write to make Ashley's email more personal and interesting.

Ask questions about Lucy:
■  ask what she did last week / month
■  ask what she is going to do
Describe past events
■  say what you did (Exercise 2, question 1)
■  say why you enjoyed / didn't enjoy it (Exercise 2, question 2)
Describe plans
■  say what you are going to do next week (Exercise 2, question 3)
■  say where you are going to go in the summer (Exercise 2, question 4)
■  say what you are going to see (Exercise 2, question 5)

■  **Plan**  Plan your email. Organise your notes into paragraphs. Use Lucy's email to help you.

Paragraph 1:  Ask questions about your friend. Include reactions to what they wrote in their last email.
Paragraph 2:  Write about something that happened last week.
Paragraph 3:  Write about your plans for the summer. Finish your letter with a personal comment or question.

■  **Write**  Write Ashley's email. Use your notes and plan to help you. Remember to use informal language.

■  **Check**  Check the following points:
■  spelling
■  grammar
■  punctuation
■  informal phrases
■  questions and details to make your email personal and interesting
■  different paragraphs for different topics

# Progress check Unit 9

Read 1–12 and evaluate your learning in Unit 9. Give yourself a mark from 1 to 3. How can you improve?
**1** I can't do this.　　**2** I have some problems with this.　　**3** I can do this well.

| A  A new model | Mark (1–3) | How can I improve? |
| --- | --- | --- |
| **1** Name five words that you can use to describe someone. | | |
| I can describe people. | | |
| **2** Name five different materials. | | |
| I can identify different materials. | | |
| **3** Complete the sentences with *be like*, *like* or *look like*.<br>　1  I .................................. dad – we've both got brown hair.<br>　2  I .................................. Vik – she's my best friend.<br>　3  I .................................. Mum – we're both hard-working. | | |
| I can use *like* in different ways. | | |

| B  A new life | Mark (1–3) | How can I improve? |
| --- | --- | --- |
| **4** Write sentences with *going to*.<br>　1  Tim / study / French / next year<br>　2  I / not go / to the cinema<br>　3  you / see Jack / later / ? | | |
| I can use *going to* to talk about future plans. | | |

| C  A new year | Mark (1–3) | How can I improve? |
| --- | --- | --- |
| **5** Write a sentence about something people do at New Year in these countries.<br>　**a** Japan　**b** Mexico　**c** Scotland | | |
| I can understand a text about New Year celebrations. | | |
| **6** Write noun forms of the verbs. Use *-ion* or *-ment*.<br>　**a** achieve　**b** celebrate　**c** disappoint　**d** predict | | |
| I can transform verbs into nouns using suffixes *-tion* and *-ment*. | | |
| **7** Write sentences with *will*.<br>　1  we / be happy / after our exams<br>　2  they / not move / house | | |
| I can use *will* to talk about future predictions. | | |

| D  A new business | Mark (1–3) | How can I improve? |
| --- | --- | --- |
| **8** Write phrasal verbs next to the definitions.<br>　**a** think of ................................<br>　**b** research ................................<br>　**c** calculate ................................ | | |
| I can use phrasal verbs. | | |
| **9** Name four phrasal verbs about phone calls. | | |
| I can use phrasal verbs to talk about phone calls. | | |
| **10** Write four useful phrases (two formal and two informal) for making phone calls. | | |
| I can use formal and informal phrases for phone calls. | | |

| E  An informal email | Mark (1–3) | How can I improve? |
| --- | --- | --- |
| **11** Complete the informal phrases.<br>　**a** I .................................. wait!<br>　**b** .................................. of love<br>　**c** .................................. again soon | | |
| I can use informal phases in an email. | | |
| **12** Write an informal email to a friend about your plans for the weekend. | | |
| I can write an informal email about future plans. | | |

**V** Holiday places

**1** Write the words next to the clues below.

- campsite ■ coast ■ island ■ lake ■ ski resort ■ temple
- theme park ■ volcano

1 a large place with exciting rides ..... **theme park** .....
2 a large area of water with land all around it

.....
3 a mountain which is open at the top – very hot gas and lava come out of it .....
4 an area of land with water all around it .....
5 a place to stay in a tent or caravan .....
6 land that is next to the sea .....
7 a place to go to do winter sports .....
8 a building which people use to pray .....

**2** Choose the correct words to complete the email.

> **Greetings from Sicily**      ↗ ✎ ✖
>
> Hi Jim
>
> Greetings from Sicily – the largest ¹lake / island in the Mediterranean Sea! I'm staying in a tent on a ²campsite / theme park on the east ³coast / bridge. From my tent I can see Mount Etna – the tallest, active ⁴volcano / bridge in Europe. It's spectacular – there are clouds of gas coming from it right now!
>
> I arrived last Saturday by boat. We sailed into the ⁵waterfall / harbour of the port of Catania.
>
> On Monday we visited an ancient city. It's got eight ⁶ski resorts / temples from the 5ᵗʰ century BC. I really liked the one for Olympian God Zeus and his son Heracles.
>
> Yesterday we went to San Giovanni – we walked on the beautiful ⁷lakes / beaches. In the past, pirates attacked the town here, so the people built a tall ⁸tower / coast to watch out for pirates.
>
> Tomorrow we're going to go to a nature reserve called the Cava Grande di Cassibile. It's got mountains to climb and ⁹coasts / lakes to swim in.
>
> I think I'll come back in the winter. There's a nice ¹⁰ski resort / temple, so I'll bring my snowboard. How about coming too?
>
> Billy

**V** insight prepositions of place: *in*, *on* and *at*

**3** Match the sentence halves. Then add the correct preposition *in*, *on* or *at*.

1 I'll see you in the PE lesson ..... **at** ..... b
2 Manchester is near Sheffield .....
3 Did you buy those vegetables .....
4 There's a great museum .....
5 Oh no! I think my camera is .....

a the north of England.
b school tomorrow.
c home on my desk.
d the city centre next to the park.
e the market?

**V** Types of holiday

**4** Complete the sentences with the words below.

- activity ■ cruise ■ farm ■ guided tour ■ sightseeing
- study ■ summer camp ■ walking

1 Jed and I went on a ..... **walking** ..... holiday. We crossed lots of hills and our feet hurt at the end!
2 My grandmother is going on a ..... around the Caribbean on a huge ship.
3 I'd love to go on a ..... holiday because I love animals.
4 Why don't you try this ..... holiday? You can go rock climbing, mountain biking and diving.
5 My sister and I are going to stay at a ..... in the school holidays. Our parents will be at work!
6 I went on a ..... around Edinburgh Castle because I wanted to know more about its history.
7 Last year I went on a ..... holiday in Spain. I learnt how to speak Spanish!
8 I want to go on a ..... holiday to Rome! I want to see the Colosseum, the Vatican and the Pantheon.

**5** Choose the correct words to complete the text.

> ### South America – West coast tour
>
>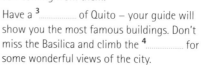
>
> **Day 1–2:** Start ¹ ..... **b** ..... Quito, a beautiful city in the mountains. Some of these mountains are ² ..... – you can see clouds of gas and ash coming from them.
>
> Have a ³ ..... of Quito – your guide will show you the most famous buildings. Don't miss the Basilica and climb the ⁴ ..... for some wonderful views of the city.
>
> **Day 3–5:** Travel to the port of Guayaquil. Join the ⁵ ..... which will take you along the coast of Peru.
>
> **Day 6:** Arrive in Salaverry. While the ship is in the ⁶ ..... , drive to Chan Chán, an ancient city with sculptures and ⁷ ..... more than 1,000 years old!
>
> **Day 7:** Travel to Arica. See what you can buy ⁸ ..... the market.
>
> **Day 8:** Join the ship again and travel to Chañaral airport.
>
> ◀ PREV   NEXT ▶   Book holiday   Flight finder

| | | | | |
|---|---|---|---|---|
| 1 | a on | ⓑ in | c at | d to |
| 2 | a volcanoes | b towers | c islands | d bridges |
| 3 | a cruise | b study holiday | c guided tour | d day trip |
| 4 | a harbour | b tower | c waterfall | d coast |
| 5 | a cruise | b coast | c temple | d campsite |
| 6 | a harbour | b volcano | c tower | d ski resort |
| 7 | a coasts | b temples | c lakes | d beaches |
| 8 | a on | b in | c to | d at |

**6** CHALLENGE! Write about a day trip or guided tour that you went on. Include the following information:

- When was it?
- Where was it?
- Who did you go with?
- What did you see?

# Grammar Adventure

## Present perfect affirmative and negative: regular verbs

**1 Complete the sentences with the present perfect form of the verbs in brackets.**

1 I _'ve travelled_ (travel) to lots of different places in my life.
2 You ........................ (not work) for a large company.
3 Liam ........................ (row) across the North Sea.
4 My grandmother ........................ (not use) an e-reader.
5 The athletes ........................ (compete) in the Olympics.
6 I ........................ (not study) Italian before.

**2 Choose the correct verbs. Then complete the text with the present perfect form of the verbs.**

Meet Jen and Brendan. They are part of the Cave Rescue Organisation (CRO) in Yorkshire. They ¹ _'ve discovered_ (finish / discover) a lot about the countryside around them – its beauty and its dangers.

The Yorkshire Dales is a national park with mountains, lakes, waterfalls and caves. Tourists ² ........................ (work / travel) to this area for years – it's very popular. A lot of them come caving here. Usually everything is fine, but sometimes people have problems and that's when Jen and Brendan, and more than 80 other volunteers with CRO can help.

The CRO ³ ........................ (help / use) thousands of people. Jen and Brendan ⁴ ........................ (rescue / watch) seven people from caves. They ⁵ ........................ (listen / climb) long distances inside caves and ⁶ ........................ (swim / stop) through deep underground rivers to find missing people. 'Caving holidays are great!' Jen says, 'but if you ⁷ ........................ (not try / not rescue) it before, you should find out how to be safe.' But it's not just people. 'We ⁸ ........................ (carry / talk) sheep and dogs out of caves too!' explains Jen. 'It's always great to see a dog back with its owner.'

## Present perfect affirmative and negative: irregular verbs

**3 Complete the sentences with the present perfect form of the verbs below.**

■ break ■ have ■ not be ■ do ■ not swim ■ not win

1 Horse riding is quite dangerous and you can get hurt. I _'ve broken_ my arm three times!
2 Kate is very kind. She ........................ a lot of work for charity.
3 Paul ........................ dinner in some famous restaurants, but he prefers eating at home.

4 I ........................ in the sea, because we live a long way away from the coast.
5 She plays the piano very well, but she ........................ a competition.
6 Mum and Dad ........................ to California before. This is their first time.

**4 Write present perfect sentences about Katy's holidays.**

■ go to Rome ✔
■ swim with dolphins ✔
■ see the Egyptian pyramids ✘
■ take lots of photos ✔
■ spend a lot of money ✘
■ be bored ✘

1 She _'s been to Rome._
2 She ........................
3 She ........................
4 She ........................
5 She ........................
6 She ........................

**5 Complete the text with the present perfect form of the verbs in brackets.**

Laura Dekker, a teenager from the Netherlands, ¹ _hasn't done_ (not do) the things other young people do.
Like other teenagers, she has been to school; she ² ........................ (study) and she ³ ........................ (take) exams, but she ⁴ ........................ (not spend) a lot of time meeting up with friends and going out. A boring life? Not at all!
Laura ⁵ ........................ (travel) around the world, but she ⁶ ........................ (go) with her parents. She ⁷ ........................ (do) most of her travelling alone.
She ⁸ ........................ (not had) rooms in hotels or a tent on a campsite – she ⁹ ........................ (sleep) in a small cabin. Why? She's a sailor. Laura ¹⁰ ........................ (sail) around the world. She ¹¹ ........................ (stay) for months of her life on her boat, *Guppy*.
Laura ¹² ........................ (be) interested in sailing since she was very young. Born in 1995, she first sailed alone at the age of six. She has wanted to sail around the world all her life, but it ¹³ ........................ (not be) easy to make her dream come true. When she was thirteen she was ready to try her world trip, but the Dutch government stopped her. They were worried about her safety.
Finally, when she was sixteen, Laura's dream came true and she became the youngest person ever to sail around the world. She ¹⁴ ........................ (not finish) her adventuring. She's got lots of sailing plans for the future.

**6 CHALLENGE! Write three sentences about adventures you have had. Then write three sentences about adventurous things you have not done, but would like to do in the future.**

_I've been on a ski trip. I haven't swum with dolphins._

# Vocabulary and grammar Travel USA

## V insight American English

**1** Replace the British English words in bold with the American English words below.

- an apartment ■ ~~fall~~ ■ eraser ■ garbage ■ pants
- soccer ■ sweater ■ yard

1  In **autumn**, the leaves on the trees are beautiful.
   fall
2  My aunt has got **a flat** in Madrid. We stay there sometimes. ............
3  Can you take out the **rubbish**, please? ............
4  How about a game of **football**? ............
5  I need some new **trousers** for school. ............
6  Put a **jumper** on. It's cold outside. ............
7  The children are playing outside in the **garden**. ............
8  Can I use your **rubber**? I've made a mistake in my homework. ............

**2** Complete the text with American English words.

> In October this ¹ ............ fall ............, my family and I are going on ² ............ to Glasgow in the UK. We're going to stay in an ³ ............ near the city centre. It's got a small ⁴ ............ so, if the weather is good, we can sit outside. But, I think it'll be too cold! I'm going to pack a ⁵ ............ so I can stay warm. Most of the time we're going to be in the city. We're going to visit museums and famous buildings. We'll probably go to the ⁶ ............ too – I love watching films! We've also got tickets to see a ⁷ ............ match – Glasgow Rangers vs Manchester Utd! It'll be very exciting.
>
> My friends told me I have to try some local food – I'll definitely try some ⁸ ............, maybe with some fish. It's good to try new things, so I'm also going to buy some ⁹ ............ – I've never tried European chocolate. People say it's a bit different to ours.

## Present perfect: questions and short answers

**3** Complete the questions with the present perfect form of the verbs in brackets. Then match questions 1–6 to short answers a–f.

1  Have you seen (you / see) the *Twilight* films?  f
2  ............ (Jack / visit) Dublin? ............
3  ............ (your friends / live) in Spain? ............
4  ............ (Mum / be) to a ski resort? ............
5  ............ (David / try) rock climbing? ............
6  ............ (you and Dan / eat) Japanese food? ............

a  Yes, he has. He loves going up in the mountains.
b  No, he hasn't. But he wants to go there next year.
c  No, we haven't. Perhaps we should try it.
d  Yes, they have. Their parents worked in Barcelona.
e  Yes, she has. She went to the Alps once.
f  ~~Yes, I have. I've got them on DVD.~~

**4** Put the words in the correct order to make present perfect questions.

1  been / to / North America / have / you / ?
   **Have you been to North America?**
2  have / in a lake / swum / the children / ?
   ............
3  Lily / studied / Italian / has / ?
   ............
4  tried / your friends / have / these candies / ?
   ............
5  Harry / competed / has / a marathon / in / ?
   ............
6  you and your brother / have / visited / the USA / ?
   ............

## Present perfect with *ever* and *never*

**5** Complete the sentences with *ever* or *never*.

1  Have you ............ ever ............ seen a volcano?
2  He's ............ been to France.
3  We've ............ gone on holiday in winter.
4  Have they ............ travelled by coach?
5  I've ............ eaten sushi.
6  Has Lucy ............ worked in a cafe?

**6** Choose the correct words.

Meg  You look really well. ¹(Have)/ Has you been on ²sweater / vacation?
Ruth  Yes, I ³have / has! I've been to Canada for a month with my brother.
Meg  Wow! That sounds great. I've ⁴never / ever been to Canada.
Ruth  I had a really good time. I stayed in ⁵an apartment / a yard in Quebec.
Meg  Is Quebec the capital city of French Canada?
Ruth  Yes, it is.
Meg  I've ⁶never / ever been to a French-speaking place before. Have you ⁷never / ever studied French?
Ruth  Yes, I ⁸haven't / have. But my brother has ⁹never / ever studied French, so I had to do most of the talking!
Meg  So, ¹⁰have / has you improved your French?
Ruth  Definitely!
Meg  And have ¹¹brought you / you brought lots of things back with you? Are the shops good?
Ruth  Yes, they are. I bought some clothes – these ¹²pants / fries, for example. And I've got you a small present – some ¹³garbage / candy because I know you like sweet things!

**7** CHALLENGE! Imagine you have met an American student and you want to find out more about them and their experiences. Write five present perfect questions to ask the American student.

**V** insight **Travel collocations**

**1  Match the sentence halves.**

1  Have you booked ..b..
2  I'll buy ...........
3  When did he catch ...........
4  We go ...........
5  He packed ...........
6  Did you send ...........

a  lots of souvenirs.
b  ~~your holiday to the USA?~~
c  a postcard to your grandfather?
d  his bag carefully, so he didn't forget anything.
e  the bus to Bath?
f  abroad every summer.

**2  Complete the postcard with the words below.**

■ abroad ■ bag ■ bus ■ hotel ■ plane ■ ~~postcard~~ ■ sites

Hi Jamie

I'm sending you this [1] ......postcard...... from Lisbon in Portugal. This is the first time I've been [2] ........................ . I'm staying in a [3] ........................ with Mum and Dad. We've seen some of the sites already — the castle and the Belém Tower. Fantastic! Tomorrow we're going to catch a [4] ........................ to Évora, a town with a Roman temple! Then on Friday I have to pack my [5] ........................ because we're going to come home on Saturday. I hope I don't miss the [6] ........................!

Love

Suzanne

**V  Holidays: phrasal verbs**

**3  Match the statements to the phrasal verbs below.**

■ chill out ■ ~~get away~~ ■ get back ■ get on
■ look forward to ■ queue up ■ take off

1  'I really want to go on holiday!' .......get away.......
2  'Let's relax!' ........................
3  'I can't wait to be on holiday!' ........................
4  'What time does the plane leave?' ........................
5  'Here's the bus. Let's go!' ........................
6  'When do you return?' ........................
7  'There are lots of people buying tickets. We have to wait for our turn.' ........................

**4  Choose the correct words to complete the sentences.**

1  We're going home today. We need to (check out of) / drop off our hotel.
2  Chill out / Get into the taxi. We're going to be late!
3  We need to get away / get off the train at this station.
4  Let's get out of / get back the car and have a walk.
5  Dad is going to pick up / queue up granddad tonight.
6  We're going to set off / take off on the tour at 10 o'clock.

**Tourist information**

**5  ◎ 3.13  Complete the dialogue with the phrases below. Then listen and check.**

■ How much do the tickets cost, please?
■ Is it possible to go there today?
■ And what time does it close?
■ I'd like some information about Lindisfarne.
■ So, what time is the road open tomorrow?
■ Is there a discount for students?

Assistant  Hello. Can I help you?
Alex       Yes, please. [1] ........................
           Is it true that it's an island sometimes?
Assistant  Yes, that's right. When the sea is at its highest level, the road is covered with water. Lindisfarne becomes an island.
Alex       Wow! [2] ........................
Assistant  I'm afraid not. It's too late today.
Alex       [3] ........................
Assistant  Tomorrow the road is open from 7.15.
Alex       [4] ........................
Assistant  It closes at 14.10, but it opens again in the evening at 19.35. Do you want to visit the Lindisfarne castle?
Alex       [5] ........................
Assistant  They're £5.
Alex       [6] ........................
Assistant  Yes, there is. It's £4.50 for students.
Alex       Thank you.
Assistant  You're welcome. Goodbye.

**6  Match questions 1–6 to responses a–f.**

1  Can I help you? ...........
2  What time does the theme park open? ...........
3  What time does it close? ...........
4  How much do tickets cost? ...........
5  Is it possible to take a dog? ...........
6  Is there a discount for students? ...........

a  At 8 o'clock in the evening.
b  Yes, I'd like some information about the boat trip.
c  It opens at 10 o'clock.
d  They're £10 for adults and £5 for children.
e  Yes, they pay £8.
f  Yes, of course. They love the park area.

**7  CHALLENGE!  Write a dialogue between a tourist and a tourist office assistant about a tourist attraction. Use the expressions in exercises 5 and 6 to help you plan your dialogue.**

**1**  Read the title of the text. What do you think *Go for it!* means? Choose the best definition.

   **1**  do something quickly
   **2**  follow your goals
   **3**  travel to different countries

**2**  Read the text quickly and check your answers.

**3**  Read the text and match sentences A–H to gaps 1–6. There are two sentences that you do not need.

   **A**  Perhaps you won't be good at it.
   **B**  At the age of eight, he walked 26 miles through the mountains of Yorkshire, England.
   **C**  Sometimes you have to save a lot of money first.
   **D**  What did they usually do?
   **E**  Any competition – a five-mile run, a marathon, a cycle ride.
   **F**  People should go camping.
   **G**  He created the concept of microadventures.
   **H**  He's also camped in Greenland and walked across its icy plains.

**4**  Read the text again. Are the sentences true (T) or false (F)? Correct the false ones.

   **1**  Alistair has been interested in adventure since he was little.
   **2**  He always travels to cold places.
   **3**  He learned about animals in place.
   **4**  He didn't go abroad in 2011.
   **5**  He put ideas for adventures on the internet.
   **6**  He organized a race for people to take part in.
   **7**  He has won a lot of races.
   **8**  He wants people to think differently about their free time.
   **9**  Anyone can go on a microadventure.
   **10**  Some people find reasons not to take part in adventures.

**5**  Complete the sentences with information from the text. Use your own words if possible.

   **1**  As a university student Alistair went on adventures in his ........holidays........ .
   **2**  He started his Indian adventure on a ........................ on the east coast.
   **3**  He could swim in the lakes and rivers in Iceland because ........................ had made them warm.
   **4**  In 2011, Alistair found adventures near his ........................ .
   **5**  Alistair is not interested in winning races – he enjoys ........................ .

# Go for it!

He's walked across India. He's camped in the Arctic and he's cycled around the world. Alistair Humphreys is a true adventurer.
His adventuring started early.
5  **1** ....................................................................

When he was at university he found time in the holidays to cycle long distances in Asia, Europe and South America.

His experiences are impressive. His Indian
10  adventure started on the country's sandy east coast, where the River Kaveri meets the sea. He followed the river up through the mountains to its source. Finally, he walked down through the mountains to India's west coast.

15  Alistair has experienced the cold, too. He's spent weeks camping in the Canadian Arctic studying the animals that live there.
**2** ....................................................................

He's seen volcanoes in Iceland and has swum in
20  the volcano-heated rivers and lakes there.

Adventurers love new experiences and they often crave bigger challenges that take them further away from home. But, in 2011, Alistair had a new idea.
25  **3** ....................................................................

He encouraged people to do something new, to go on their own adventures. He did it, too. That year, he didn't go abroad, but stayed in the UK and looked for microadventures there. He didn't
30  want these adventures to cost a fortune or to take a lot of time, but, they had to be interesting.

Using the internet he connected with people and gave them challenges. The first was to enter a race.
35  **4** ....................................................................

# Go on a microadventure!

**6** Replace the words in bold with the highlighted words in the text.

1 He won a **lot of money** on the TV show.
...........fortune...........

2 The **start** of the Danube is in Germany.
..........................................

3 I always find **reasons** not to do my homework.
..........................................

4 The view from the top of the mountain was **spectacular and amazing**. ..........................................

5 I've got a great **idea and a plan** for our holidays.
..........................................

6 Is there anything you **often really want to do or have**? ..........................................

7 Look at this! It's **very small**! ..........................................

8 I gave myself a **goal to achieve** this year – learn to ski.
..........................................

**7** Complete the sentences with the correct form of the words in exercise 6.

1 Have you got a ......suggestion...... for what we can do for our science project?

2 We can't go to Australia. It costs a .......................... to get there!

3 Have you seen this .......................... phone? It's tiny!

4 Where is the .......................... of the River Thames?

5 Josh is very lazy. He's got lots of .......................... not to do exercise.

6 My sister wanted a new .........................., so she joined a drama club.

7 When my dad is very tired, he .......................... coffee!

8 The story you wrote is very ........................... You're a great writer.

**8 CHALLENGE!** Write a short text to get students in your school interested in a microadventure. Explain what a microadventure is and include some suggestions about what you can do near where you live. Remember – this should be something you have never done before.

Alistair's never won a race in his life, but he's always loved the fun of taking part.

Next he got people to think about their weekends.

40 5 ..........................................

Go shopping? Watch TV? He suggested they go somewhere new. So, what did he do? He got up early, left his home in the city and was up in the hills by lunchtime ready to go down – fast – by

45 mountain bike.

Another suggestion was to follow a river from its source to its end. Alistair has done this more than once, and it's something anyone can do. It doesn't have to be the Amazon, just a river that's

50 near you.

There are lots of excuses not to go on an adventure. You don't have time. You haven't got the money. You've never done it before.

6 ..........................................

55 But, Alistair believes, anyone can, and should, have an adventure. So, what are you waiting for?!

# Writing  A profile

## 1  Complete the text with *so* and *because*.

### My heroine:
### Rosie Swale Pope

My hero is the author and adventurer, Rosie Swale Pope. She was born in 1946 in Switzerland. Her mother was Swiss and her father was Irish. Her mother died when she was two, [1]............................ Rosie went to live in Ireland with her grandmother.

She has been an adventurer for most of her life. She's sailed around the world. She's ridden a horse across South America. She is most famous for her running. She's competed in marathons all over the world. She's run 27 marathons in 27 days! Rosie has also written several books about her adventures.

In 2002, her husband died [2]............................ he had cancer. Rosie wanted people to know more about this terrible disease, [3]............................ she decided to go on a new adventure – to run around the world! People started to find out about her trip, [4]............................ she appeared in newspapers and on TV to talk about it. This meant she had a chance to talk about her husband being ill. It's a long way around the world, [5]............................ her adventure took five years, but she did it! On her way, she also raised money for a children's charity in Russia.

I really admire Rosie Swale Pole, [6]............................ she has big ideas for big adventures. She was very sad when her husband died, [7]............................ she decided to do something positive. I love her way of thinking about life.

## 2  Answer the questions.

1  List four adventurous things Rosie Swale Pope has done.
......................................................................................................

2  Why do most people know about her?
......................................................................................................

3  What happened in 2002?
......................................................................................................

4  What did Rosie decide to do after 2002?
......................................................................................................

5  Why does the writer admire Rosie Swale Pole?
......................................................................................................

## Linking words: *so* and *because*

## 3  Read the sentences. Correct the sentences that are incorrect.

1  In 2009, Malala Yousafzai started to write a blog for the BBC **because** she wanted the world to know about life in her town in Pakistan.

2  There was fighting in her country **because** she was often scared, but she didn't give up her fight for education.

3  Girls found it difficult to get an education, **so** some people didn't want girls to go to school.

4  It was dangerous for Malala to use her own name on the blog, **so** she used the name, Gul Makai.

5  She had to leave her town, **so** it wasn't safe for her to stay.

6  The KidsRights Foundation wanted to give Malala the International Children's Peace Prize, **because** of her work to help girls have an education.

7  In 2012, she was shot **so** of her opinions about education and it made some people very angry.

8  The hospitals in Pakistan couldn't help her **because** her injuries were very bad, **because** she travelled to the UK.

---

### WRITING GUIDE

- **Task**  Write a profile of Malala Yousafzai or a hero / heroine of your choice.

- **Ideas**  Answer the questions and make notes about Malala or your hero / heroine. Use the internet to help you.

  1  What is your hero / heroine's name?
  2  What does he / she do?
  3  When was he / she born?
  4  What did he / she do as a child?
  5  What has he / she done in his / her life?
  6  What has he / she achieved?
  7  Has he / she done any charity work?
  8  Why do you admire him / her?

- **Plan**  Use the profile in exercise 1 as a model. Organize your notes into paragraphs.

  Paragraph 1:  introduction, details of when and where he / she was born
  Paragraph 2:  life as a child and after
  Paragraph 3:  interesting things he / she has done
  Paragraph 4:  things he / she achieved
  Paragraph 5:  summary, why you admire him / her

  **Think about what tenses you need to use – present simple, past simple or present perfect?**

  - Which facts are about a situation in the present (e.g. what he / she does, why you admire him / her)?
  - Which facts are about things he / she has done in their life, but with no definite time in the past (e.g. interesting things he / she has done or achieved)?
  - Which facts are things which happened at a definite time in the past (e.g. when he / she was born, when something happened)?

- **Write**  Write your profile. Use your notes and plan to help you. Remember to use the linking words *so* and *because*.

- **Check**  Check the following points:
  - spelling
  - grammar
  - punctuation
  - correct tenses to describe different types of facts and information
  - *so* and *because*
  - different paragraphs for different topics

# Progress check Unit 10

Read 1–13 and evaluate your learning in Unit 10. Give yourself a mark from 1 to 3. How can you improve?

1 I can't do this.    2 I have some problems with this.    3 I can do this well.

| A  Tourists ... Who wants them? | Mark (1–3) | How can I improve? |
|---|---|---|
| 1  Name four holiday places and five types of holidays. | | |
| I can identify holiday places and types of holidays. | | |
| 2  Complete the phrases with *in, on* or *at*. <br> a .................... the countryside   b .................... school <br> c .................... an island | | |
| I can use prepositions of place *in, on* and *at*. | | |

| B  Adventure | Mark (1–3) | How can I improve? |
|---|---|---|
| 3  Write present perfect sentences with the regular verbs. <br> 1  she / travel / around the world   2  we / not be / to Italy | | |
| I can use the present perfect with regular verbs in affirmative sentences and negative sentences to describe experiences. | | |
| 4  Complete the present perfect sentences with the irregular verbs. <br> a  He .................... (not be) to New Zealand. <br> b  You .................... (break) your leg. | | |
| I can use the present perfect with irregular verbs in affirmative and negative sentences. | | |

| C  Travel USA | Mark (1–3) | How can I improve? |
|---|---|---|
| 5  Name three holiday places in the USA. | | |
| I can understand a text about travel in the USA. | | |
| 6  Name the American English word for the British English words. <br> a  rubbish   b  trousers   c  garden   d  chips | | |
| I can use American English words. | | |
| 7  Write present perfect questions and short answers. <br> a  .................... (your teacher / teach) you the present perfect? ✔ .................... <br> b  .................... (you / be) to New York? ✘ .................... | | |
| I can use present perfect questions and short answers. | | |
| 8  Complete the sentences with *ever* and *never*. <br> a  Has he .................... listened to this band? <br> b  I've .................... watched travel programmes on TV. | | |
| I can use *ever* and *never* with the present perfect. | | |

| D  Trans–Siberian | Mark (1–3) | How can I improve? |
|---|---|---|
| 9  Match the verbs *go, buy* and *pack* with the words. <br> a  souvenirs   b  your bag   c  abroad | | |
| I can use travel collocations. | | |
| 10  Name the phrasal verbs that describe the situations. <br> a  arrive at a hotel   b  relax   c  leave a train or bus | | |
| I can use holiday phrasal verbs. | | |
| 11  Write phrases for the situations. <br> 1  ask about opening times   2  ask about ticket prices | | |
| I can use phrases to find out information for tourists. | | |

| E  A profile | Mark (1–3) | How can I improve? |
|---|---|---|
| 12  Choose the correct words. <br> a  I like him **because** / **so** he's kind. <br> b  I like swimming **because** / **so** I'm going on a beach holiday. | | |
| I can use linking words *so* and *because*. | | |
| 13  Write a profile of someone you admire. | | |
| I can write a profile. | | |

## BEFORE YOU READ

1 Read about Mark Twain. How old was he when he left school? What was his first job?
2 Read the background to the story on page 93. Who does Tom live with?

## About the author

**Mark Twain** (real name Samuel Langhorne Clemens)
**Born:** 1835 in Missouri, USA
**Died:** 1910
**Important works:** *The Adventures of Tom Sawyer* (1876), *The Prince and the Pauper* (1881), *The Adventures of Huckleberry Finn* (1884), *A Connecticut Yankee in King Arthur's Court* (1889)
**Did you know?** Mark Twain grew up in Hannibal, Missouri, on the Mississippi River. The Mississippi is a very important river in the USA. When Twain was growing up, many slaves escaped from their owners on this river. The river offered them freedom. This is where he set the story of Tom Sawyer and many of his other books.
Like Tom, Twain didn't like school. He left when he was twelve and got a job as a printer. He had many jobs in his life. He worked on boats on the Mississippi and he was a journalist. He also fought in the army during the Civil War. Later he became a writer. He had lots of pen names before he chose the name Mark Twain. He signed some of his stories Thomas Jefferson Snodgrass and W. Epaminondas Adrastus Blab.
Mark Twain loved cats. There were nineteen of them in his house when he was a child. Later, he had three dogs. He called them 'I know', 'You know' and 'Don't know'. He also loved science. His book *A Connecticut Yankee in King Arthur's Court* is about a time traveller. He travels back in time to the court of King Arthur and introduces modern technology to the King.

1 Read the extract on page 93. Where is Joe going?

2 Read the extract again. Match sentences A–G to gaps 1–7 in the extract.
   A More friends came to laugh at Tom.
   B 'You call this work?' he said.
   C He was the richest boy in St Petersburg.
   D 'I can go to the river any day.'
   E Joe began to get interested and said:
   F He sat down and ate Joe's apple.
   G Tom thought for a second.

3 **SPEAKING** Work in pairs. Answer the questions.
   1 Why is Tom painting the fence?
   2 Why do Tom's friends help?
   3 What do you think happens next?

4 **Read what happens next. What do the boys decide to do?**

## READ ON

One evening, Tom climbs out of his bedroom window. He goes to the graveyard with his friend Huckleberry Finn. They are looking for ghosts. They don't see any ghosts, but they do see a murder. Injun Joe murders Doctor Robinson. Tom and Huck don't tell anyone, because they're afraid. Injun Joe is a dangerous man. Then it's the summer holidays. There's no school and Tom wants to do something exciting. Tom, Huck and Joe Harper run away to Jackson Island.

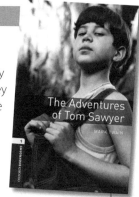

5 🔊 **3.14 Listen to the next part of the story. What are the two activities they do in the river?**

6 🔊 **3.14 Listen again. Are the sentences true (T) or false (F)? Correct the false ones.**
   1 Tom can hear planes.
   2 All the boats from St Petersburg are on the river.
   3 Bill Turner fell in the river last winter.
   4 Huck can't sleep that night.
   5 The next morning Joe isn't there.
   6 Tom tells them his story at lunch.

7 **SPEAKING Work in pairs. Answer the questions.**
   1 Why do the three boys go to Jackson Island?
   2 What do they do on the island?
   3 When do they see the boats? How many boats are looking for them?
   4 Where does Tom go?

## Writing

8 **Write an email to a friend. Tell him / her about your weekend on an island. Include the following ideas and your own ideas:**
   - who you went with (friends, family)
   - what you did (swimming, tennis, games)
   - what you ate (barbecues, a picnic)
   - why you liked it / didn't like it (fun, exciting, boring, cold).

## BACKGROUND TO THE STORY

Tom Sawyer is a twelve-year-old boy. He lives with his Aunt Polly and his half-brother Sid in St Petersburg, Missouri. This is a town in America on the Mississippi River. Tom likes swimming in the river, fishing and having adventures with his friends. He doesn't like school and he's always in trouble. Aunt Polly is often angry with him. One day, she makes him paint the garden fence. Tom doesn't want to do this. He thinks of a clever plan. He tells his friends that painting is fun. Soon all his friends are helping.

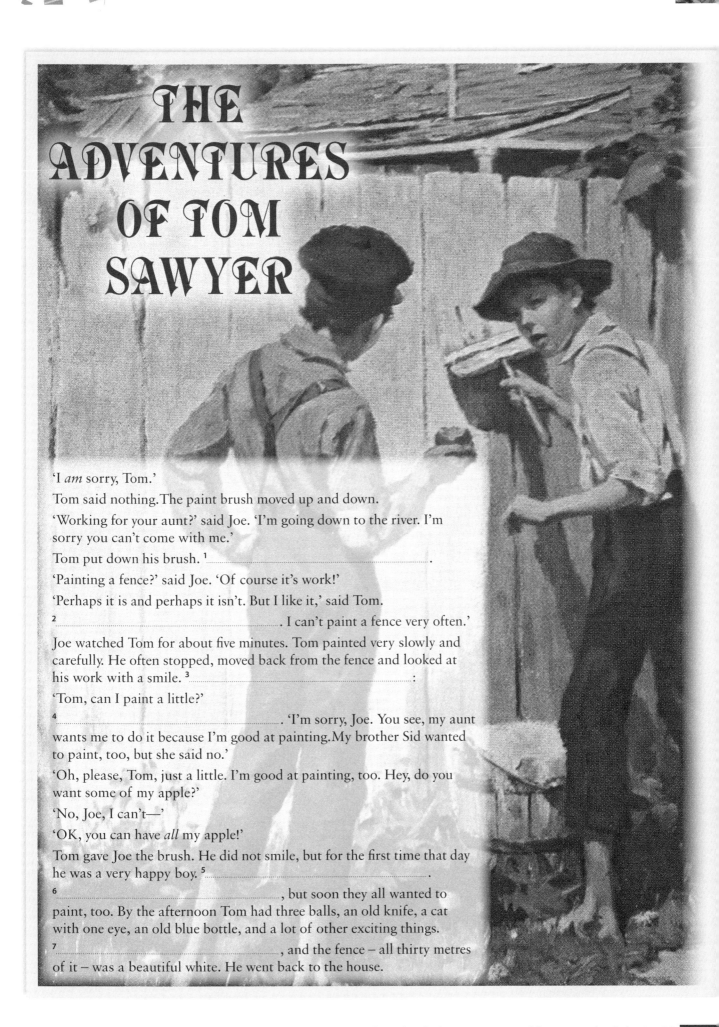

# THE ADVENTURES OF TOM SAWYER

'I *am* sorry, Tom.'

Tom said nothing. The paint brush moved up and down.

'Working for your aunt?' said Joe. 'I'm going down to the river. I'm sorry you can't come with me.'

Tom put down his brush. [1] ..................................................... .

'Painting a fence?' said Joe. 'Of course it's work!'

'Perhaps it is and perhaps it isn't. But I like it,' said Tom.

[2] ..................................................... . I can't paint a fence very often.'

Joe watched Tom for about five minutes. Tom painted very slowly and carefully. He often stopped, moved back from the fence and looked at his work with a smile. [3] ..................................................... :

'Tom, can I paint a little?'

[4] ..................................................... . 'I'm sorry, Joe. You see, my aunt wants me to do it because I'm good at painting. My brother Sid wanted to paint, too, but she said no.'

'Oh, please, Tom, just a little. I'm good at painting, too. Hey, do you want some of my apple?'

'No, Joe, I can't—'

'OK, you can have *all* my apple!'

Tom gave Joe the brush. He did not smile, but for the first time that day he was a very happy boy. [5] ..................................................... .

[6] ..................................................... , but soon they all wanted to paint, too. By the afternoon Tom had three balls, an old knife, a cat with one eye, an old blue bottle, and a lot of other exciting things.

[7] ..................................................... , and the fence – all thirty metres of it – was a beautiful white. He went back to the house.

From *The Adventures of Tom Sawyer*, Oxford Bookworms. Text adaptation by Nick Bullard.

## BEFORE YOU READ

1 Read about L. Frank Baum. What did his father build him in 1880?
2 Read the background to the story on page 95. Where does the storm blow Dorothy's house?

## About the author

**Lyman Frank Baum** (always called Frank)
**Born:** 1856 in Chittenango, New York
**Died:** 1919 in Hollywood, California
**Important works:** *Mother Goose in Prose* (1897), *Father Goose, His Book* (1899), *The Wizard of Oz* (1900)
**Did you know?** L. Frank Baum was an actor and a writer. When he was a child he didn't like his first name, Lyman. He always used his middle name, Frank. He had a bad heart, so he didn't go to school. A tutor taught him at home. Baum liked reading, writing, selling fireworks and keeping chickens. He also loved the theatre. His parents were very rich and his father built him a theatre in 1880. Baum was an actor, until he married Maud Gage in 1882. They had four sons, and every evening he invented stories for them. In 1897, he wrote his first children's book. He worked with a friend, W.W.Denslow, who was an artist and did the illustrations for Baum's books. In 1900, they published *The Wonderful Wizard of Oz*, now usually called *The Wizard of Oz*.
It was a great success and Baum became famous. He published many other books about Oz and in 1911 he moved to Hollywood. Baum wasn't a good businessman and he lost all his money, but he wrote one new book about Oz every year. After Baum died, MGM made a film of *The Wizard of Oz*. Judy Garland played the part of Dorothy.

1 Read the extract on page 95. Who runs out of the trees?

2 Read the extract again. Put the events a–h in the correct order.
  a The Emerald City is far away.
  b The Lion says that he's a coward.
  c Dorothy, Toto and the Lion sleep under a big tree.
  d The Lion and Toto become good friends.
  e Dorothy hits the Lion on the nose with her bag.
  1 f They can hear noises in the trees.
  g A lion chases Toto.
  h Dorothy tells the Lion about the Wizard of Oz.

3 SPEAKING Work in pairs. Answer the questions.
  1 Why does Dorothy not like the noises which came from the trees?
  2 Think of three adjectives which describe the lion.
  3 What do they all want to ask the Wizard of Oz for?

4 Read what happens next. What do the monkeys do to Dorothy and her friends?

## READ ON

When Dorothy and her friends reach the Emerald City they meet the great Wizard. He can help them but first he wants them to kill the Wicked Witch of the West. Dorothy, the Scarecrow, the Tin Man and the Lion leave the Emerald City. They walk to where the Witch of the West lives. But the Witch has a magic eye. She can see the friends on the road and she becomes very angry. She calls her magic monkeys. She asks them to kill the people and the dog and bring the lion to her. The monkeys leave, but when they find Dorothy, they can't kill her. The kiss from the Good Witch of the North protects Dorothy and Toto. The monkeys take the straw out of the Scarecrow, they break the Tin Man and they put the Lion in the cellar. They carry Dorothy and Toto to the Witch's house.

5 🌐 3.15 Listen to the next part of the story. What does the witch want?

6 🌐 3.15 Listen again. Complete sentences 1–10 with characters A and B.
  A Dorothy        B The Witch

  1 ................................. didn't know the red shoes were magic.
  2 ................................. only took off the red shoes to wash.
  3 ................................. was afraid of water.
  4 ................................. lost a shoe.
  5 ................................. took one of the red shoes.
  6 ................................. got angry.
  7 ................................. threw water.
  8 ................................. disappeared.
  9 ................................. put the Witch's black hat on.
  10 ................................. called fopr the magic monkeys.

7 SPEAKING Work in pairs. Answer the questions.
  1 Do you think that the Wizard can help Dorothy and her friends? How?
  2 Imagine that you have a pair of magic shoes. What wish do you make?

## Writing

8 Dorothy goes on a journey from Kansas to the Emerald City. She makes some new friends. Imagine you went on an unusual journey. Include the following:
  ■ where you went        ■ what happened
  ■ who you met           ■ how you got home

# The Wizard of Oz

So they all walked along the yellow brick road. There were many tall trees next to the road, and sometimes the three friends heard noises from animals behind the trees. Dorothy did not like these noises very much.

'How far is it to the Emerald City?' she asked the Tin Man. 'Do you know?'

'It's a long way, I think,' said the Tin Man. 'And we must be careful because—'

But just then a big lion suddenly ran out from the trees, into the road. It opened its mouth – it had long yellow teeth – and began to run after Toto.

Dorothy was afraid for Toto. She ran up to the lion and hit it on the nose with her bag. 'Don't hurt my dog!' she cried angrily. 'He's smaller than you!'

'I didn't hurt him,' said the Lion. 'Don't hit me again – please!'

'Why – you're afraid!' said Dorothy. 'Be quiet, Toto, he isn't going to hurt you. He's more afraid than you are. He's just a big coward.'

'It's true,' said the Lion. 'I am a coward. Everyone thinks lions are brave. I make a lot of noise, but I'm not brave. I'm just a coward.' And the Cowardly Lion began to cry.

Then Dorothy told him about the Wizard of Oz. 'Come with us to the Emerald City,' she said. 'I want to go back to Kansas, the Scarecrow wants some brains, and the Tin Man wants a heart. Perhaps the Wizard of Oz can make you brave.

'Oh, thank you!' said the Lion. 'I would very much like to be brave.'

And so the Cowardly Lion came with them. At first Toto was afraid of him, but very soon he and the Lion were good friends.

That night Dorothy and Toto slept under a big tree, next to the Cowardly Lion's big, warm body. In the morning they ate the last of their bread.

From *The Wizard of Oz*, Oxford Bookworms. Text adaptation by Rosemary Border.

# Literature insight 3 *Macbeth* – William Shakespeare

**BEFORE YOU READ**

1 Read about William Shakespeare. How old was he when he got married?
2 Read the background to the story on page 97. What do the witches tell Banquo? What do you think this means?

## About the author

**William Shakespeare** (also called The Bard)
**Born:** 1564 in Stratford-upon-Avon, England
**Died:** 1616 in Stratford-upon-Avon
**Important works:** *Richard III* (1592), *Romeo and Juliet* (1594), *A Midsummer Night's Dream* (1595), *Hamlet* (1600).
**Did you know?** Historians do not know the exact date of Shakespeare's birth. They think he was probably born on 23 April, St George's Day (St George is the patron saint of England). William went to the grammar school in Stratford and studied Latin. In 1582, when he was only eighteen, he married Anne Hathaway. She was eight years older than him. They had three children, a daughter Susanna and twins Hamnet and Judith.

William became an actor and he went to London with a theatre company called the Lord Chamberlain's Men. He began to write plays, which became very popular. He wrote historical plays, comedies and tragedies. When London theatres closed because of the plague, Shakespeare wrote poetry. His theatre company built the Globe Theatre in London in 1599. Queen Elizabeth I often went there. The theatre was rebuilt and reopened in 1997 and you can see performances of Shakespeare's plays there.

William Shakespeare died a rich and respected man in Stratford-upon-Avon on 23 April 1616. Many people today believe that he is the greatest writer in the English language.

1 **Read the extract on page 97. Who can Macbeth see in his chair?**

2 **Read the extract again. Are the sentences true (T) or false (F)? Correct the false ones.**
   1 At the king's castle they are having a banquet in the kitchen.
   2 There is food and wine on the table.
   3 There is blood on the ghost's face.
   4 The ghost speaks to Macbeth.
   5 The dinner guests can see the ghost.
   6 Lady Macbeth tells the guests that her husband is well.
   7 Macbeth drinks a toast to Banquo.
   8 Banquo's ghost does not appear again.

3 **SPEAKING Work in pairs. Answer the questions.**
   1 When Macbeth arrives, what does he say to the guests about his friend Banquo?
   2 Where is Banquo's ghost sitting? How does Macbeth react?
   3 Do you think Macbeth is happy now he is king? Why / Why not?

4 **Read what happens next. Who is Macbeth afraid of?**

**READ ON**

Alone in the castle, Macbeth tells his wife that he is afraid of Macduff, another general. He thinks that Macduff plans to kill him. Macbeth cannot sleep, so he searches for the witches. He wants to know more about the future.

Macbeth finds them in a dark cave. They are throwing things into a pot on a fire. The witches tell him to be careful of Macduff. They say that no child born from a woman can hurt him. They tell him to be careful when trees near his castle begin to move. Then the ghost of Banquo, with his children and grandchildren wearing crowns, appears.

Macbeth sends soldiers to Macduff's castle. They kill his wife and children. Macduff and Malcolm plan to attack Macbeth's castle.

5 **3.16 Listen to the next part of the story. What strange things does Lady Macbeth do?**

6 **3.16 Listen again. Choose the correct answers.**
   1 Lady Macbeth's servant is talking to
      a a doctor.   b a servant.   c a soldier.
   2 When Lady Macbeth is asleep she
      a gets up.   b wakes up.   c reads.
   3 She carries a candle in her hand because she is afraid of
      a murderers.   b Macbeth.   c the dark.
   4 Lady Macbeth talks of washing her
      a face.   b hands.   c hair.
   5 She says that Duncan was old, but had a lot of
      a money.   b gold.   c blood.
   6 She is sad because
      a Banquo's sons are dead.
      b Macbeth isn't dead.
      c Macduff's wife and children are dead.

7 **SPEAKING Work in pairs. Answer the questions.**
   1 The murders started with King Duncan. Lady Macbeth persuaded her husband to murder the king. Do you think that she is sorry? Why / why not?
   2 Is Macbeth a moral play? What is the moral?

## Writing

8 **Imagine you are Banquo. You are worried. You think it is dangerous for King Duncan to go to Macbeth's castle. Write a letter to him. Tell him:**
   - about your meeting with the witches
   - about Macbeth's wife who wants to be queen
   - not to go to the castle

# Macbeth

Macbeth went into the dining room. There were a lot of people in the room, and there was a lot of food and wine on the table.

'Where's my good friend Banquo?' asked Macbeth. 'He isn't here. He's late!'

'It doesn't matter,' said Lady Macbeth. 'Come and sit down. Your chair is here.'

Macbeth walked to the table, then he stopped suddenly. There was a ghost in his chair! The ghost looked up at him. It was Banquo and his face was bloody!

'What's happening?' cried Macbeth. He was afraid.

The ghost looked at him, but didn't speak. 'Why are you looking at me? I didn't do it!' Macbeth cried.

Everyone at the table looked at Macbeth. 'What's wrong, my lord?' they asked. 'Why are you worried?'

They couldn't see the ghost – but Macbeth could see it.

'I'm sorry, everyone, my husband isn't well,' said Lady Macbeth.

She took Macbeth out of the room. 'What's the matter with you?' she asked angrily. 'You're imagining things again. First it was a dagger in front of you on the night of Duncan's murder, and now this ghost. What's wrong? Don't be afraid. Be a man. Be brave. There's no one in your chair!'

'But he's a dead man. How can he come back?' said Macbeth. 'And how can you look at him and not be afraid?'

'What are you talking about? What are people going to think? There is no ghost! Your friends at the table are worried. Now, go back and sit in your chair!'

They went back into the dining room. Macbeth couldn't see the ghost now, so he sat down happily.

'I'm sorry, my friends,' he said to his visitors. 'Sometimes I feel ill and I begin to imagine things; but please don't worry about me. I'm better now. Come on, let's have some wine! Let's drink to our friend Banquo! He isn't here with us tonight and I'm sorry for that!'

Just then, Banquo's ghost came through the door and walked across the room. Macbeth cried out again. 'Get away from me!'

## BEFORE YOU READ

1 Read about Thomas Hardy. Hardy set his novels in Wessex. Is Wessex a real place name? Where is it?
2 Read the background to the story on page 98. Who does Farmer Lodge bring home one day?

## About the author

**Thomas Hardy**

**Born:** 1840 near Dorchester, England
**Died:** 1928 Dorchester
**Important works:** *Far from the Madding Crowd* (1874), *The Mayor of Casterbridge* (1886), *Tess of the d'Urbervilles* (1891), *Jude the Obscure* (1895).
**Did you know?** As a child Thomas Hardy loved school, and he studied many subjects including Latin and Greek. In 1856, when he left school, he worked for a local architect and church restorer. In 1862, he studied architecture in London, but returned home two years later. He wrote poems and stories. It was his second novel, *Far from the Madding Crowd*, that made him successful and famous.
Hardy set his novels in the countryside of Wessex. This was a fictional name he gave to the south-western part of England, where he lived all his life. He wrote four great tragic novels, all of which display a pessimistic view of life. In his novels *Tess of the d'Urbervilles* and *Jude the Obscure*, Hardy criticised Victorian morals. This caused a scandal and some people burned his books. Hardy didn't write any more novels after this, but wrote poetry for the rest of his life. He wrote *Wessex Poems* in 1898. Hardy's ashes are buried in Westminster Abbey in London, but his heart is buried in the graveyard at Stinsford Church, alongside the graves of his parents, his grandparents and his first wife.

1 Read the extract on page 99. In Rhoda's dream, what does the phantom have on her third finger?

2 Read the extract again. Choose the correct answers.
1 One evening Rhoda's son is
   a at the table. b in front of the fire. c in bed.
2 Rhoda stares at the fire and she can see a picture of
   a her son. b Gertrude Lodge. c Farmer Lodge.
3 The phantom … on Rhoda's body.
   a kneels b sits c stands
4 The phantom had a cruel
   a laugh. b smile. c look.
5 Rhoda is afraid and she … the phantom's arm.
   a pulls b breaks c hits
6 The dream makes Rhoda feel
   a cold. b hot. c warm.

3 SPEAKING Work in pairs. Answer the questions.
1 Who appears to Rhoda in the dream? Why is the phantom laughing?
2 Does Rhoda sleep again? How does she feel next morning?

4 Read what happens next. The story is called *The Withered Arm*. Who has a withered arm?

## READ ON

The next morning a woman comes to Rhoda's cottage. It is Gertrude Lodge and she has some shoes for Rhoda's son. Gertrude looks the same as the phantom in Rhoda's dream, but her eyes are kind and not cruel. Rhoda and Gertrude become friends.
One day Gertrude tells Rhoda that she had a bad dream and then her arm hurt. There are yellowy-brown marks on her left arm. They look like finger marks. Rhoda is afraid that she did this to Gertrude. Only witches can harm people in dreams. Is Rhoda a witch? Gertrude asks Rhoda to take her to Mr Trendle's house. He is a wise man and he can look at her arm. Rhoda doesn't want to meet the wise man. He understands dreams and witches.

The Withered Arm

5 🌐 3.17 Listen to the next part of the story. How does Gertrude see the face of her enemy?

6 🌐 3.17 Listen again. Complete sentences 1–7 with characters A–C.

**A** Rhoda       **B** Gertrude       **C** Mr Trendle

1 ......................................... is at home.
2 ......................................... looks at Rhoda for a long time.
3 ......................................... is surprised she has an enemy.
4 ......................................... can see into the room.
5 ......................................... sees the face of her enemy in the egg.
6 ......................................... can't hear the name Gertrude whispers.
7 ......................................... has a very pale face.

7 SPEAKING Work in pairs. Answer the questions.
1 What does Mr Trendle look like?
2 Whose face do you think Gertrude sees in the egg?
3 What do you think will happen next?

## Writing

8 Witches in stories can do good things and bad things. In the story, Rhoda has a dream and she hurts Gertrude's arm. Imagine that she can also make Gertrude's arm better. Use the ideas to write a good ending to this story.
   ▪ describe Rhoda / in front of / fire
   ▪ goes to bed / has a dream
   ▪ Gertrude appears / they speak
   ▪ Rhoda touches Gertrude's arm / better
   ▪ Rhoda / Gertrude / friends again

# The Withered Arm

One night, two or three weeks later, when the boy was in bed, Rhoda Brook sat by the dying fire in her little house. She stared at the fire for a long time, but she saw only the picture in her head of the new wife. At last, tired from her day's work, she went to bed.

But the picture of Gertrude Lodge did not go away. When Rhoda slept, the young wife was still there in Rhoda's dreams. She sat on Rhoda's body in the bed, staring into Rhoda's face. Her blue eyes were cold, and with a cruel laugh, she put her left hand in front of Rhoda's eyes. There, on the third finger, was her wedding-ring. And the phantom of Gertrude Lodge laughed again.

Rhoda turned this way and that way, but the phantom was still there. It sat, heavier and heavier, on Rhoda's body, and now Rhoda could not move. Always in her ears was that cruel laugh, and always in front of her eyes was that left hand with its wedding-ring.

At last, half-dead with terror, Rhoda suddenly put out her right hand, took hold of the phantom's left arm, and pulled it hard.

The phantom fell off the bed onto the floor, and Rhoda sat up.

'Dear God!' she cried. She felt cold, so cold. 'That was not a dream – she was here!'

She could still feel the young woman's arm under her hand – a warm, living arm. She looked on the floor for the woman's body, but there was nothing there.

Rhoda Brook slept no more that night, and at the dairy early the next morning, she looked pale and ill. She could not forget the feel of that arm under her hand.

## BEFORE YOU READ

1 Read about Arthur Conan Doyle. Who gave him the idea for the character of Sherlock Holmes?
2 Read the background to the story on page 101. How did the Duke's son leave the school at night?

## About the author

**Sir Arthur Ignatius Conan Doyle**

**Born:** 1859 in Edinburgh, Scotland
**Died:** 1930 in Crowborough
**Important works:** *A Study in Scarlet* (1887), *Micah Clarke* (1889), *The Hound of the Baskervilles* (1902)
**Did you know?** Conan Doyle studied medicine at Edinburgh University. When he finished university, he worked as a ship's doctor. He went on voyages to Antarctica and West Africa. Then he became a doctor in Southsea, in the south of England. While he was waiting for patients, he wrote stories. Dr Joseph Bell, one of Conan Doyle's teachers at medical school, gave him the idea for a new character – a very clever private detective. This character was Sherlock Holmes, and his friend was called Watson. The first Holmes story, *A Study in Scarlet*, was published in 1887.

*A Scandal in Bohemia* (1891) was the first Holmes story to become very popular. The public loved this unusual detective, who smoked a pipe, played the violin and lived at 221B Baker Street in London. Fifty-six Sherlock Holmes stories appeared in *Strand* magazine from 1891–1927. The stories are set in Victorian London, the English countryside and abroad, for example, in the USA and Switzerland. Since then, many other writers have written stories about Holmes, including comics and graphic novels. More than 70 actors have played him in more than 200 films.

1 Read the extract on page 101. What did Arthur receive the day before he disappeared?

2 Read the extract again. Answer the questions.
   1 Where does Holmes write things down?
   2 How do they know that Arthur didn't go home?
   3 Who is the unhappiest man in England?
   4 Who doesn't like people talking about his life?
   5 Where did the police find a man and a boy?
   6 What language does Arthur not learn at school?
   7 Which train did Dr Huxtable catch?
   8 Who owns a bicycle?

3 SPEAKING Work in pairs. Answer the questions.
   1 Do you think Arthur is with the German teacher? Where do you think Arthur is?
   2 What skills do you need to be a great detective?
   3 Do you like mystery stories? Why / Why not?

4 Read what happens next. What does Holmes find on the moors?

## READ ON

Holmes and Watson catch a train to Dr Huxtable's school. They meet the Duke and Mr James Wilder, his secretary. The Duke is surprised to see Holmes. He does not want people to know about his son's disappearance.
The Duke leaves and Sherlock Holmes studies a map of the area. When the gardener finds a school hat on the moors, Holmes knows that Arthur and the German teacher did not travel by road.
The next day Holmes and Watson walk across the moor. They don't find any footprints, but they find cow tracks, bicycle tracks and blood.

5 🔘 **3.18** Listen to the next part of the story. What does the workman do when he sees the body?

6 🔘 **3.18** Listen again. Complete the sentences.
   1 Watson offers to run back to the ...................... .
   2 Holmes writes a ...................... to Dr Huxtable.
   3 The workman runs down the ...................... .
   4 Then Holmes ...................... carefully.
   5 The German teacher left without his ...................... .
   6 The German teacher ...................... eight kilometres from the school.
   7 The German teacher needed a bicycle because Arthur was moving ...................... .
   8 The person travelling with Arthur hit the German teacher on the ...................... .

7 SPEAKING Work in pairs. Answer the questions.
   1 In your opinion, did Arthur kill the German teacher? Why / Why not?
   2 Would you like to go to a school like Arthur's? Why / Why not?
   3 In pairs, imagine that one of you is Sherlock Holmes and the other is the Duke of Holdernesse. Ask and answer questions to find out more about Arthur. Find out what he looks like, what his hobbies are and what sport he plays.

## Writing

8 **Arthur is a new boy at school and his mother is in France. Imagine that you are Arthur. Write a letter to your mother, the Duchess. Include the following ideas and your own ideas:**

   ■ where the school is        ■ what your friends are like
   ■ what you do every day      ■ what your room is like
   ■ what your teachers and lessons are like

# Sherlock Holmes and the Duke's Son

Holmes took out a little notebook, and began to write things down.

'The boy didn't go home, of course,' he said.

'No, no. We asked at Holdernesse Hall at once,' said Dr Huxtable. 'The Duke is very afraid for his son – and I am the unhappiest man in England. Mr Holmes, you are a famous detective – please help me!'

'You make things very difficult for me,' Holmes said. 'How can I find marks in the ivy or on the ground after three days? Why didn't you come to me at once?'

'Because of the Duke,' Dr Huxtable said. 'He doesn't like people talking about his unhappy family life.'

'And what are the police doing?'

'Well, they heard about a boy and a young man at the station early on Tuesday. They looked for them, and last night they found them in Liverpool – but it was a man and his son going to visit a friend. We lost three days because of that. And last night I couldn't sleep, so I took the first train down to London this morning.'

'Well, Dr Huxtable, some more questions,' said Holmes. 'Did the boy take German lessons?'

'No.'

'So he didn't know the German teacher well, then.'

'He probably never spoke to him,' said Dr Huxtable.

'Mmm,' said Holmes. 'Does the boy have a bicycle?'

'No.'

'Was any other bicycle missing?'

'No.'

'So. Did the German teacher ride away on his bicycle in the night, with the boy on his back? I don't think so. But what happened to the bicycle? Now, what about visitors? Did the boy have any visitors the day before?'

'No.'

'Did he get any letters?'

'Yes, one letter. From his father.'

'Do you open the boys' letters, Dr Huxtable?'

'No.'

'Then how do you know that the letter was from the father?'

'I know the Duke's handwriting. And he says that he wrote a letter to his son.'

From *Sherlock Holmes and the Duke's Son*, Oxford Bookworms. Text adaptation by Jennifer Bassett.

## Listening

**1** Look at the questions in exercise 2. Match the words below with the recording you think you will hear them in.

■ skateboard ■ water ■ teach ■ drawing ■ pool ■ singing ■ picture ■ musical

**2** EXAM TASK ● 3.19 **Listen to recordings 1–4 and choose the correct answers.**

1 On which days does the boy do his swimming training?
   a Tuesday and Thursday
   b Tuesday, Thursday and Saturday
   c Tuesday, Thursday, Saturday and Sunday
2 What does Ben think about skateboarding?
   a His friend Maria isn't very good at it.
   b He doesn't like it.
   c He isn't very good at it.
3 What does the girl say about her family and music?
   a Her mother sings, her sister plays the piano and her dad plays the guitar.
   b Her mother sings, her sister plays the guitar and her dad listens to rock music.
   c Her mother sings, her sister plays the piano and her dad listens to rock music.
4 What does Dan want Gemma to do?
   a Draw a picture of Dan.
   b Draw a picture of Mr Granger.
   c Draw a picture of a football.

## Reading

**3** Read the article about Sophie quickly. Find the following information.

1 The name of the football team
2 The name of the stadium.
3 The name of Sophie's favourite player

**4** EXAM TASK **Read the article about Sophie. Are statements 1–6 true (T) or false (F)?**

|   |   | T | F |
|---|---|---|---|
| 1 | Everyone in Sophie's family likes Tottenham Hotspur. | | |
| 2 | Sophie plays football for Tottenham Hotspur. | | |
| 3 | Sophie and the other mascots meet the Tottenham players in the family room. | | |
| 4 | Sophie's family waits in the tunnel for Sophie. | | |
| 5 | The match starts at three o'clock. | | |
| 6 | The mascots watch the football game with their families. | | |

## Real Lives

### Sophie – the Tottenham Hotspurs Mascot

Sophie Sayeed, 14, describes her amazing experience as a Tottenham Hotspur's Mascot

It is two o'clock in the afternoon on Saturday, 12th June, and this is a very exciting day! I'm with my parents and my brother in the family room at White Hart Lane, in north London – home of Tottenham Hotspurs football club. My whole family – my mum, my dad, my eight-year-old brother, Steve, and I are big fans of Tottenham. It's a special day for me because I am one of the mascots for Tottenham's match today. Tottenham Hotspur chooses eleven young mascots – one person for each member of the football team – for every important match.

Now it's half past two. I walk into the tunnel area with the other ten mascots. We meet the Tottenham players and talk to them. The players sign autographs and pose for photographs with us. Then we all return to the family room. We change into the Tottenham kit – special clothes for the match – and say goodbye to our families. My mum, dad and brother go to their seats in the stadium and wait for the match to begin, but I go back to the tunnel with the other mascots.

It is now three o'clock and the players are in the tunnel and ready to start the game. The bell rings and we all run out onto the pitch. Each mascot runs together with one member of the team. I am with Mousa Dembélé – my favourite player! I can hear shouting and singing from the crowds. There are more than 30,000 spectators for today's match at White Hart Lane and the noise is incredible! The players and the mascots stand together on the pitch for a photo session. The mascots shake the hands of the players and of the referee. Then, finally, we run around the pitch and wave at the crowds for one last time before we join our families to watch the match. What an amazing experience!

## Use of English

**EXAM STRATEGY**

- Read the text first.
- Try to guess the missing words. Then look at the words in the box. Are they the same as your guesses?
- Complete the gaps you are certain about first.
- Remember that there are two words you do not need.

**5** **EXAM TASK** Complete the gaps in the text with the words in the box. There are two words that you do not need.

■ their ■ go ■ hasn't ■ to ■ fast ■ into ■ don't ■ for
■ listening ■ him ■ can ■ them

# My hero

My grandfather is my hero. He's tall and he's got short curly hair. He's eighty-six years old and he lives in a small flat next ¹........................ the university. It's got a living room, a small kitchen, a bathroom and a bedroom but it ²........................ got a garden. He loves ³........................ to music and he has got more than 500 CDs. He keeps ⁴........................ in a box under his bed. He ⁵........................ play the piano and the violin. He's in a band called 'The Old Timers' and sometimes they perform at a café in town. Everyone in the band is more than eighty years old! He can't walk very ⁶........................, but he goes out every day and meets his friends in the library or in the park. They read the newspapers together and play chess. Sometimes they ⁷........................ swimming on Friday afternoons at the sports centre. On Sundays, we usually have lunch at his flat. He's really ⁸........................ cooking and he often prepares unusual food. We ⁹........................ always like his food, but he's very funny and we always enjoy spending time with ¹⁰.........................

## Speaking

**EXAM STRATEGY**

- Read the task carefully.
- Think of one or two pieces of information for each point and one or two questions for the other person.
- Remember to show interest in the other person's information.

**6** Match these words with the four points in the exam task below. There are three words for each point. Then use the words to write two sentences for each point.

■ grandmother ■ often ■ garden ■ at the weekend
■ brother ■ bedroom ■ have a shower ■ play tennis
■ chat online ■ sofa ■ cousin ■ photography

**7** **EXAM TASK** Role-play the situation below at a party.

**Student A: Talk to another guest. Find out about the person's:**

- daily routine
- likes and dislikes
- family
- home

**Student B: One of the other guests talks to you. Answer his/her questions about:**

- your daily routine
- your likes and dislikes
- your family
- your home

## Writing

**EXAM STRATEGY**

- Read the task carefully and make notes for each point.
- Use a new paragraph for each new point.
- Remember to check your grammar, spelling and punctuation.

**8** **EXAM TASK** Write a letter to your penfriend in another country. Describe your best friend. Include information about:

- your friend's appearance
- your friend's personality
- your friend's interests
- when you meet and what you do together

## Listening

**1 Match the words to the definitions.**

1 forest rangers    **a** these places keep animals in
2 farmers           captivity
3 zoos             **b** protecting the environment
4 conservation    **c** these people keep animals for food
                 **d** these people protect the forest

> **EXAM STRATEGY**
>
> - Look at the questions before you listen.
> - Think about what kind of information you need to answer them, for example:
>   a number
>   a price
>   a verb
>   a noun

**2** **EXAM TASK** 🔊 **3.20** **Listen to a radio interview. Then answer the questions with no more than four words or numbers.**

1 How many mountain gorillas are there in the wild?

2 How many mountain gorillas are there in zoos and wildlife parks?

3 Where does The Gorilla Organization send information about mountain gorillas?

4 What is the mountain gorillas' habitat?

5 What does the organization teach forest rangers to do?

6 What meat are local farmers now producing?

## Reading

> **EXAM STRATEGY**
>
> - Read the gapped sentences carefully. Think about what kind of information you need to complete them.
> - Read the text and underline the key information.
> - Remember to check your answers for grammar and spelling.

**3 Read the text quickly and choose the best answers.**

1 Farm:shop is in a **small town** / **big city**.
2 There are **plants** / **animals** and plants in the shop.
3 Susan and Pierre **often** / **rarely** visit the shop.

**4** **EXAM TASK** **Read the text again. Complete the sentences 1–6 with the missing words.**

1 The writer of the text thinks that the shop is very .................................... from the noisy street outside.
2 Some of the plants are not inside the shop, they are in .................... ..................................... .
3 The chickens live ................... .................... of the shop.
4 ................................. .................................... can have meetings on the third floor.
5 Susan Turner is buying vegetables and .................................... at the shop.
6 Pierre Dupont works as a .................................... .

# Farm:shop

It's a warm day in April when I visit the Farm:shop in Dalston, London. Outside, the street is busy and noisy, with cars, buses and people. But when I walk into the shop, I find a very different part of London: a peaceful, calm and green space.

Farm:shop in Dalston is a farm, it's a shop, it's a café and it's a school. The shop has got a small garden, where they grow lots of vegetables, herbs and mushrooms. There are more plants and fruit inside the shop – on the floor, on shelves and growing up the walls! There are also large tanks of fish and even chickens on the roof!

You can eat food from the shop at the café and you can learn about farming and gardening at special classes. Upstairs, on the third floor, there is a meeting room for local businesses. You can have a party here or you can hire a desk and work here.

Susan Turner visits the shop once or twice a week. 'I love the fresh food,' she says, 'and I like visiting the chickens on the roof! There are always new things in the shop. Today I'm buying carrots, potatoes and some eggs.'

Pierre Dupont is enjoying a cup of coffee and a piece of homemade cake in the café. 'I'm a writer,' he says, 'but it's difficult and boring to stay at home all day. I come here in the afternoons and I use a desk upstairs in the meeting room. Sometimes I help in the shop. There are always interesting people here.'

## Use of English

### EXAM STRATEGY

- Read through the text first.
- Look at the words before and after each gap.
- Read the complete sentences aloud. Do they make sense?

**5** **EXAM TASK** Read the text and choose the correct answers to complete gaps 1–9. Write the correct letter (a–d) in the gaps.

## We grow our own food

We live in a small house in the country. It's got a big garden and we grow **1** ........ of food in it. We grow potatoes, beans, onions, peas and tomatoes. We haven't got **2** ........ carrots in our garden because no one in our family likes carrots! We've got **3** ........ apple trees at the bottom of the garden, but they don't produce **4** ........ fruit at the moment because they're very young. We also keep some animals; we've got **5** ........ pigs and a goat called Tilly. I love the pigs, but I don't like Tilly. She's always trying to eat the plants!

It's early April now and **6** ........ rains quite often at this time of year. I don't like getting wet, but I know it's really good for the plants. Today, though, it isn't raining. It's a warm, **7** ........ day and my dad and I are in the garden. My dad **8** ........ a hole for some new potatoes. It's hard work and he's very tired and hot. I'm chasing Tilly, but she's running **9** ........ from me!

| | a | b | c | d |
|---|---|---|---|---|
| **1** | much | a lot | many | some |
| **2** | a | much | some | any |
| **3** | some | any | a little | much |
| **4** | many | much | some | a few |
| **5** | a few | much | a little | any |
| **6** | are | there | do | it |
| **7** | sunny | sun | suns | shines |
| **8** | digs | dig | is digging | are digging |
| **9** | in | for | away | out |

## Speaking

### EXAM STRATEGY

- Look at the photo carefully and think about the vocabulary you need to describe it.
- Remember to use phrases like: *in the background, in the foreground, on the left/right*, etc. to describe where things are in a picture.
- Use the present continuous to describe what people are doing in the photo.

**6** Look at the photo below and think about how to describe it. Make notes about:

- the people: (their appearance, what they are feeling, what they are doing)
- the animals
- the scenery
- the weather

**7** **EXAM TASK** Answer the questions about the photo. Give reasons for your answers.

1 What are the people in the photo doing?
2 Do you think they are enjoying this activity? Why / Why not?
3 What kinds of outdoor activities do you enjoy doing? How often do you do them?

## Writing

### EXAM STRATEGY

- Read the task carefully and think about the type of text. Is it formal or informal?
- Write a plan first. Make a list of five or six key words to include in each paragraph.
- Remember to check your grammar, punctuation and spelling.

**8** Look at the sentences (1–6) below. Are they formal (F) or informal (I)?

1 Dear Mrs Smith
2 Best wishes
3 Hi John
4 Yours sincerely
5 Write soon!
6 I look forward to hearing from you.

**9** **EXAM TASK** Write an email to a foreign friend. Describe a traditional meal from your country. Answer these questions in your email:

- when do people usually eat this food?
- do people usually eat it at home or at a restaurant?
- is the food healthy or unhealthy?
- do you like it?

## Listening

**1 Find synonyms and antonyms for words 1–5 below.**

■ expensive ■ difficult ■ bad ■ not into ■ easy ■ a few
■ like ■ half price ■ great ■ lots of

| | antonym | synonym |
|---|---|---|
| 1 enjoy | | |
| 2 many | | |
| 3 hard | | |
| 4 good | | |
| 5 cheap | | |

**2 EXAM TASK 3.21 Listen to the conversation. Are the sentences true (T) or false (F)?**

| | | T | F |
|---|---|---|---|
| 1 | Jackie has to get a birthday present for her brother. | | |
| 2 | Jackie's brother is sixteen. | | |
| 3 | Jackie's brother enjoys reading about basketball. | | |
| 4 | Jackie's brother hasn't got many DVDs. | | |
| 5 | Adam thinks that it's hard to choose a present. | | |
| 6 | Jackie wants to spend more than £20. | | |
| 7 | Jackie thinks that a hat is a good idea. | | |
| 8 | The clothes in Albatross are usually very cheap. | | |

## Reading

**3 Read the article quickly and choose the best option.**

**The article is about:**

**a** where you can buy a good birthday present in Brighton.
**b** some different places to eat in Brighton.
**c** one small part of Brighton with lots of interesting places.

# North Laine

Are you looking for the perfect present for an unusual friend? Do you want to find a pair of vegetarian shoes? Perhaps you need to buy an electric guitar or a bunch of flowers. Or maybe you want to meet your friends for a Chinese meal and then go to the cinema or watch a comedy show? You can do all of these things in North Laine – a small but lively area in the centre of Brighton. Here's our guide to the five most interesting places in North Laine.

### A Snooper's Paradise

It's not one shop, it's a group of ninety small shops all together in one large building. You can buy second-hand clothes, antique furniture, old magazines and unusual jewellery here – as well as lots of other things.

### B Komedia

This is a fantastic arts venue with comedy shows every weekend and special performances for children. You can also listen to live music here. It's got a small café with an excellent kitchen, so you can eat good food and watch a great show at the same time.

### C Canteen

There are more than thirty cafés and restaurants in North Laine, but Canteen is our favourite. It serves fresh pies with potatoes and peas. All the ingredients are local and the food is delicious!

### D Pen to Paper

You can buy cheap pencils for 50p here or you can spend £300 on a Mont Blanc pen. This shop has got diaries, journals, notebooks, pens and pencils. You can also find unusual birthday cards here.

### E The Animal House

There are a lot of different things in this shop – cards, toys, games, clothes – but everything has an animal theme here. You can find a toy monkey for your baby brother, a zebra-patterned bag for you and a lovely mug with a picture of a cat on it for your grandmother!

**4 EXAM TASK Read the text again. Match the information in sentences (1–6) to paragraphs (A–E). There is one heading that you do not need.**

1 This place sells writing supplies. ☐
2 This place provides entertainment. ☐
3 This place has got things for people of different ages ☐
4 This place is a café and also a shop. ☐
5 There is more than one shop here. ☐
6 The food here is from the area around Brighton. ☐

## Use of English

**5** **EXAM TASK** Read the text. Complete the gaps in the text (1–10) with the correct form of the words in brackets.

# The perfect job

Everyone in our village knows my brother Jed because he's always doing sport and he wears very ¹ .................... (usual) clothes with bright colours and strange patterns. Jed is twenty-five years old and he has got a really ² .................... (interest) job. He works as a clothes ³ .................... (design) for a sports company. It's the perfect job for him because he was really good at art and design at school, and he loves playing sport. He is the ⁴ .................... (good) football player in our town and he's also an excellent horse ⁵ .................... (ride). But his favourite sport is triathlon: running, cycling and swimming. Even when it's very cold, wet and ⁶ .................... (wind), Jed spends three hours every day training. He often cycles twenty kilometres to work and then the same distance home in the evening! We live in a village at the top of a hill and his office is in the town at the bottom of the hill, so he travels very ⁷ .................... (quick) in the morning, but his journey home in the evening is much ⁸ .................... (slow)! 'Cycling is ⁹ .................... (fast) than walking and ¹⁰ .................... (exciting) than driving,' he says. 'It's the best way to travel!'

## Speaking

**6** Look at the sentences below. Decide if they are from a patient (P) or a doctor (D).

1 Are you worried about anything? ☐
2 You should take these pills. ☐
3 I've got a bad headache. ☐
4 What's the problem? ☐
5 Can you give me some advice? ☐
6 I feel dizzy. ☐

**7** **EXAM TASK** Role-play the situation below at a doctor's surgery.

**Student A: You don't feel well. Talk to a doctor about your problems.**

- Describe the problem
- Ask for some advice
- Listen to the doctor's suggestions
- Thank the doctor

**Student B: You are a doctor. Give advice to a patient.**

- Listen to the patient's problem
- Ask questions about the problem
- Give some advice
- Say goodbye to the patient

## Writing

**8** Look at the task below and make notes. Think of one piece of advice for each point.

**9** **EXAM TASK** You write an advice column for your school magazine. A student is worried about an interview for a holiday job in a local shop. Write a letter of advice. Include information about:

- how to prepare for the interview
- what kind of clothes to wear
- what questions she should ask
- what things she should/shouldn't do

## Listening

**1** Match the words to make collocations. Then predict which collocations will match questions A–F below.

| | | | |
|---|---|---|---|
| 1 | revise | a | a word of a language |
| 2 | I'm so | b | an adventure |
| 3 | it's a great | c | really hard for something |
| 4 | it's | d | excited |
| 5 | set | e | opportunity |
| 6 | can't speak | f | up a sports club |

**2** **EXAM TASK** 🔊 **3.22** Listen to five young people talking about their plans for the future. Match question (A–F) to speakers (1–5). There is one question you do not need.

| Which speaker is going to: | 1 | 2 | 3 | 4 | 5 |
|---|---|---|---|---|---|
| **A** start a new job? | | | | | |
| **B** learn a new language? | | | | | |
| **C** move to a new country? | | | | | |
| **D** teach? | | | | | |
| **E** buy a new car? | | | | | |
| **F** take an exam? | | | | | |

## Reading

**3** Read the text about Steve Jobs quickly. Put these events into the correct order.

**a** He set up NeXt.
**b** He returned to Apple.
**c** He met Steve Wozniac.
**d** He and Wozniac started a company in his garage.
**e** He went to Reed College.

**4** **EXAM TASK** Read the text again. Match the sentences A–G to the gaps 1–6. There is one sentence that you do not need.

## Steve Jobs

Steve Jobs was born in 1955 in San Francisco, California. [1] ....... This part of Northern California is famous because there are lots of technology companies here.

Steve's father, Paul, was a mechanic and he encouraged his son's early interest in electronics and technology. [2] ....... In 1971, Jobs met Steve Wozniac. Wozniac was twenty-one: five years older than Jobs. They were both interested in electronics and computers and they immediately became friends.

Jobs was very clever but he didn't enjoy school. He joined Reed College in 1972, but he didn't finish the course. [3] ....... He worked as a video game designer at Atari electronics. For the next two years, between 1974 and 1976, Jobs worked for Atari and at the same time, he joined a computer club with Steve Wozniac. The members of the club talked about their ideas together and built their own computers.

In 1976, Wozniac and Jobs decided to set up their own computer company. They chose the name Apple and their first office was Jobs' garage. [4] ....... This was a new idea, and it became popular very quickly. By 1980, Apple Computers was worth more than $200 million.

But Jobs wasn't always popular with other people in the company. [5] ....... In 1985 he left Apple and formed a different computer company, NeXt. He also became the chairman of Pixar Animation Studios. Pixar made several very successful films, including *Toy Story* and *Finding Nemo.*

In 1996, Apple bought NeXt and Jobs returned to Apple. Between 1996 and 2010, Jobs and Apple launched several very successful products, including: the i-mac, the iPod, the iPhone and the iPad. [6] ....... He fought the illness for many years, but finally died in 2011.

Jobs was a very important influence in the world of computing. His sense of design and his interest in new and exciting ideas, helped to make computers popular with a whole generation.

**A** But Jobs became very ill with cancer in 2003.
**B** He got married to Laurene Powell in 1991.
**C** Five years later, in 1960, his family moved to 'Silicon Valley'.
**D** They wanted to make computers for people at home - personal computers.
**E** He taught Steve how to build radios and televisions from basic materials.
**F** He had a lot of arguments and got angry very quickly.
**G** In 1974, when he was nineteen years old, he left college and started his first job.

## Use of English

**5** **EXAM TASK** Read the text about planning a journey. Complete the text with the correct form of the verbs in brackets.

### An Amazing Journey

Last year my family ¹.................... (make) a big decision. We decided to leave our house and our comfortable lives and to spend one year travelling around the world. My parents didn't want ².................... (travel) by plane because they don't enjoy ³.................... (fly). So they bought a big bus and put a small kitchen and some beds in it. Then we all sat down together and started to plan our journey. There was one big problem, though – my mother couldn't drive! So she ⁴.................... (take) some lessons with a driving school. There's a big car park near our house, and my mum practised driving the bus round and round the car park every evening. She ⁵.................... (pass) her test last month and she's already a really confident driver.

It's Saturday today and I usually ⁶.................... (go) out with my friends at the weekend, but today, I ⁷.................... (pack) my suitcase, because we ⁸.................... (start) our amazing journey tomorrow. My father ⁹.................... (drive) the bus to Dover and then we ¹⁰.................... (take) the ferry to Calais. I hope the weather ¹¹.................... (be) good for the boat journey!

## Speaking

**6** Match these statements to the photos. One statement matches both photos.

1 They are dancing and laughing.
2 It's probably summer because the sun is shining.
3 I think it's inside.
4 Everyone is very happy.
5 I can see some food on the table.

**7** **EXAM TASK** These two photos show people at a party. Compare and contrast them. Include the following points:

- what the people are doing
- what the people are wearing
- what kind of celebration it is
- which celebration you would enjoy more and why

## Writing

**8** **EXAM TASK** Write a story with the title, 'A very bad day'. Include information about:

- where you were
- who you were with
- what happened
- why it was a bad day

## Listening

**1** Match the sentences in exercise 2 to the gaps in 1–4.

  **1** a type of person / people ................................ and

  ................................

  **2** a place ................................ ,

  ................................ and

  ................................

  **3** an amount of money ................................

  **4** a possession ................................

**2** [EXAM TASK] 🌐 **3.23** **Listen to Tara talking about her bike ride from Ireland to Croatia. Complete sentences 1–7 with information from the text. Write only one word or number in each gap.**

  **1** Tara spent time in ................................ when she was a child.

  **2** She stayed with different ................................ during her journey.

  **3** She didn't always cycle 100 km per day because she had to cross some ................................ .

  **4** She rode her bike in seven different ................................ .

  **5** Someone stole her ................................ in France.

  **6** Some ................................ helped her when she was lost in Switzerland.

  **7** She donated more than £................................ to Guy's Hospital in London.

## Reading

**3** [EXAM TASK] **Read the text quickly. Which text is about:**

  **a** a place for dead people

  **b** a very old city

  **c** a place which has got trees and plants all around it

**4** [EXAM TASK] **Read the text again and choose the correct answers.**

**AROUND THE WORLD: THREE CONTINENTS – THREE ANCIENT WORLDS**

### 1 ASIA

Angkor Wat, in Cambodia, is the largest religious monument in the world. It's a group of 12th century temples, originally dedicated to the Hindu God Vishnu. In the 14th century it became a Buddhist site and today it is a major religious monument for both Hindus and Buddhists. The temples are still in good condition, but the jungle has grown around them so that between and inside the temples there are trees and plants. The whole monument covers more than 400 square kilometres – that's an area bigger than Paris! About 500,000 tourists visit Angkor Wat every year.

### 2 SOUTH AMERICA

In the fifteenth century, high up in the Andes mountains in Peru, the Incas built a stone city, Machu Picchu, with palaces, temples and about 150 houses. The construction of this city was an amazing achievement. The Incas cut huge steps into the side of the mountain and then carried the stone up the mountain to build the city. When Spain conquered the Inca people in 1533, they destroyed many Inca cities, but they never discovered Machu Picchu at the top of the mountain. Between 1570–1580, all the Incas left Machu Picchu. Perhaps they became ill, but no one really knows why. Then, in 1911, Hiram Bingham discovered it again.

### 3 AFRICA

More than 3,500 years ago, the Ancient Egyptians began to build amazing tombs – places for their dead Kings. They built them in a valley by the Nile River, and we now call this the 'Valley of the Kings'. The most famous tomb in the Valley of the Kings is probably the tomb of Tutankhamun. Howard Carter discovered it in 1922. Inside the tomb there were beautiful objects, gold jewellery and decorations on all the walls. There was also the body of the Pharaoh (Egyptian King) Tutankhamun. Cairo Museum is now the home of many of these objects and sometimes there are special exhibitions in other major museums, including London and New York, but Tutankhamun still rests in his tomb in the Valley of the Kings.

**1** What can visitors see in Angkor Wat?

  **a** One main Hindu temple and some other, smaller Buddhist temples.

  **b** Lots of Buddhist temples and a few Hindu temples.

  **c** Lots of temples that are important for Buddhists and Hindus.

  **d** One large temple that was Hindu and is now Buddhist.

**2** Why does the writer mention Paris?

  **a** Angkor Wat and Paris are the same size.

  **b** Paris is smaller than Angkor Wat.

  **c** Angkor Wat is 4,000 kilometres from Paris.

  **d** Paris and Angkor Wat both get a lot of tourists.

**3** It was difficult to build Machu Picchu because
  a  the buildings used lots of different materials.
  b  the Inca people took stone from the mountains to build it.
  c  there was a war with Spain at the same time.
  d  the main material for the buildings was at the bottom of the mountains.
**4** You can see Tutankhamun's body
  a  in Cairo.
  b  in London.
  c  in the Valley of the Kings.
  d  in New York.

## Use of English

### EXAM STRATEGY

- Read the text quickly to understand the general meaning.
- Look at the words before and after the gap.
- Think about the kind of word you need – preposition, pronoun, auxiliary verb, etc.
- Read through the completed text to check that it makes sense.

**5**  **EXAM TASK**  Read the text about Kira Salak. Complete gaps 1–8 with the missing words. Use one word in each gap.

### PROFILE OF AN ADVENTURER: KIRA SALAK

Kira Salak is a novelist, a travel writer and an adventurer. She ¹................ visited some of the world's ²................ dangerous places, including Madagascar, Borneo, Rwanda, and the Democratic Republic of Congo. *Book Magazine* described her as '³................ craziest woman adventurer of our day.' And the *New York Times* said, 'she's a real life Lara Croft.'

Kira was born ⁴................ Chicago, USA, in 1971. She loved sport ⁵................ school, and when she was a teenager she wanted to train as an Olympic athlete. But she was also very interested in writing and finally she decided to give ⁶................ her Olympic training and to focus on travel writing.

When Kira was twenty-four ⁷................ old, she became the first woman to travel across Papua New Guinea, and later she wrote a book about her experience. In 2005 she cycled over 1,200 kilometres across Alaska to the Arctic Ocean and in 2006 she travelled 966 kilometres by kayak down the Niger River to Timbuktu.

She's also written a novel, won several journalism awards, and when she isn't travelling, she enjoys taekwondo, camping and mountain climbing.

What are her plans for the future? 'I want ⁸................ ride a horse across Mongolia,' she says.

## Speaking

### EXAM STRATEGY

- Use adjectives and adverbs to make your description more interesting.
- Make sure you include information about each point.
- You can always include extra information about the topic.

**6** Write at least three more holiday words for each heading.

**HOLIDAYS**

| | |
|---|---|
| Activities | sightseeing, |
| | ................................, |
| | ................................, |
| Places | beach, |
| | ................................, |
| | ................................, |
| People | friends, |
| | ................................, |
| | ................................, |
| Adjectives | exciting, |
| | ................................, |
| | ................................, |

**7**  **EXAM TASK**  Talk about your favourite holiday experience. Include answers to the questions below.

- Where did you go?
- What did you do there?
- Who did you go with?
- Why did you enjoy it?

## Writing

### EXAM STRATEGY

- Read the task carefully and make notes for each point.
- Include your personal opinion as well as facts and information.
- Remember to check your writing carefully for grammar, punctuation and spelling.

**8**  **EXAM TASK**  Your friend in the USA is going to visit your country. Write a letter about the best places to visit and things to do in your country. Include information about:

- the best time of the year to visit and why
- different ways of travelling around your country
- some important buildings or monuments
- some beautiful scenery in your country – e.g. mountains or beaches

# Grammar reference and practice

## W.1 ◾ be

### Affirmative

| | | |
|---|---|---|
| I | 'm (= am) | |
| We / You / They | 're (= are) | at home. |
| He / She / It | 's (= is) | |

### Negative

| | | |
|---|---|---|
| I | 'm not (= am not) | |
| We / You / They | 're not / aren't (= are not) | at home. |
| He / She / It | isn't (= is not) | |

### Questions and short answers

| | | | |
|---|---|---|---|
| Am | I | | Yes, I am. No, I'm not. |
| Are | we / you / they | at home? | Yes, you are. No, we aren't. |
| Is | he / she / it | | Yes, he is. No, she isn't. |

**1** Complete the sentences with first the affirmative form and then the negative form of the verb *be*.

1 She's a student. She __isn't__ a teacher.
2 They _____ big. They _____ small.
3 We _____ hot. We _____ cold.
4 It _____ a good school. It _____ a bad school.
5 My mother _____ in the garden. My mother _____ in the house.
6 I _____ fifteen. I _____ eighteen.

**2** Write questions and short answers.

1 you / English?
   __Are you English?__
   Yes, __I am__ .
2 the girl / happy?
   _____
   No, _____ .
3 they / sixteen?
   _____
   Yes, _____ .
4 we / in London?
   _____
   No, _____ .
5 you / my friend?
   _____
   No, _____ .
6 the boy / your brother?
   _____
   Yes, _____ .

## W.2 ◾ Possessive adjectives

| Subject pronoun | Possessive adjective |
|---|---|
| I | my |
| you | your |
| he | his |
| she | her |
| it | its |
| we | our |
| they | their |

- We use possessive adjectives to show who possesses something.
  *This is my bag.*
  *He's in their house.*

**1** Complete the sentences with the correct possessive adjectives.

1 We are from England. ___Our___ home is in London.
2 He is from France. _____ home is in Paris.
3 They are from Germany. _____ home is in Berlin.
4 She is from Spain. _____ home is in Madrid.
5 You are from Italy. _____ home is in Rome.
6 I am from Poland. _____ home is in Warsaw.

## W.3 ◾ this, that, these, those

### Singular

| | ☐ |
|---|---|
| this box ☐ | that box |

### Plural

| | ☐☐☐ |
|---|---|
| these boxes ☐☐☐ | those boxes |

- We use *this* and *these* for things and people that are near to us.
- We use *that* and *those* for things and people that aren't very near.

**1** Choose the correct words.

1 (This)/ These girl is my sister.
2 That / Those houses are very big.
3 Is this / these dog your dog?
4 Are this / these books from the library?
5 That / Those chair is red.
6 That / Those desks are small.

## W.4 ■ *have got*

### Affirmative

| I<br>We<br>You<br>They | 've (= have) got | a new phone. |
|---|---|---|
| He<br>She<br>It | 's (= have) got | |

### Negative

| I<br>We<br>You<br>They | haven't (= have not) got | a cat. |
|---|---|---|
| He<br>She<br>It | hasn't (= has not) got | |

### Questions and short answers

| Have | I<br>we<br>you<br>they | got a<br>brother? | Yes, I have.<br>No, we haven't. |
|---|---|---|---|
| Has | he<br>she<br>it | | Yes, he has.<br>No, she hasn't. |

**1** Complete the sentences with the correct form of *have got*.

1 ✔ He __has got__ short hair and blue eyes.
2 ? A: __Have__ you __got__ a computer?
    B: Yes, I __have__.
3 ✘ We ................................ a dog.
4 ✘ My parents ................................ a car.
5 ? A: ................................ Anna ................................
    a new bag?
    B: No, she ................................ .
6 ✔ I ................................ three sisters.
7 ✔ My school ................................ 600 students.
8 ✘ Tom ................................ a dictionary.

**2** Match the sentence halves.

1 Have you got a
2 She's got a lot of
3 The town's got a
4 They haven't got a
5 I've got two sisters,

a great shopping centre.
b a brother and a cat.
c homework tonight.
d new laptop for homework?
e big house, but it's nice.

## W.5 ■ Object pronouns

| Subject pronoun | Object pronoun |
|---|---|
| I | me |
| you | you |
| he | him |
| she | her |
| it | it |
| we | us |
| they | them |

**1** Rewrite the sentences. Replace the words in italics with object pronouns.

1 I like *the boy*. __I like him__ .
2 She's got *my bag*. ................................ .
3 I haven't got *your books*. ................................ .
4 Jude likes *me and my friends*. ................................ .
5 We are with *the girl*. ................................ .

## W.6 ■ Articles: *a / an* and *the*

### *a / an*

■ We use *a* with singular nouns when the next word starts with a consonant sound (b, c, d, f, etc.):
**a ball, a desk, a tree**
■ We use *an* with singular nouns when the next word starts with a vowel sound (a, e, i, o, u):
**an apple, an insect**

We use *a / an* with singular nouns when:
■ we mention something for the first time.
**There is a house near my school.**
■ we describe a person or thing.
**We've got an old dog.**
**She's a tall, slim young woman now.**
■ we say what someone's job is.
**Her mother is a doctor.**

### *the*

We use *the* before singular and plural nouns when:
■ we refer to something that was mentioned before.
**I've got a new computer and a new phone. I like the computer but I don't like the phone.**
■ there is only one of something
**I'm at the park.** (There is only one park.)

**1** Choose the correct words.

1 They've got (a)/ an new house and a new car.
   A / **The** car is red.
2 We're at a / the cinema.
3 Has she got a / an brother?
4 There's a / the computer club and a / the music club
   at our school. A / **The** computer club is on Mondays.
5 He's a / an old man and he's got a / an big dog.
6 We've got a / an maths exam tomorrow.

# Grammar reference and practice

## 1.1 ■ Present simple affirmative and negative

| Affirmative | | |
|---|---|---|
| I<br>We<br>You<br>They | watch TV | every evening. |
| He<br>She<br>It | watches TV | |
| **Negative** | | |
| I<br>We<br>You<br>They | don't (= do not) watch TV | every evening |
| He<br>She<br>It | doesn't (= does not) watch TV | |

### Spelling rules: third person singular
- Most verbs: add -s
- Verbs ending in -s, -sh, -ch, -o, -x: add -es
- Verbs ending in consonant + -y: change -y to -ies
- The verb to have: change have to has

### Negative
We make the negative form with do and does + n't (= not) + verb. We don't add -s to the verb.

### Use
We use the present simple to talk about:
- habits and everyday routines. We often use time expressions such as *every day, all the time, in the morning, in summer, on Sundays, at weekends* etc.
  I get up at six o'clock every morning.
  Mikhail doesn't play football on Saturdays.
- facts and general truths.
  The temperature changes a lot outside the space station.
  The President of the USA lives in the White House.
- states. Some verbs that describe states are *believe, hate, know, like, love, need, prefer, understand, want.*
  I don't like Spanish food.
  Sarah knows my grandmother.

**1** Choose the correct words.
1 My mother go /(goes) to work by bus.
2 I **study / studies** French and German at school.
3 My school day **finish / finishes** at 3.30 p.m.
4 Piotr **have / has** a big car.
5 She **write / writes** to her cousin every month.
6 They **meet / meets** their friends at the weekend.
7 We **love / loves** romantic films.
8 My friends **live / lives** in the town centre.

**2** Rewrite the sentences from exercise 1 in the negative.
1 My mother ......doesn't go...... to work by bus.
2 I ..................................................... at school.
3 My school day ................................. at 3.30 p.m.
4 Piotr ..................................................... a big car.
5 She ........................ to her cousin every month.
6 They ..................................... their friends at the weekend.
7 We ............................................. romantic films.
8 My friends ............................. in the town centre.

**3** Complete the sentences with the present simple form of the verbs in brackets.
1 I ..........get up.......... (get up) at six o'clock.
2 My father ..................... (not / make) breakfast on Saturday mornings.
3 Stella ..................... (start) school at half past eight.
4 We ..................... (watch) films after dinner.
5 Your friends ..................... (not / like) pizza.
6 You ..................... (not / go) to the gym at the weekend.
7 Dan ..................... (have) a shower every day.
8 My cat ..................... (sleep) 14 hours a day.

## 1.2 ■ Present simple questions and short answers

| Yes / No questions and short answers | | | |
|---|---|---|---|
| Do | I / we / you / they | teach English? | Yes, I do.<br>No, I don't. |
| Does | he / she / it | | Yes, he does.<br>No, he doesn't. |

### Yes / no questions
- Yes / no questions always expect the answer *yes* or *no.*
- We form yes / no questions in the present simple with *Do / Does* + subject + verb.
NOTE: We always put a question mark (?) at the end of a question.

### Short answers
- We make short answers with Yes + subject + *do / does* or No + subject + *don't / doesn't.*

**1** Match questions 1–6 to answers a–f.
1 Do you know that girl? — e
2 Does your brother go swimming before school? — ☐
3 Do they know the answer to the question? — ☐
4 Does Anna play football at the weekend? — ☐
5 Does your dog like cats? — ☐
6 Do we have this CD? — ☐

a Yes, she does.　d No, we don't.
b No, it doesn't.　e Yes, I do.
c No, he doesn't.　f Yes, they do.

**2** Write *yes / no* questions. Then write short answers.

1  you / like / sport
   Do you like sport?
   ✔ Yes, I do.

2  your friend / live / in London
   ............................................................
   ✔ ..........................................................

3  your parents / get up / before you
   ............................................................
   ✗ ..........................................................

4  William / ride / his bike / to school
   ............................................................
   ✔ ..........................................................

5  we / have / a maths lesson today
   ............................................................
   ✗ ..........................................................

6  Eloise / listen / to music / every evening
   ............................................................
   ✗ ..........................................................

# 1.3 ◼ *Wh*- question words

*Wh*- questions ask for specific information.

| Word | Information |
|------|-------------|
| Where | places |
| What | things |
| When | time |
| Who | people |
| How old | age |
| How many | number |

**1** Choose question words to complete the questions.

1  Where / (When) do you get up in the morning?
2  What / Where does your uncle work?
3  What / Why is your name?
4  Who / Where lives in this house?
5  How many / How old is your brother?
6  How many / How old students are there in your class?

**2** Match the answers to the questions in exercise 3.

1  There are thirty-six.  ☐ 6
2  At my school.  ☐
3  At 6.30 a.m.  ☐
4  My friend, Katie.  ☐
5  He's fifteen.  ☐
6  Tom.  ☐

**3** Put the words in the correct order to make *wh*- questions.

1  your / when / birthday / is / mother's / ?
   When is your mother's birthday?

2  house / is / how / your / old / ?
   ............................................................

3  live / Tessa / does / Where / ?
   ............................................................

4  teacher / your / who / favourite / is / ?
   ............................................................

5  answer / what / this / is / question / to / the / ?
   ............................................................

6  family / how / in / people / are / your / many / ?
   ............................................................

# 2.1 ◼ Adverbs of frequency

| | |
|---|---|
| **100%** | always |
| | usually  normally |
| | often  frequently |
| **50%** | sometimes |
| | not often  occasionally  rarely |
| **0%** | never |

## Use

We use adverbs of frequency to describe how often we do something.

A:  How often do you see your cousins?
B:  I usually see them at weekends. I never see them during the week.

## Word order

Adverbs of frequency usually come:

◼ before the main verb.
   My parents often make pizza on Friday nights.
   Rachel always has a shower in the morning.
◼ after the verb *be*.
   He is never late.
   They are usually at drama club on Wednesdays.

The following adverbs can also come at the beginning of the sentence:
*usually, sometimes,*
Usually I sit at this desk.
Sometimes we go swimming on Wednesday afternoons.

**1** Put the words and phrases in the correct order to make sentences. In some cases, more than one answer is possible.

1  sometimes / play tennis / you / after school
   You sometimes play tennis after school.

2  before breakfast / we / train / for two hours / always
   ............................................................

3  never / Sarah / her text messages / reads
   ............................................................

4  go cycling / occasionally / Ahmed and Natalie / after work
   ............................................................

5  bored / at the weekend / I'm / often
   ............................................................

6  rarely / my cousins / on Sundays / are / at the sports centre
   ............................................................

# Grammar reference and practice

**2** Complete the answers to the questions. Use the adverbs in brackets.

1 How often do you buy magazines? (not often)
I _don't often buy magazines._

2 How often does your sister go to the cinema? (never)
My sister ....................................... .

3 How often do you play football in the park? (sometimes)
I ....................................... .

4 How often are you late for school? (usually)
I ....................................... .

5 How often do your parents drive to work? (occasionally)
My parents ....................................... .

6 How often does your dog sleep on your bed? (always)
My dog ....................................... .

## 2.2 ■ *can / can't* for ability

**Affirmative**

| I You He / She / It We They | can | play the piano. |
|---|---|---|

**Negative**

| I You He / She / It We They | can't (= cannot) | ride a bicycle. |
|---|---|---|

**Questions and short answers**

| Can | I you he / she / it we they | speak Italian? | Yes, I can. No, she can't. |
|---|---|---|---|

### Form

■ To form the affirmative we use *can* + infinitive without *to*.
NOTE: We do not add *-s* after *can* in the third person.
**He can jump.** NOT **He cans jump.**

■ To form the negative we use *can't* (= *cannot*) + infinitive without *to*.
**She can't hear you.**

■ To form questions we use *Can* + subject + infinitive without *to*.
**Can they swim?**

### Use

■ We use *can / can't* to talk about ability.
**I can ride a bicycle but I can't ride a horse.**
**Can Fred run fast?**

**1** Choose the correct options.

1 Can they hear the music?
a Yes, they can't.   b No, they can't.
c No, they don't.

2 Can she speak French?
a Yes, she can.   b Yes, she is.
c No, she doesn't.

3 Can you see the whiteboard?
a Yes, I am.   b Yes, I can.   c No, can't I.

4 Can David play the violin?
a No, he can't.   b Yes, he does.   c Yes, it is.

5 Can Olga and Tanya read?
a Yes, they are.   b Yes, they can.
c No, they don't.

6 Can you swim?
a Yes, I swim.   b Yes, I am.   c No, I can't.

**2** Complete the sentences about Jim and Kath using information from the chart.

|  | Jim & Kath | Abi |
|---|---|---|
| fly a plane | ✗ | ✔ |
| do karate | ✔ | ✗ |
| play the drums | ✔ | ✗ |
| sing | ✗ | ✔ |
| make a cake | ✔ | ✗ |
| speak Spanish | ✔ | ✔ |

1 Jim and Kath ......_can't fly_...... a plane.
2 They ....................................... karate.
3 They ....................................... drums.
4 They ....................................... sing.
5 They ....................................... a cake.
6 They ....................................... Spanish.

**3** Study the chart in Exercise 2 again. Write questions and short answers about Abi.

1 _Can Abi fly a plane?_
_Yes, she can._

2 ................ she ................ karate?

3 ................ she ................ the drums?

4 ................ she ................ ?

5 ................ she ................ a cake?

6 ................ she ................ Spanish?

## 2.3 ■ Adverbs of manner

### Form
■ We usually form adverbs of manner by adding -ly to the adjective.

quiet → quietly
loud → loudly

■ Adjectives ending in -y: change -y to -ily.

noisy → noisily
happy → happily

■ There are some common irregular forms.

fast → fast          good → well
hard → hard          late → late

### Use
We use adverbs of manner to describe how someone does something.

He plays the piano well.
She speaks quietly.

### Word order
Adverbs of manner usually come:
■ after the main verb.

She runs fast.

■ after the object of the sentence, if there is one.

I learn new languages quickly.
Kylie plays the piano beautifully.

### Modifiers
■ We often use modifiers, for example: very, really, quite, a bit to give more information about adverbs of manner.

My friends play football really well.
He plays the guitar quite loudly.

**1 Complete the sentences using the adverbs below.**

■ fast ■ quietly ■ easily ■ well ■ slowly ■ badly

1 You're speaking too ........quietly........ . I can't hear you!
2 He's an amazing musician. He can play the drums very ......................... .
3 She wins all the races. She can run really ......................... .
4 Our team always loses. We play really ......................... !
5 I love maths. It's not difficult. I can usually do my homework quite ......................... .
6 Grandpa can ride a bike, but he's not very fast. He usually rides very ......................... .

**2 Write sentences with adverbs of manner.**

1 Harry / swim / good.
   Harry swims well.
2 I / play tennis / bad.
   .........................................................
3 They / play / the piano / slow.
   .........................................................
4 We / usually / finish / our homework / quick.
   .........................................................
5 Dad / sometimes / shouts / angry / at our dog.
   .........................................................
6 Your little brother / plays / very / noisy.
   .........................................................

**3 Put the words in the correct order to make sentences.**

1 the / plays / beautifully / flute / Kate / really
   .........................................................
2 speaks / teacher / very / our / loudly
   .........................................................
3 tests / do / I / quite / in / well
   .........................................................
4 very / the / trains / volleyball / hard / team
   .........................................................
5 eat / quickly / really / I / breakfast
   .........................................................

## 3.1 ■ there is / there are with some, any and a / an

### Affirmative
■ We use There is + a / an before singular nouns.

There is a book on the table.
There is an apple in my bag.

■ We use There are + some before plural nouns.

There are some posters on the wall.

■ We can also use There are + a number (e.g. one, two, three) before plural nouns.

There are five desks in the classroom.

### Negative
■ We use There isn't (= is not) + a / an before singular nouns.

There isn't a cup on the table.
There isn't an orange in my bag.

■ We use There aren't (= are not) + any before plural nouns.

There aren't any pens on the desk.

### Questions and short answers
■ We use Is there + a / an before singular nouns.

Is there a computer in your classroom?
Yes, there is. / No, there isn't.

■ We use Are there + any before plural nouns.

Are there any plants in your garden?
Yes, there are. / No, there aren't.

**1 Complete the sentences with There is or There are.**

1 ............There are............ fifteen students in the science club.
2 ......................... a table in their kitchen.
3 ......................... a TV in my bedroom.
4 ......................... some clothes shops in your town.
5 ......................... two bathrooms in our house.
6 ......................... five children on the beach.

## 2 Choose the correct words.

1 Are there (any)/ a good hotels in this town?
   Yes, there **is** / **are**.
2 There isn't **any** / **an** armchair in my living room.
3 **Are** / **Is** there a washbasin in your room?
   **Yes** / **No**, there isn't.
4 There are **some** / **any** bottles in the fridge.
5 There **are** / **aren't** any cupboards in my kitchen.
6 There **is** / **are** a spider on the wall!

## 3 Write questions with *Is there a / an...* or *Are there any ...* . Then write short answers.

1 stairs / in Mary's house?
   **Are there any stairs in Mary's house?**
   **✔ Yes, there are.**
2 armchair / in your room?
   ....................................................
   ✗ ...............................................
3 bin / in your classroom?
   ....................................................
   ✔ ...............................................
4 curtains / at the window?
   ....................................................
   ✗ ...............................................
5 university / in your town?
   ....................................................
   ✔ ...............................................

# 3.2 ▪ Possessive *'s*

We use *'s* to show possession.
- Add *'s* to a singular noun.
  **The boy has got a dog. This is the boy's dog.**
  **The girl has got two cats. These are the girl's cats.**
- Add *'* to a plural noun which ends in -s.
  **The girls have got a computer.**
  **This is the girls' computer.**
- Add *'s* to irregular plural nouns which don't end in -s.
  **The children have got a ball. This is the children's ball.**

REMEMBER: We also use *'s* in contracted forms of *is* and *has*.
**John's got a sofa in his bedroom. The sofa's very small.**
(= John has got a sofa in his bedroom. The sofa is very small.)

## 1 Complete the sentences with possessive *'s* or *s'*.

1 Tanya has got a blue bag. This is Tanya**'s** blue bag.
2 My friend has got a big house. This is my friend................ big house.
3 My parents have got a car. This is my parent................ car.
4 Mrs White has got some plants in her garden. These are Mrs White................ plants.
5 The men have got sandwiches for lunch. These are the men................ sandwiches.
6 The classroom has got fifteen desks. These are the classroom................ desks.
7 The students have got new books. These are the student................ books.
8 The people have got a new president. This is the people................ new president.

## 2 Correct the sentences by adding apostrophes.

1 Sophie's brother lives in France.
2 My childrens room is very messy.
3 This is my friends new song. They are in a band.
4 I've got one cat. The cats bed is under the table.
5 A: Are those bikes Tims?
   B: Yes, they are. He's got five bikes!
6 My sisters daughters name is Alice.

# 3.3 ▪ Possessive pronouns and *whose*

We use possessive pronouns to show possession.

| Subject pronoun | Possessive adjective | Possessive pronoun |
|---|---|---|
| I | my | mine |
| you | your | yours |
| he | his | his |
| she | her | hers |
| it | its | - |
| we | our | ours |
| they | their | theirs |

- We use possessive adjectives before a noun.
  **It's my bag.**
  **They are our books.**
  **The TV is in her bedroom.**
- We use possessive pronouns to replace nouns.
  **It's mine.     They're ours.     It's hers.**
- We use the question word *whose* to ask about possession.
  **A: Whose desk is this?**
  **B: It's mine.**
  **A: Whose pens are these?**
  **B: They're yours.**

REMEMBER: We always put a question mark (?) at the end of a question.

## 1 Choose the correct possessive pronouns.

1 Bob, is this guitar ............**yours**...........?
   **a** theirs     **b** yours     **c** his
2 This is my cousins' house. It's ............................ .
   **a** ours     **b** theirs     **c** hers
3 These are Jim's books. They're not mine, they're
   ............................ .
   **a** his     **b** ours     **c** mine
4 This is my bag. Where is ............................?
   **a** yours     **b** ours     **c** mine
5 A: Whose shoes are these?
   B: They're not yours. They're my sister's. They're
   ............................ .
   **a** hers     **b** his     **c** yours
6 My brother and I have got this new computer.
   It's ............................ .
   **a** mine     **b** hers     **c** ours

**2 Choose the correct words.**

1 A: Whose are these sandwiches? Are they **her** / **hers**?
  B: No, they aren't **her** / **hers** sandwiches. They're **our** / **ours**.
2 A: Why is **your** / **yours** bag on **my** / **mine** desk?
  B: That isn't **your** / **yours** desk. It's **my** / **mine**.
3 This purse is **your** / **yours** but the money inside it is **our** / **ours**.
4 A: Whose house is this? Is it **your** / **yours** grandparents' house?
  B: No, it isn't **their** / **theirs**. It's **my** / **mine** cousins' house.
5 A: I can't find **my** / **mine** dictionary. Can I use **your** / **yours**?
  B: Sorry, **my** / **mine** is at home.
6 **Your** / **Yours** bedroom is big, but **her** / **hers** is small.

**3 Complete the sentences with the correct possessive pronouns.**

1 I don't like my new phone, but Anna loves ....**hers**.....
2 We haven't got our homework, but those students have got ............................... .
3 A: Whose is this present?
  B: It's for me and my brother. It's ............................... .
4 Have you got a blue jacket? Is this blue jacket ............................... ?
5 A: Is this Tom's picture?
  B: No, it isn't ............................... .
6 A: Are these your clothes, Amy?
  B: Yes, they're ............................... .

# 4.1 ■ Present continuous

### Affirmative and negative

| I | 'm (= am)<br>'m not (= am not) | |
|---|---|---|
| He<br>She<br>It | 's (= is)<br>isn't (= is not) | eating breakfast. |
| We<br>You<br>They | 're (= are)<br>aren't (= are not) | |

### Questions and short answers

| Am | I | | Yes, I am.<br>No, I'm not. |
|---|---|---|---|
| Is | he<br>she<br>it | eating<br>breakfast? | Yes, he is.<br>No, he isn't. |
| Are | we<br>you<br>they | | Yes, we are.<br>No, we aren't. |

**Spelling rules: *-ing* form**

- Most regular verbs: add *-ing*.
- Verbs ending in *-e*: remove *-e* and add *-ing*.
- Verbs ending *-ie*: change *-ie* to *-ying*.
- Short verbs ending consonant + vowel + consonant: double the final consonant and add *-ing*.

**Use**

We use the present continuous to talk about:

- actions that are happening at the time of speaking, often with expressions such as *at the moment* and *now*.
  What are you doing? ~ I'm watching TV.
  She's doing her homework at the moment.
- actions that are happening around now, but perhaps not at the moment of speaking.
  I'm travelling around Australia. (I'm not travelling right now.)
  We're studying English at university. (We're not studying at the moment.)

**1 Complete the sentences with the present continuous form of the verbs in brackets.**

1 I 'm sitting (sit) on the sofa and watching (watch) TV at the moment.
2 My parents ............................... (prepare) dinner.
3 A: ............................... (you / look) at me?
  B: Yes, I ............................... at you.
4 She ............................... (not / talk) on the phone, she ............................... (sleep).
5 We ............................... (learn) about rivers in geography this term.
6 A: ............................... (your brother / listen) to the radio?
  B: No, he ............................... .

**2 Write sentences about what is happening now.**

1 A you / eat / breakfast / at the moment?
  Are you eating breakfast at the moment?
  B No / I / read / the newspaper.
  No, I'm not. I'm reading the newspaper.
2 My dog / chase / a cat in the garden.
  ...............................................................
3 We / take / photographs / of tigers / at London Zoo.
  ...............................................................
4 The foxes / dig / a hole in the ground.
  ...............................................................
5 The hungry wolves / look for / food.
  ...............................................................
6 I / not do / my homework. / I / drink / a cup of tea.
  ...............................................................
7 She / listen / to some music / at the moment.
  ...............................................................
8 Why / you / laugh?
  ...............................................................

# Grammar reference and practice

**3** Complete the sentences with the verbs in brackets. Then match questions 1–4 to answers a–d.

1 .................... he .................... (chat) online?
2 .................... you .................... (download) some music?
3 .................... she .................... (do) housework?
4 .................... they .................... (enjoy) their holiday?

a Yes, she is. She's doing the ironing.
b No he isn't. He's doing his homework.
c Yes, I am. I'm buying a new album.
d No, they're not. It's raining!

## 4.2 ■ Present simple or present continuous

We use the present simple to talk about:
■ general truths
■ habits and routines

We often use frequency expressions, e.g. *sometimes*, *never*, *every week*, *once a month* with the present simple.

We use the present continuous to talk about:
■ activities that are happening now.
■ temporary situations.

We often use expressions like *right now* and *at the moment* with the present continuous.

**1** Read the sentences and decide if they are present simple (PS) or present continuous (PC).

1 I never go to bed before 10 p.m. ☐ PS
2 I'm not getting up now. I'm staying in bed for a bit longer. ☐
3 We're playing cricket in the park at the moment. ☐
4 We usually play football after school on Wednesdays. ☐
5 She isn't talking to me. ☐
6 She doesn't talk very much. I think she's quite shy. ☐
7 Giraffes don't eat meat. ☐
8 The giraffes are eating that man's picnic! ☐

**2** Choose the correct options.

1 A: Do you usually phone / Are you usually phoning your cousin on Fridays?
   B: Yes, I do. / I am.
2 My parents cook / are cooking in the kitchen at the moment.
3 He doesn't read / isn't reading a book. He listens / 's listening to music right now.
4 We visit / are visiting my aunt every Sunday.
5 I often watch / am watching TV programmes about animals.
6 What do you do / are you doing?
   I write / 'm writing an email to my friend.

**3** Complete the sentences with the present simple or present continuous form of the verbs in brackets.

1 She usually _____drinks_____ (drink) tea in the morning, but today she 's having _____ (have) some orange juice.
2 I .................... (not / ride) my bike to school in the mornings. I usually .................... (take) the bus.
3 A: .................... she .................... (swim) at the moment?
   B: No, she ..................... She never .................... (go) swimming before lunch.
4 We .................... (not / study) in the classroom today. We .................... (visit) a farm on a school trip.
5 A: .................... you usually .................... (meet) up with friends at the weekend?
   B: Yes, I ..................... But today, I .................... (stay) at home.
6 My friends .................... (work) in the library today.
7 A: What .................... (you / do) after school on Mondays?
   B: I usually .................... (go) to the park.
8 They .................... (watch) a great film on TV at the moment.

## 5.1 ■ Countable and uncountable nouns

### Countable nouns

■ Countable nouns have a singular and a plural form.
■ We use *a / an* with the singular form and *some / any* with the plural form.
   I eat an apple every day.
   I've got some apples in my bag.
   I haven't got any apples in my bag.

### Uncountable nouns

■ Uncountable nouns only have a singular form.
■ We don't use *a / an* with an uncountable noun. We only use *some / any* or no article.
■ There is no plural form of uncountable nouns.
   I eat some bread every day.
   My brother loves bread.
   Have we got any bread in the cupboard?
   We haven't got any bread.

REMEMBER! We use *some* in affirmative sentences and *any* in negative sentences and questions.

■ We often use units of quantity with uncountable nouns. These units of quantity can describe:
   a part or portion
   *a piece of cake, a slice of cheese, a loaf of bread*
   a container
   *a carton of milk, a bottle of juice*
   a measurement
   *a kilo of meat, fifty grammes of sugar*

**1** Write U (uncountable) or C (countable).

| | | | | |
|---|---|---|---|---|
| **1** | rice | U | **6** | water | |
| **2** | apple | | **7** | cheese | |
| **3** | chair | | **8** | pen | |
| **4** | juice | | **9** | biscuit | |
| **5** | milk | | **10** | bread | |

**2** Complete the sentences with *a* / *an* or *some*.

**1** We've got _____some_____ cheese and _____some_____ biscuits.

**2** A: What's in your lunchbox?
B: _____ tomato, _____ carrot and _____ sandwiches.

**3** I want to do my homework. I need _____ pen and _____ paper.

**4** A: Do you need anything from the supermarket?
B: Yes please! We need _____ milk and _____ sugar. And please get _____ newspaper!

**5** They live in _____ big house with _____ beautiful garden.

**6** There's _____ glass on the table and there's _____ juice in the fridge.

# 5.2 ■ Quantifiers: *much, many, a lot of*

We use *much*, *many* and *a lot of* to talk about large quantities.

### much

■ We use *much* with uncountable nouns.

■ We usually use *much* in questions and in negative sentences.

■ When we ask questions with *much*, we use the phrase: *How much … ?*
A: How much bread have you got?
B: Not much.
We haven't got much time – we're late!

### many

■ We use *many* with countable nouns.

■ We usually use *many* in questions and in negative sentences.

■ When we ask questions with *many*, we use the phrase: *How many … ?*
A: How many apples have you got?
B: Not many. Three, I think.
I haven't got many flowers in my garden.

### a lot of

■ We use *a lot of* with countable and uncountable nouns.

■ We use *a lot of* in affirmatives, negatives and questions.
She's got a lot of money but she hasn't got a lot of friends.
A Have you got a lot of books?
B Yes, I have. I've got a lot of books and a lot of bookshelves!

**1** Choose the correct words.

**1** How *much* / many milk is in the fridge?
**2** How **much** / **many** space is there in your bag?
**3** I haven't got **some** / **many** pictures in my room, but I've got **a lot of** / **much** photos.
**4** How **much** / **many** bananas are in the bowl?
**5** We haven't got **a lot of** / **many** flour but we've got **a lot of** / **much** butter.
**6** They don't have **many** / **much** food in the house.
**7** I play **much** / **a lot of** different sports.
**8** Have you got **many** / **much** homework tonight?

**2** Write questions with *How much* or *How many*.

**1** students / be / in your class / ?
How many students are in your class?

**2** people / be / in your family / ?
_____

**3** time / you / usually spend / on your homework / ?
_____

**4** water / you / drink / every day / ?
_____

**5** armchairs / you / have got / in your living room / ?
_____

**6** chicken / you / eat / every week / ?
_____

**7** eggs / be / in the box / ?
_____

**8** pets / you / have got / ?
_____

# 5.3 ■ Quantifiers: *a little / a few*

We use *a little* and *a few* to refer to small amounts.

### a little

■ We use *a little* with uncountable nouns.
I only take a little sugar in my tea.

### a few

■ We use *a few* with plural countable nouns.
There are a few problems with this homework.

**1** Choose the correct words.

**1** There's *a little* / a few milk in the jug.
**2** There are **a little** / **a few** tomatoes in the fridge.
**3** I've only got **a little** / **a few** bread. There are **a little** / **a few** slices in the bread bin.
**4** Do you want **a little** / **a few** cheese?
**5** There are **a little** / **a few** boxes of pens in the stationery cupboard.
**6** Would you like **a little** / **a few** potatoes with your chicken?

**2** Complete the sentences with *a little* or *a few*.

1 There are ............... *a few* ............... letters on the desk. Are they yours?
2 I can only speak ........................................ English.
3 Do you want ........................................ chocolate?
4 We've got ........................................ days before the beginning of term.
5 She always eats ........................................ raspberries with yoghurt in the morning.
6 Can I try ........................................ of the stew?
7 There are ........................................ children in the park today, but not many because it's very cold.
8 I sometimes have apple pie with ........................................ custard for pudding. It's delicious!

## 6.1 ■ Comparative adjectives

### Spelling rules

■ For short adjectives, add -*er* to form the comparative.
small → smaller
young → younger
■ For short adjectives ending in -*e*, add -*r*.
large → larger
nice → nicer
■ For short adjectives ending in vowel + consonant (except -*w*), double the consonant and add -*er*.
hot → hotter
wet → wetter
■ For adjectives ending in consonant + -*y*, remove the -*y* and add -*ier*.
early → earlier
busy → busier
■ For adjectives of two or more syllables (except adjectives ending in -*y*), add more before the adjective.
beautiful → more beautiful
expensive → more expensive
■ Some adjectives are irregular, for example:
good → better
bad → worse
far → farther / further

### Use

We use comparative adjectives to compare two people or things. Comparative adjectives are often followed by *than*.
Your trousers are more expensive than mine.
This house is bigger than that house.

**1** Complete the sentences using the comparative form of the adjectives in brackets.

1 My brother goes swimming every day. He's ............ *fitter* ............ (fit) than me!
2 Your house is ........................................ (close) to the school than my house.
3 Grant is ........................................ (friendly) than Ben, and he's also ........................................ (intelligent).
4 I'm ........................................ (good) at languages than my sister, but ........................................ (bad) at sport.
5 Do you think a good diet is ........................................ (important) than a lot of exercise?
6 The film and the book are both very sad, but I think the film is ........................................ (sad) than the book.
7 Let's study in the library. It's much ........................................ (quiet) than it is at home.
8 My dad is always ........................................ (late) than my mum.

**2** Write sentences using the correct comparative form of the adjectives and *than*.

1 My sister's room / is / tidy / my room.
**My sister's room is tidier than my room.**
2 Jim's dog / is / thin / Hal's dog.
........................................
3 Your house / is / large / our house.
........................................
4 Pete's exam results / are / bad / Jay's exam results.
........................................
5 Today / is / wet / yesterday.
........................................
6 Your dress / is / pretty / my dress.
........................................
7 These jeans / are / cheap / those jeans.
........................................
8 The supermarket / is / convenient / the shops on the high street.
........................................
9 The film / is / exciting / the book.
........................................
10 I think maths / is / easy / geography.
........................................

**3** Choose the correct word.

1 It's **hotter** / **hoter** today than yesterday.
2 My mum is **youngger** / **younger** than my dad.
3 I get up **earlyer** / **earlier** than my sister.
4 My phone is **smaller** / **smaler** than yours.
5 This film is **better** / **gooder** than the book.
6 Andy is **nice** / **nicer** than Robert.
7 Your bag is **expensiver** / **more expensive** than mine.
8 The school is **farther** / **farer** than the cinema.

## 6.2 ■ Superlative adjectives

### Spelling rules

- For short adjectives, add -est.
  - small → the smallest
  - young → the youngest
- For short adjectives ending in -e, add -st.
  - large → the largest
  - nice → the nicest
- For short adjectives ending in vowel + consonant (except -w), double the consonant and add -est.
  - hot → the hottest
  - wet → the wettest
- For adjectives ending in consonant + -y, remove the -y and add -iest.
  - early → the earliest
  - busy → busiest
- For adjectives of two or more syllables (except adjectives ending in -y), add the most before the adjective.
  - beautiful → the most beautiful
  - expensive → the most expensive
- Some adjectives are irregular, for example:
  - good → the best
  - bad → the worst
  - far → the farthest / the furthest

### Use

We use superlative adjectives to compare a person or thing with the whole group. Superlative adjectives are always preceded by *the …* or *the most …*.

We do not use *than* after superlatives.

Sarah is the shortest girl in our class.
This is the most expensive dress in the shop.

**1** Write the comparative and superlative forms of the adjectives.

|   |   |   |   |
|---|---|---|---|
| 1 | different | more different | the most different |
| 2 | rainy | | |
| 3 | delicious | | |
| 4 | far | | |
| 5 | famous | | |
| 6 | traditional | | |
| 7 | smart | | |
| 8 | good | | |
| 9 | baggy | | |
| 10 | fat | | |
| 11 | safe | | |
| 12 | nice | | |

**2** Complete the sentences with the superlative form of the adjectives in brackets.

1 When we go on holiday, my mum's suitcase is always the heaviest (heavy).
2 Death Valley, in California, is one of ............................ (hot) places in the world.
3 Rob is ............................ (friendly) boy in our class.

4 My aunt isn't ............................ (rich) person in our town, but she's definitely ............................ (popular).
5 You are ............................ (strange) person I know!
6 I want to buy ............................ (big) cake in the shop.
7 You are my ............................ (good) friend.
8 I think my uncle Sam is ............................ (interesting) person in our family.

**3** Write comparative and superlative sentences using the information in the chart.

|           | Price | Age          | Speed           | Length     |
|-----------|-------|--------------|-----------------|------------|
| Red car   | £300  | 10 years old | 100 km per hour | 4.3 metres |
| Blue car  | £500  | 8 years old  | 150 km per hour | 3.9 metres |
| Black car | £150  | 40 years old | 90 km per hour  | 4.8 metres |

1 The red car is __more expensive than__ (expensive) the black car.
3 The black car is __the cheapest__ (cheap) car.
2 The blue car is ............................ (expensive) car.
4 The black car is ............................ (old) car.
5 The red car is ............................ (old) the blue car.
6 The red car is ............................ (fast) the black car.
7 The blue car is ............................ (fast) car.
8 The black car is ............................ (long) car.
9 The red car is ............................ (short) the black car.
10 The blue car is ............................ (short) car.

## 7.1 ■ *have to* and *should*

### *have to* and *don't have to*

| Affirmative and negative | | |
|---|---|---|
| I<br>We<br>You<br>They | have to<br>don't (= do not) have to | work. |
| He<br>She<br>It | has to<br>doesn't (= does not) have to | |

| Questions and short answers | | | | |
|---|---|---|---|---|
| Do | I<br>we<br>you<br>they | have to | work? | Yes, I do.<br>No, I don't. |
| Does | he<br>she<br>it | | | Yes, he does.<br>No, he doesn't. |

# Grammar reference and practice

## Use

- In affirmative sentences, we use *have to* to show that it is necessary to do something.
  We have to tidy our rooms on Saturday mornings.
  He has to wear black shoes at school.
- We use *don't have to* when it isn't necessary for someone to do something.
  You don't have to pay for this course. It's free.
  She doesn't have to get up early at the weekend. She can stay in bed until 10.
- We use the question form *Do I / you / we / they have to … ?* or *Does he / she / it have to … ?* to ask if it is necessary to do something.
  Do we have to buy the tickets now?
  Does he have to take the test?

**1** Write sentences with the correct form of *have to*.

1 She / not / sweep the floor.
  <u>She doesn't have to sweep the floor.</u>

2 They / empty the bins / after breakfast.

3 you / do your homework / on Friday night?

4 We / make our beds / in the morning.

5 My friends / not / wear / school uniform.

6 Julie and I / walk / home every afternoon.

7 I / not / go to school / at the weekend.

8 My dog / sleep / in the kitchen.

**2** Study the chart and complete the sentences with *has to / have to* and *doesn't have to / don't have to*.

What are the rules at Joe's school and at Sue and Kate's school? Do they have to …

|  | Joe | Sue & Kate |
|---|---|---|
| wear school uniform? | ✔ | ✔ |
| do homework every night? | ✘ | ✔ |
| be at school before 8.30 a.m.? | ✘ | ✔ |
| eat lunch at school? | ✔ | ✘ |
| tidy the classroom every day? | ✘ | ✘ |

1 Joe <u>has to wear</u> school uniform.
2 Sue and Kate ............................ school uniform.
3 Joe ............................ homework every night.
4 Sue and Kate ............................ homework every night.
5 Joe ............................ at school before 8.30 a.m.
6 Sue and Kate ............................ at school before 8.30 a.m.
7 Joe ............................ lunch at school.
8 Sue and Kate ............................ lunch at school.

9 Joe ............................ his classroom every day.
10 Sue and Kate ............................ their classroom every day.

## *should* and *shouldn't*

| Affirmative and negative | | |
|---|---|---|
| I<br>You<br>He / She / It<br>We<br>They | should<br>shouldn't (= should not) | sit on this sofa. |

| Questions and short answers | | | |
|---|---|---|---|
| Should | I<br>you<br>he / she / it<br>we<br>they | sit on this sofa? | Yes, you should.<br>No, you shouldn't. |

### Form

- *Should* is used with an infinitive without *to*.
- The forms of *should* are the same for all persons.
- There is no auxiliary *do* in questions or negatives.

### Use

- We use *should* to give advice, or when the speaker feels that it is important for someone to do something.
  You should always wear a helmet when you ride a bike.
  We should send an email to our cousin.
- We use *shouldn't* to give advice, or when the speaker feels that it is important for someone not to do something.
  You shouldn't worry so much!
  He shouldn't shout at his little sister.

**3** Complete the sentences with *should* or *shouldn't*.

1 You .......<u>should</u>....... wear a coat – it's cold outside.
2 We ............................ take the train. It's very expensive. We ............................ go by bus.
3 Suzie's bike is really dirty. She ............................ clean it.
4 Your mother isn't well at the moment. You ............................ help her with the housework.
5 The children ............................ spend all their money on sweets.
6 I ............................ go to bed so late. I always feel so tired at school.
7 We ............................ study for the test tomorrow.
8 My friends ............................ do more exercise. They're not very fit.

**4** Put the words in the correct order to make sentences.

1 tonight / should / we / out / go / ?
  <u>Should we go out tonight?</u>
2 so / they / work / late / shouldn't

3 should / water / drink / I / more

4 doctor / to / should / the / go / you

..............................................................

5 that / he / computer / buy /expensive / shouldn't

..............................................................

6 phone / my / should / sister / I / ?

..............................................................

# 7.2 Past simple: *be* and *can*

## Past simple: *be*

| Questions and short answers | | | |
|---|---|---|---|
| Was | I<br>he / she / it | at home yesterday? | Yes, I was.<br>No, he wasn't. |
| Were | you<br>we<br>they | | Yes, you were.<br>No, you weren't. |
| **Affirmative and negative** | | | |
| I<br>He / She / It | was<br>wasn't (=was not) | | at home yesterday. |
| You<br>We<br>They | were<br>weren't (=were not) | | |

### Form

- The past simple affirmative forms of *be* are *was* and *were*.
- The negative is formed by adding *n't* (= *not*).
  You / We / They were in London last night.
  You / We / They weren't in London last night.
  I / He / She / It was on the bus.
  I / He / She / It wasn't on the bus.
- The past simple question form of *be* is formed by changing the order of the subject and the verb.
  Were you / we / they in London last night?
  Was I / he / she / it on the bus?

### Use

We use the past simple form of *be* to talk about situations in the past.

**1 Complete the sentences with *was* or *were*.**

1 I .....was..... at Ted's house last night.
2 They .................... very friendly.
3 My sister and I .................... very busy last week.
4 My parents .................... in Paris for their anniversary last weekend.
5 She .................... happy, but her brothers .................... sad.
6 A: .................... you in the garden?
B: Yes, I .................... .
7 You .................... the most hardworking student in our class at primary school.
8 They .................... at the supermarket.

**2 Rewrite the sentences using the past simple.**

1 I'm not hungry, but I am tired.
I wasn't hungry, but I was tired.
2 She is at school.
..............................................................
3 A Are you a student?
..............................................................
B No, I'm not. I'm a teacher!
..............................................................
4 A Is your sister in her bedroom?
..............................................................
B Yes, she is.
..............................................................
5 We aren't very rich, but we are happy.
..............................................................
6 They are at the station.
..............................................................

## Past simple: *can*

| Affirmative and negative | | | |
|---|---|---|---|
| I<br>You<br>He / She / It<br>We<br>They | could<br>couldn't (= could not) | | play the piano. |
| **Questions and short answers** | | | |
| Could | I<br>you<br>he / she / it<br>we<br>they | speak English? | Yes, I could.<br>No, we couldn't. |

### Form

- *Could* is used with an infinitive without *to*.
- The forms of *could* are the same for all persons.

### Use

- We use *could* to describe ability in the past.

**3 Write sentences using *could* and *couldn't*.**

1 Jane / ride a bike / when she was three ✔
Jane could ride a bike when she was three.
2 My friends / hear / the music at the concert. ✘
..............................................................
3 I / swim / when I was a child. ✘
..............................................................
4 you / play the violin / when you were younger? ✔
..............................................................
5 We / remember / the teacher's name. ✔
..............................................................
6 they / climb / up the ladder? ✔
..............................................................

# Grammar reference and practice

**4** Rewrite sentences 1–3 in the negative and sentences 4–6 in the positive.

**1** They could find the car keys.
**They couldn't find the car keys.**

**2** Orla could speak two languages.

**3** I could play the trumpet.

**4** I couldn't swim when I was five.

**5** We couldn't understand English films.

**6** Maya couldn't visit her grandparents.

## 8.1 ▪ Past simple: affirmative

| Affirmative | | |
|---|---|---|
| I<br>You<br>He / She / It<br>We<br>They | lived | 20,000 years ago. |

### Spelling rules
- Most regular verbs: add *-ed*
- Regular verbs ending in *-e*: add *-d*
- Short regular verbs ending in consonant + vowel + consonant: double final consonant and add *-ed*
- Regular verbs ending consonant + *-y*: change *-y* to *-ied*

### Use
We use the past simple for:
- a completed past action or a past state. We often use it with expressions that show when things happened, such as *yesterday, … ago, when I was a child, in April / in 2008, last night / last week / last month / last year*, etc.
  The girls played football with their friends yesterday.
  We travelled from Kazakhstan to Kenya last year.
- a past habit, often with an adverb of frequency or a time expression, such as *every week / every Monday / every summer / every year*.
  We usually walked to the sports centre after school.
  They phoned their uncle every Monday.
- a sequence of actions in the past.
  He smiled at the girl and then disappeared.

**1** Choose the correct word.

**1** They **look** / **looked** for their dog in the garden.
**2** She **chats** / **chatted** to her friends last night.
**3** We often **used** / **use** the internet for our homework when we were students.
**4** Thomas Edison **invented** / **invents** the light bulb.
**5** You **tried** / **try** very hard yesterday. Well done.
**6** The students **want** / **wanted** to change their course last year.

**2** Complete the sentences with the past simple form of the verbs in brackets.

**1** Jess and Amy _____watched_____ (watch) an interesting programme on TV.
**2** We _____ (stay) at a hotel.
**3** You _____ (copy) my homework!
**4** My father _____ (wait) for me outside the station.
**5** The film _____ (start) at 7.20 and it _____ (finish) at 9.00.
**6** She _____ (like) her new phone.
**7** They _____ (study) Japanese at college.
**8** I _____ (hate) cheese when I was a child.

## 8.2 ▪ Past simple affirmative: irregular verbs

- Many verbs have irregular past simple forms, for example, *have → had, know → knew, teach → taught*.

### Common irregular past simple verbs

| | | | |
|---|---|---|---|
| become | became | know | knew |
| buy | bought | leave | left |
| catch | caught | make | made |
| come | came | meet | met |
| do | did | put | put |
| eat | ate | run | ran |
| find | found | see | saw |
| get | got | sing | sang |
| give | gave | teach | taught |
| go | went | think | thought |
| grow | grew | understand | understood |
| have | had | wear | wore |
| hear | heard | write | wrote |

**1** Write sentences in the past simple.

**1** My father / teach / English and Russian / when he was younger.
**My father taught English and Russian when he was younger.**
**2** We / buy / a new armchair / last weekend.
**3** I / wear / a beautiful green dress / at my friend's party.
**4** Jude and Max / go / to Australia / in 2013.
**5** My sister / make / a cheese and mushroom pizza / and I / eat / it.
**6** We / write / a letter / to the President of the USA / last year.

**7** My friends / give / me / a wonderful present / for my birthday.

**8** Gemma / leave / her homework / in her bag.

**2** **Complete the sentences with the past simple form of the verb in brackets.**

**1** He ................................ (write) beautiful poems for my sister.
**2** We ................................ (find) an expensive phone in the park.
**3** I ................................ (have) an amazing holiday last month.
**4** Sam ................................ (put) the book on his teacher's desk.
**5** They ................................ (go) to the café in the morning.
**6** I ................................ (hear) a strange noise last night.
**7** Jan ................................ (leave) her house an hour ago.
**8** Luca ................................ (run) in a race last weekend.

# 8.3 ▪ Past simple: negative and questions

## Past simple: negative form

| Negative | | |
|---|---|---|
| I<br>You<br>He / She / It<br>We<br>They | didn't (= did not) study | German at school. |

▪ We form the negative of regular and irregular verbs with *didn't* + infinitive without *to*.

**1** **Rewrite the sentences in the negative.**

**1** She liked the film.
**She didn't like the film.**
**2** We saw a cat in the road.

**3** My cousins wrote a book about Spanish history.

**4** Ned played tennis with his friend, James.

**5** I planted a tree in our garden.

**6** The children waited for their friends.

**7** I bought a new pair of jeans yesterday.

**8** The dog ate all the biscuits on the table.

## Past simple: questions and short answers

| Yes / No questions and short answers | | | |
|---|---|---|---|
| Did | I<br>you<br>he / she / it<br>we<br>they | understand the homework? | Yes, I did.<br>No, we didn't. |

| Wh- questions | | | |
|---|---|---|---|
| Where | did | I<br>you<br>he / she / it<br>we<br>they | go? |
| Who | | | see? |

▪ We make past simple *yes/no* questions with:
*Did* + subject + infinitive + ?
▪ We make past simple *wh-* questions with:
Question word + *did* + subject + infinitive + ?

**2** **Write questions in the past simple.**

**1** your friends / travel / to Sweden last year ?
**Did your friends travel to Sweden last year?**
**2** Where / your sister / find / her phone ?

**3** she / like / the ice cream ?

**4** What / Tom / put / on the table ?

**5** How / you / get / here ?

**6** you / remember / your book ?

**7** he / read / my magazine ?

**8** we / see / this film / last year ?

**3** **Match the questions from exercise 2 to the answers. There are two answers that you do not need.**

**a** It was in her bag! [2]
**b** His phone. ☐
**c** No, you didn't. ☐
**d** No, we didn't. ☐
**e** Oh no! I forgot it! ☐
**f** They didn't. ☐
**g** No, she didn't. ☐
**h** I rode my bike. ☐
**i** Yes, they did. ☐
**j** Yes, he did. ☐

# Grammar reference and practice

## 9.1 ■ *going to*: future plans

| Affirmative and negative | | |
|---|---|---|
| I | 'm (= am) <br> 'm not (= am not) | |
| He <br> She <br> It | 's (= is) <br> isn't (= is not) | going to meet our friends. |
| We <br> You <br> They | 're (= are) <br> aren't (= are not) | |

| Yes / No questions and short answers | | | |
|---|---|---|---|
| Am | I | | Yes, I am. <br> No, I'm not. |
| Is | he <br> she <br> it | going to meet our friends? | Yes, he is. <br> No, he isn't. |
| Are | we <br> you <br> they | | Yes, they are. <br> No, they aren't. |

| Wh- questions | | | | |
|---|---|---|---|---|
| Where | am | I | | stay? |
| Who | is | he <br> she <br> it | going to | see? |
| What | are | we <br> you <br> they | | watch? |

### Use

We use *be* + *going to*:

- to describe an intention.

  I'm going to finish my homework tonight.

  I'm not going to meet my friends tonight.

- to talk about a future plan.

  We are going to move to Germany next year.

  We aren't going to see our grandparents this weekend.

**1** Study the information and write affirmative and negative sentences with *going to* about Amy's plans.

| | | | |
|---|---|---|---|
| pack suitcase | ✔ | watch a film | ✘ |
| phone her friend | ✘ | drive to airport | ✔ |
| find passport | ✔ | play football | ✘ |
| do homework | ✘ | fly to Madrid | ✔ |

1 She 's going to pack ............... her suitcase.
2 She isn't going to phone ............... her friend.
3 She ............... her passport.
4 She ............... her homework.
5 She ............... a film.
6 She ............... to the airport.
7 She ............... football.
8 She ............... to Madrid.

**2** Complete the sentences with *going to* and the verbs in brackets.

1 A: What are you going to do (you / do) next weekend?
  B: I ............... (play) tennis with my friends.
2 She ............... (not / buy) any new clothes. She ............... (save) her money.
3 ............... (you / make) supper tonight?
4 Where ............... (they / stay) while they're on holiday?
5 The twins ............... (not / have) a party for their birthday this year.
6 A: ............... (he / tidy) his room this afternoon?
  B: No, he ............... . He ............... (visit) his cousins.
7 My brother and I ............... (join) the drama club next term.
8 You ............... (start) your new job next week.

## 9.2 ■ *will*: predictions

| Affirmative and negative | | |
|---|---|---|
| I <br> You <br> He / She / It <br> We <br> They | will <br> won't (= will not) | be very lucky. |

| Yes / No questions and short answers | | | |
|---|---|---|---|
| Will | I <br> you <br> he / she / it <br> we <br> they | win the competition? | Yes, I will. <br> No, they won't. |

| Wh- questions | | | |
|---|---|---|---|
| Where | will | I <br> you <br> he / she / it <br> we <br> they | live? |

### Use

- We use *will* and *won't* (= will not) to express predictions about the future.

  It will rain next week.

  We won't use cars or planes in the future.

- We often use *I think*, *maybe* and *probably* with *will*.

  I think I'll stay at home tonight.

  You'll probably hate this film!

  She probably won't come after all.

## 1 Complete the sentences with the phrases below.

■ won't get married ■ won't go ■ ~~will they have~~
■ will move ■ will be ■ will earn ■ will win ■ will sell
■ will it be

1 What job ___will you have___ when you leave school?
2 I think my team _____ the match.
3 You probably _____ before you are thirty.
4 I think the next president of the USA _____ a woman.
5 _____ sunny tomorrow?
6 I think my family _____ to another country next year.
7 She probably _____ to university, but she _____ a lot of money.
8 I think my parents _____ their car soon.

## 2 Write sentences with *will* and *won't*.

What will the world be like in 2050?
1 Robot teachers / teach / our children.
   ___Robot teachers will teach our children.___
2 Many people / take / holidays on the moon.
   _____
3 Families /probably / live / in smaller houses.
   _____
4 People / not eat / meat.
   _____
5 We / grow plants / in space.
   _____
6 I think / there / not be / any wars.
   _____
7 It / not rain / very often.
   _____
8 We / probably / not use / desktop computers.
   _____

## 3 Prediction or plan? Choose the correct options.

1 I think we (will)/ are going to all live in underground houses by 2050.
2 My mum **will** / **'s going to** start her new job tomorrow.
3 They **won't** / **aren't going to** take the train to the shops. They **will** / **'re going to** walk.
4 She probably **won't** / **isn't going to** stay in this country. She loves travelling.
5 I've got my ticket! I **'ll** / **'m going to** fly to Rome on Thursday!
6 In the future, people **will** / **are going to** have much smaller families.

# 10.1 ■ Present perfect: affirmative and negative

## Regular verbs

| Affirmative and negative | | |
|---|---|---|
| I<br>We<br>You<br>They | have<br>haven't (= have not) | competed in the Olympics. |
| He<br>She<br>It | has<br>hasn't (= has not) | |

### Form

■ We form the present perfect with *have* / *has* and the past participle of the main verb.
■ The past participle of regular verbs is the same as the past simple form.
   Past simple: We played football in the park yesterday.
   Present perfect: We have played football three times this week.

### Use

We use the present perfect:
■ to talk about experiences and things that have happened at an indefinite time in the past.
   I've worked in a lot of different places in my life.
   He's rowed across the Atlantic Ocean three times.
   They've travelled a lot in Africa and Asia.
■ to talk about an action or event that started or happened in the past, but has a connection with the present. The action or event might be finished or unfinished.
   I've opened a box of chocolates. Do you want one?
   She's used the last clean cup in the house!
   We've lived in this town all our life. (We were born here and we still live here now.)
■ to talk about recent events.
   Our head teacher has resigned!

## 1 Choose the correct words.

1 She **have** / (**has**) danced in some major competitions around the world.
2 We **don't** / **haven't** phoned our friends in Australia this month.
3 I've **post** / **posted** your letter for you.
4 The college has **offer** / **offered** me a place to study physics.
5 I **hasn't** / **haven't** prepared lunch, because I'm not hungry.
6 He **hasn't** / **haven't** returned the book to the library.

**2 Complete the sentences with the present perfect form of the verbs below.**

■ finish ■ not visit ■ ~~pack~~ ■ answer ■ not tidy ■ bake ■ talk ■ walk

1 I've packed _____ my bag and I'm ready to go.
2 My sister _____ a delicious cake. Would you like a slice?
3 Henry _____ from Brighton to Edinburgh – that's 600 kilometres!
4 The programme _____ , so let's switch off the TV.
5 We _____ to lots of people and they all love our idea.
6 Nick's grandmother is feeling a bit lonely, because he _____ her this week.
7 I _____ all the questions in the test, but I don't know what my score will be.
8 You _____ your room. It's really messy.

## Irregular verbs

■ Many verbs have irregular past participle forms.

### been and gone

The verb go has two past participle forms: been and gone.

■ We use been when we know that someone has returned from a place.
**Dad has been to the supermarket.** (He is back home now.)

■ We use gone when the person has not returned.
**Dad has gone to the supermarket.** (He is still at the supermarket.)

**Common irregular past participles**

| | | | |
|---|---|---|---|
| become | become | make | made |
| buy | bought | meet | met |
| break | broken | put | put |
| catch | caught | ride | ridden |
| come | come | run | run |
| do | done | say | said |
| eat | eaten | see | seen |
| find | found | sing | sung |
| get | got | swim | swum |
| give | given | teach | taught |
| go | gone / been | think | thought |
| have | had | understand | understood |
| hear | heard | wear | worn |
| know | known | win | won |
| leave | left | write | written |

**3 Write sentences in the present perfect.**

1 She / write / five books for children.
**She's written five books for children.**
2 My parents / teach / at different schools / around the world.
_____
3 They / not give / any money / to charity.
_____
4 I / not hear / this song before.
_____
5 Mike / run / two marathons / this year.
_____
6 You / make / a terrible mistake.
_____
7 My sister / met / several famous actors.
_____
8 We / not have / a reply from him.
_____

**4 Write positive ✔ and negative ✗ sentences in the present perfect.**

1 We _____ haven't eaten _____ (eat) chocolate today. ✗
2 I _____ (write) a story for my homework. ✔
3 I _____ (know) Sara for ten years. ✔
4 She _____ (go) to the USA. ✗
5 We _____ (break) the phone. ✔
6 They _____ (win) any football matches. ✗
7 He _____ (ride) a horse. ✔
8 She _____ (meet) my brother. ✗

## 10.2 ■ Present perfect: questions and short answers

| Yes / No questions and short answers | | | |
|---|---|---|---|
| Have | I / we / you / they | met my brother? | Yes, I have. No, they haven't. |
| Has | he / she / it | | Yes, he has. No, she hasn't. |
| **Wh- questions** | | | |
| Where | have | I / we / you / they | been? |
| What | has | he / she / it | done? |

■ We make present perfect yes/no questions with:
Have / Has + subject + past participle + ?
■ We make present perfect wh- questions with:
Question word + have / has + subject + past participle + ?

**1** Put the words in the correct order to make questions.

1 you / why / taken / have / bag / my / ?
*Why have you taken my bag?*

2 he / has / book / your / read / ?

3 received / have / you / email / my / ?

4 you / homework / where / put / have / your / ?

5 you / your / have / dog / found / ?

6 glass / has / broken / the / ?

7 said / has / what / she / ?

8 people / how / seen / have / many / this film / ?

## 10.3 ■ Present perfect with *ever* and *never*

■ In present perfect questions, we often use *ever* (= at any time in the past).
  *Have you ever eaten Japanese food?*
■ To express a negative, we can use *never* (= at no time in the past) + affirmative verb.
  *She's never left her home town.*

**2** Write questions and short answers.

1 you / ever / sail / to France? ✔
*Have you ever sailed to France?*
*Yes, I have.*

2 Sara / ever / teach / English? ✔

3 they / ever / visit / the museum? ✔

4 you / ever / climb / a mountain? ✗

5 he / ever / sing / in public? ✔

6 the girls / ever / play / basketball? ✗

7 you and your friends / ever / go / camping? ✔

8 Dan / ever / win / a competition? ✗

**3** Study the chart. Write sentences in the present perfect about Max's experiences and Bob and Sam's experiences.

|  | Max | Bob & Sam |
|---|---|---|
| sail across the Atlantic | ✗ | ✗ |
| swim in the sea | ✔ | ✔ |
| walk across a desert | ✗ | ✔ |
| jump out of an aeroplane | ✔ | ✗ |
| ride an elephant | ✔ | ✗ |

1 Max *has never sailed* across the Atlantic.
2 He *has swum* in the sea.
3 He .......................... across a desert.
4 He .......................... out of an aeroplane.
5 He .......................... an elephant.
6 Bob and Sam .......................... across the Atlantic.
7 They .......................... in the sea.
8 They .......................... across a desert.
9 They .......................... out of an aeroplane.
10 They .......................... an elephant.

# Pronunciation insight 1

## Present simple -s endings

The third person present simple form always ends in -s. We always say the final -s. There are three different ways to pronounce the final -s.
/s/ as in chats    /z/ as in plays    /ɪz/ as in teaches

**1** Choose the correct -s ending. Complete the table with the verbs below.

■ teaches ■ does ■ eats ■ finishes ■ likes ■ goes
■ watches ■ loves ■ talks

| /ɪz/ | /z/ | /s/ |
|------|-----|-----|
| teaches | | |
| | | |
| | | |

**2** 🌐 **3.24** Listen and check your answers to exercise 1. Then listen and repeat.

**3** 🌐 **3.25** Listen to the -s endings and tick (✔) the sound you hear.

| | /ɪz/ | /z/ | /s/ |
|---|------|-----|-----|
| 1 gets | | | |
| 2 has | | | |
| 3 feels | | | |
| 4 takes | | | |
| 5 washes | | | |
| 6 uses | | | |
| 7 lives | | | |
| 8 walks | | | |

**4** 🌐 **3.26** Listen and check your answers to exercise 3. Then listen and repeat.

**5** 🌐 **3.27** Listen to the sentences. Write the -s ending sound you hear.

1 /......./        2 /......./        3 /......./

**6** 🌐 **3.28** Complete the sentences with the the verbs below. Then write the correct symbols: /ɪz/, /z/ or /s/. Then listen and check.

■ chat ■ get ■ have ■ play ■ start ■ study ■ use ■ watch

1 Jenny ......plays...... basketball on Saturdays. /z/
2 Jasmin .................... TV every evening. ...........
3 Zoe .................... breakfast at 9.00 on Saturdays. ...........
4 Jim .................... dressed before breakfast. ...........
5 Tom .................... school at 8.30 in the morning. ...........
6 Lauren .................... her computer to do her homework. ...........
7 Callum .................... on the phone to Kelly every evening. ...........
8 Lucy .................... Portuguese after school on Thursday. ...........

# Pronunciation insight 2

## can and can't

Look at the pronunciation and stress of can and can't in these sentences.

I can run fast. /kən/          I can't run fast. /kɑ:nt/

Can you run fast? /kæn/

**1** 🌐 **3.29** Listen to the sentences and underline the stressed words.

1 I can't act.              4 I can't ride a bike.
2 Carl can swim.           5 Can they speak French?
3 Can Sally sing?          6 Lisa can play football.

**2** 🌐 **3.30** Listen and tick (✔) the sentences you hear.

1 a I can play the guitar. ☐
  b I can't play the guitar. ☐
2 a Ethan can ride a bike. ☐
  b Ethan can't ride a bike. ☐
3 a You can come to my house. ☐
  b You can't come to my house. ☐
4 a I can speak Spanish. ☐
  b I can't speak Spanish. ☐
5 a They can swim. ☐
  b They can't swim. ☐
6 a We can sing well. ☐
  b We can't sing well. ☐

**3** 🌐 **3.31** Listen to Bethany and Leo talking. Tick (✔) what each person can do.

| | Bethany | Leo |
|---|---------|-----|
| play football | | |
| play basketball | | |
| do karate | | |
| draw | | |
| act | | |
| sing | | |
| dance | | |
| speak Spanish | | |
| speak German | | |

**4** 🌐 **3.32** Write sentences with can (✔) and can't (✘). Underline the stressed words. Then listen and check.

1 Harry / run / fast (✔)
....................................................
2 we / sing (✘)
....................................................
3 Mum and Dad / dance (✘)
....................................................
4 you / speak / English (?)
....................................................
5 you / play / tennis (✔)
....................................................
6 Carla / cook (?)
....................................................

# Pronunciation insight 3

## Final -s

The final -s is always pronounced in English. Sometimes it is pronounced /s/ and sometimes it is pronounced /z/.

/z/ Eva's bag.    How's your friend?
/s/ It's my bag.  Where are the toilets?

**1** 🔊 **3.33** **Listen to the words. Do they end in /s/ or /z/? Then listen and repeat.**

1 beds /............/
2 wardrobes /............/
3 cats /............/
4 cupboards /............/
5 roofs /............/
6 parents /............/

**2** 🔊 **3.34** **Say these sentences. What is the sound for the underlined -s? Then listen and repeat.**

1 There's a nice hotel here. /............/
2 That house is ours. /............/
3 There's a big house. /............/
4 It's Jack's bike. /............/
5 There's a TV next to the window. /............/
6 Is this their dog? Yes, it's theirs. /............/
7 Is this book yours? /............/
8 There's a flag on the beach. /............/
9 Are you Pat's daughter? /............/

## Being polite when asking for directions

Intonation is important if you want to be polite in English. When you ask for directions, it's polite for your intonation to go down and then up at the end of your question.

Excuse me!          How do you get to the museum?

Where is the station, please?

**3** 🔊 **3.35** **Listen to the people asking directions. Tick (✔) the questions that sound polite.**

1 a How do you get to the shopping centre? ☐
  b How do you get to the shopping centre? ☐
2 a Where's the theatre? ☐
  b Where's the theatre? ☐
3 a How do you get to the library, please? ☐
  b How do you get to the library, please? ☐
4 a Where's the bus stop? ☐
  b Where's the bus stop? ☐
5 a Excuse me! ☐
  b Excuse me! ☐

**4** 🔊 **3.35** **Listen and repeat the questions from exercise 3.**

# Pronunciation insight 4

## Stress in two-syllable nouns

We usually pronounce two-syllable nouns with the stress on the first part of the word.

Oo          Oo
insect      raven

**1** 🔊 **3.36** **Say the two-syllable words below. Mark the stressed syllable. Then listen, check and repeat.**

1 mountain        6 cactus
2 chicken         7 tiger
3 eagle           8 rabbit
4 desert          9 flower
5 monkey          10 pigeon

We pronounce a few words with the stress on the second syllable.

oO          oO
giraffe     hotel

## Vowel sounds: /iː/ /ɪ/ /æ/ /ɑː/ /ɒ/ /ə/

**2** 🔊 **3.37** **Listen to the six vowel sounds. Then listen and repeat.**

1 /iː/  me, see, three
2 /ɪ/   big, dig, hit
3 /æ/   rabbit, man, bank
4 /ɑː/  garden, dance, can't
5 /ɒ/   clock, dog, shop
6 /ə/   colour, never, centre

**3** 🔊 **3.38** **Listen to the words and write the vowel sound. Use /iː/, /ɪ/, /æ/, /ɑː/, /ɒ/, /ə/.**

1 chicken /............/     6 cactus /............/
2 giraffe /............/     7 rock /............/
3 rat /............/         8 lizard /............/
4 budgie /............/      9 dog /............/
5 plant /............/       10 spider /............/

**4** 🔊 **3.39** **Listen and check your answers to exercise 3.**

/ə/ is a very important vowel sound in English. It's the vowel sound that we use the most. We use it in weak or unstressed syllables.
spider    tiger

**5** 🔊 **3.40** **Listen to the words and underline the syllable where you hear /ə/.**

1 flower      5 tortoise    9 polar bear
2 cactus      6 lizard      10 kangaroo
3 butterfly   7 desert
4 water       8 hamster

**6** 🔊 **3.40** **Say the words in exercise 5 again and mark the stress. Then listen and check.**

Oo
flower

# Pronunciation insight 5

## Stress in compound nouns

When we put two words together, they are called compound nouns. For compound nouns, the stress is on the first word.

swimming + pool = swimming pool

chocolate + cake = chocolate cake

ice + cream = ice cream

**1** 🌐 **3.41** Match words 1–8 to words a–h to make names for places in a town. Listen and check your answers. Then listen and repeat.

1 train            a centre
2 leisure        b station
3 police         c stop
4 bus             d shop
5 shopping      e stadium
6 football       f centre
7 swimming     g station
8 clothes        h pool

**2** 🌐 **3.42** Complete the pairs of compound nouns with the words below. Then listen and check.

▪ station ▪ ball ▪ room ▪ book

1 bath      ............................    3 text   ............................
    bed                             exercise
2 train     ............................   4 foot  ............................
    bus                              volley

## Stress in quantities

We don't stress *of* in quantities. We pronounce it /əv/ and we link it to the final consonant sound of the word before.

a bottle of water

**3** 🌐 **3.43** Choose the correct words. Then listen and check. Pay attention to the pronunciation of *of*.

1 a loaf of **bread** / crisps
2 a bottle of **coffee** / milk
3 a carton of **milk** / pasta
4 a slice of **potatoes** / pizza
5 a can of **ice cream** / cola
6 a tin of **tomatoes** / onions
7 a jar of **coffee** / juice
8 a packet of **crisps** / pizza
9 a kilo of **water** / apples
10 a litre of **milk** / bread

**4** Practise saying the food quantities in exercise 3 with the correct pronunciation and linking of *of*.

# Pronunciation insight 6

## Comparatives and superlatives

Comparative adjectives and *than* are weak. They have the vowel sound /ə/.
The choice of music online is bett**er** th**an** in music shops.

*The* is also weak when it's used in superlative sentences. However, it isn't weak in the superlative adjective.
I go to town by bus – it's th**e** eas**ie**st way to travel. (easiest = /ɪ/)

**1** 🌐 **3.44** Listen to the comparative and superlative forms. Choose the correct sound for the underlined parts of the words.

|  | /ə/ | /ɪ/ |
|---|---|---|
| bigg**er** |  |  |
| bigg**e**st |  |  |
| old**e**st |  |  |
| bett**er** |  |  |
| easi**e**r |  |  |
| furth**e**st |  |  |

**2** 🌐 **3.45** Mark where the sounds /ə/ and /ɪ/ are in the sentences. Say the sentences. Then listen and check your pronunciation.

1 My cat is thinner than your cat.
2 Berlin is the most exciting city I know.
3 Rosa is better at dancing than me.
4 This dress is the cheapest in the shop.
5 Jasmine's skirt is prettier than Claire's.
6 My bedroom is the smallest room in the house.

## Vowel sounds: /ʊ/ /ʌ/ /ɜː/ /uː/ /ɔː/ /e/

**3** 🌐 **3.46** Match sounds in words 1–6 to sounds in words a–f. Listen, check and repeat.

1 /ʊ/ bookshop               a shorts
2 /ʌ/ jumper                b cook
3 /ɜː/ skirt                   c necklace
4 /uː/ shoes                 d shirt
5 /ɔː/ sports shop       e rucksack
6 /e/ dress                  f boots

**4** 🌐 **3.47** Circle the correct sounds. Listen, check and repeat.

| 1 short | /ʊ/ | /ɔː/ | /uː/ |
|---|---|---|---|
| 2 good | /ʌ/ | /uː/ | /ʊ/ |
| 3 small | /ɔː/ | /ɜː/ | /e/ |
| 4 hungry | /uː/ | /ʌ/ | /ʊ/ |
| 5 worse | /ɔː/ | /uː/ | /ɜː/ |
| 6 friendly | /ɜː/ | /e/ | /ʌ/ |
| 7 further | /e/ | /ɜː/ | /ɔː/ |
| 8 lucky | /ʊ/ | /uː/ | /ʌ/ |

**5** Choose four of the adjectives in exercise 4 and write two comparative and two superlative sentences. Then say your sentences to a partner. Remember to use the correct pronunciation for the weak forms.

# Pronunciation insight 7

## Negative forms

In spoken English, *was/wasn't, were/weren't* and *could/couldn't* are usually weak forms and the negative forms are often contracted.

**1** 🔊 **3.48** **Listen and repeat.**

1 /wəz/      Who **was** at the party?
2 /wɒznt/    Tim **wasn't** there.
3 /wə/       My parents **were** happy.
4 /wɜ:nt/    They **weren't** rich.
5 /kəd/      He **could** dance well.
6 /kʊ[d]nt/  I **couldn't** watch TV last night.

**2** 🔊 **3.49** **Listen to the sentences. Put a tick (✔) for affirmative verbs and a cross (✘) for negative verbs.**

1 I ............... ✘ at school today. I ............... ☐ at home.
2 I ............... ☐ dance when I was younger, but I ............... ☐ sing.
3 We ............... ☐ safe. The road ............... ☐ dangerous.
4 You ............... ☐ popular, because you ............... ☐ play football really well.
5 Josh ............... ☐ cycle to school, because it ............... ☐ near his house.
6 You ............... ☐ happy last night. I ............... ☐ worried about you.
7 Kelly and I ............... ☐ well. We ............... ☐ at the cinema.
8 They ............... ☐ go to the concert, because they ............... ☐ get tickets.

**3** 🔊 **3.49** **Listen again and complete the sentences in exercise 2.**

/w/ is a difficult sound for many learners of English. Start by practising the /u:/ sound – your mouth makes the same shape when you say /u:/ and /w/.
   uuu … where
/w/ is silent when it comes before *r. write, wrong*
/w/ is silent when it comes before *h* and *o. two, who*

**4** 🔊 **3.50** **Listen to the sentences and underline the letters that make the** /w/ **sound.**

1 There were two women next to the window.
2 Are you going to wear that coat for the whole winter?
3 Where were you when I was at my swimming lesson?
4 I want to write on this white paper.
5 Who is with you?
6 Are we walking in the wrong direction?

**5** **Practise saying the sentences in exercise 4. Pay attention to the pronunciation of** /w/.

# Pronunciation insight 8

## Past simple -*ed* endings

-*ed* at the end of past simple forms is pronounced in three different ways:
   ▪ /t/ **liked** ▪ /d/ **listened** ▪ /ɪd/ **waited**

**1** **Say the past simple form of the regular verbs below. Put the verbs with the correct end sound in the table below.**

   ▪ chat ▪ invent ▪ like ▪ listen ▪ love ▪ stop ▪ visit ▪ talk ▪ change

| /t/ | /d/ | /ɪd/ |
|---|---|---|
| .......... | .......... | .......... |
| .......... | .......... | .......... |
| .......... | .......... | .......... |

**2** 🔊 **3.51** **Listen and check your answers to exercise 1. Then listen and repeat.**

**3** 🔊 **3.52** **Complete the sentences with the past simple affirmative form of the verbs below. Write the correct symbols for the endings: /t/, /d/ or /ɪd/. Then listen and check.**

   ▪ finish ▪ open ▪ live ▪ start ▪ want ▪ watch

1 I ............... school at 9.30 yesterday morning. /......./
2 We ............... our exams yesterday and now we're on holiday! /......./
3 I ............... a funny film with Dad last night. /......./
4 Harry ............... to make new friends, but it wasn't easy. /......./
5 They ............... the front door and went into the house. /......./
6 My family ............... in Delhi in the 1970s. /......./

**4** 🔊 **3.53** **Listen to the sentences. Are the sentences present simple or past simple? Then listen again and complete the sentences with the correct form of the verb you hear.**

1 We ............... cycling to school.
2 I ............... to my friend every evening.
3 They ............... in the morning.
4 Charlotte ............... hard.
5 My brother ............... maths at university.
6 Jake and I ............... drama.

## Past simple irregular verbs

**5** 🔊 **3.54** **Listen to the pairs of verbs. Tick (✔) the verbs that rhyme. Then listen and repeat.**

1 rode   thought  ☐      4 wrote  wore   ☐
2 read   said     ☐      5 left   grew   ☐
3 grew   knew     ☐      6 made   stayed ☐

# Pronunciation insight 9

## Saying telephone numbers

When we say phone numbers, we usually say each digit separately. We usually use pauses between groups of three or four numbers. We usually say *oh* for 0, not *zero*.

(01973) 754683 = oh-one-nine-seven-three (pause) seven-five-four (pause) six-eight-three

0797 2093572 = oh-seven-nine-seven (pause) two-oh-nine (pause) three-five-seven-two

**1** 🔊 **3.55** **Listen to the telephone numbers. Mark the pauses. Then listen and repeat.**

1 (01729) 752456
2 07895380485
3 07982509461
4 (0208) 725198

**2** 🔊 **3.56** **Listen to the telephone numbers. How do we say numbers like 77 or 888 when they are in telephone numbers? Then listen and repeat.**

1 (01779) 753556
2 0777 4895214
3 0789 3332461
4 (0207) 334455

**3** **Work in pairs. Write three telephone numbers. Don't show your partner. Say your numbers to each other and write the numbers you hear. Check your partner's answers.**

## Phrasal verbs

When we say phrasal verbs, we usually link the words and this can make them difficult to understand. Listen:

Let's work it out.
Can you pick it up, please?

**4** 🔊 **3.57** **Listen and complete the sentences with the phrasal verbs below. Then listen and repeat. Pay attention to the links between the words in the phrasal verbs.**

■ come up with ■ find out about ■ go ahead ■ look up
■ put together ■ set up

1 I usually ............................................ information online.
2 Can you ............................................ a report, please?
3 You need to ............................................ a plan.
4 Liz is going to ............................................ prices later.
5 Dad is going to ............................................ a new business.
6 We are going to ............................................ with our plans.

## *like*

**5** 🔊 **3.58** **Listen to the sentences with *like* and tick (✔) the sentence you hear.**

1 a Billy is like his brother. ☐
  b Billy likes his brother. ☐
2 a What's your friend like? ☐
  b What does your friend like? ☐
3 a They don't look like their dinner. ☐
  b They don't like their dinner. ☐
4 a I like my cousin a lot. ☐
  b I look a lot like my cousin. ☐
5 a Do you like your brother? ☐
  b Are you like your brother? ☐

# Pronunciation insight 10

## Pronunciation of *have* in present perfect

■ When we use the present perfect we usually use contractions.
I've = /aɪv/    haven't = /hævənt/
He's = /hiːz/    hasn't = /hæzənt/

■ In questions, the weak form is used. In short answers, *have* and *has* are strong.
/həv/
Have you seen the new Bond film?
  /hæv/      /hævənt/
Yes, I have.    No, I haven't.

■ *ever* /evə/ and *never* /nevə/ end with the sound /ə/.

**1** 🔊 **3.59** **Listen and tick (✔) the sentence you hear. Then listen and repeat. Pay attention to the pronunciation of *have/haven't*.**

1 a I've never won a competition. ☐
  b I never won a competition. ☐
2 a She's swum 25 metres. ☐
  b She swam 25 metres. ☐
3 a We've had a great day. ☐
  b We had a great day. ☐
4 a Harry's climbed Mount Everest. ☐
  b Harry climbed Mount Everest. ☐
5 a Granddad has enjoyed dancing all his life. ☐
  b Granddad enjoyed dancing all his life. ☐
6 a Mum's broken her mobile phone. ☐
  b Mum broke her mobile phone. ☐

**2** 🔊 **3.60** **Listen to the questions and answers. Underline the weak forms.**

1 'Have you swum in a lake?' 'Yes, I have.'
2 'Has she visited Thailand?' 'No, she hasn't.'
3 'Have you ever been to Egypt?' 'Yes, we have.'
4 'Have your parents seen the Eiffel Tower?' 'No, they haven't.'
5 'Has David won the match?' 'Yes, he has!'

**3** **Work in pairs. Practise saying the questions and answers in exercise 2. Pay attention to the weak forms.**

**4** 🔊 **3.61** **Match questions 1–6 to answers a–f. Then listen and check.**

1 Have you ever been to the USA?
2 Has David ever worked abroad?
3 Have they ever cycled in France?
4 Has Maria ever visited Canada?
5 Have you ever seen The Parthenon?
6 Have we ever met him before?

a Yes, they have. They took their bikes there last June.
b No, we haven't. We've never been to Greece.
c Yes, I have. I went to New York last year.
d No, we haven't. We've never seen him before.
e No, he hasn't. He's never had a job outside this country.
f Yes, she has. She stayed with her friend in Toronto.

**5** 🔊 **3.61** **Underline the weak forms in exercise 4. Listen, check and repeat.**

# Wordlist

## Welcome

**angry** (adj) /ˈæŋgri/ feeling or showing anger: *My father was angry with me when I got home late.*

**apple** (n) /ˈæpl/ a hard round fruit with green or red skin: *Would you like a glass of apple juice?*

**aunt** (n) /ɑːnt/ the sister of your mother or father, or the wife of your uncle: *My aunt is a lovely lady.*

**autumn** (n) /ˈɔːtəm/ the part of the year between summer and winter: *In autumn, the leaves fall from the trees.*

**bag** (n) /bæg/ a thing made of cloth, paper, leather, etc., for holding and carrying things: *She brought some sandwiches in a plastic bag.*

**(read a) book** (n) /bʊk/ a thing that you read or write in, that has a lot of pieces of paper joined together inside a cover: *I'm reading a new book.*

**bored (with sth)** (adj) /bɔːd/ not interested; unhappy because you have nothing interesting to do: *I'm bored with this book.*

**brother** (n) /ˈbrʌðə(r)/ a man or boy who has the same parents as you: *My brother is called Brian.*

**cold** (adj) /kəʊld/ not hot or warm; with a low temperature: *I'm cold. Will you put the heater on?*

**computer** (n) /kəmˈpjuːtə(r)/ a machine that can store and find information, calculate amounts and control other machines: *I love playing on the computer.*

**cousin** (n) /ˈkʌzn/ the child of your aunt or uncle: *Paul and I are cousins.*

**cricket** (n) /ˈkrɪkɪt/ a game for two teams of eleven players who try to hit a small hard ball with a piece of wood (called a bat) on a large field: *We watched a cricket match.*

**curly** (adj) /ˈkɜːli/ with a lot of curls: *He's got curly hair.*

**dad** (n) /dæd/ an informal word for father: *This is my dad.*

**dark** (adj) /dɑːk/ A dark colour is nearer to black than to white: *He's got dark brown hair.*

**daughter** (n) /ˈdɔːtə(r)/ a girl or woman who is sb's child: *They have two daughters and a son.*

**excited (about sth)** (adj) /ɪkˈsaɪtɪd/ not calm, for example because you are happy about sth that is going to happen: *He's excited about his holiday.*

**fair** (adj) /feə(r)/ Fair skin or hair is light in colour: *He's got fair hair.*

**(play) football** (n) /ˈfʊtbɔːl/ a game for two teams of eleven players who try to kick a round ball into the other team's goal on a field: *Peter's playing in a football match tomorrow.*

**granddaughter** (n) /ˈgrændɔːtə(r)/ the daughter of your son or daughter: *Mr and Mrs May are excited about the birth of their first granddaughter.*

**grandfather** (n) /ˈgrænfɑːðə(r)/ the father of your mother or father: *My grandfather has died.*

**grandmother** (n) /ˈgrænmʌðə(r)/ the mother of your mother or father: *I always go to my grandmother's house after school.*

**grandparent** (n) /ˈgrænpeərənt/ the mother or father of your mother or father: *This is a picture of two of my grandparents*

**grandson** (n) /ˈgrænsʌn/ the son of your son or daughter: *Their grandson is a doctor.*

**happy** (adj) /ˈhæpi/ feeling pleased or showing that you are pleased: *You look very happy today.*

**hot** (adj) /hɒt/ having a high temperature: *I'm hot. Can you open the window?*

**hungry** (adj) /ˈhʌŋgri/ wanting to eat: *Let's eat soon – I'm hungry!*

**husband** (n) /ˈhʌzbənd/ the man that a woman is married to: *Her husband is Chinese.*

**into sth** /ˈɪntə/ very interested in sth, for example as a hobby: *I'm really into canoeing.*

**long** (adj) /lɒŋ/ far from one end to the other: *She has long black hair.*

**mobile phone** (n) /ˌməʊbaɪl ˈfəʊn/ a telephone that you can carry around with you: *I'll ring you on your mobile phone tonight.*

**mum** (n) /mʌm/ an informal word for mother: *This is my mum.*

**nephew** (n) /ˈnefjuː/ the son of your brother or sister: *This is my youngest nephew, Charlie.*

**niece** (n) /niːs/ the daughter of your brother or sister: *My niece, Jenny, will be two next month.*

**old** (adj) /əʊld/ having lived for a long time: *My grandfather is very old.*

**parent** (n) /ˈpeərənt/ a mother or father: *Her parents live in Italy*

**sad** (adj) /sæd/ unhappy: *He looked very sad.*

**short** (adj) /ʃɔːt/ a small distance from one end to the other: *Her hair is very short.*

**sister** (n) /ˈsɪstə(r)/ a girl or woman who has the same parents as you: *I've got two older sisters.*

**son** (n) /sʌn/ a boy or man who is sb's child: *They have a son and two daughters.*

**spring** (n) /sprɪŋ/ the part of the year after winter, when plants start to grow: *The flowers of this plant bloom in spring.*

**straight** (adj) /streɪt/ with no curve or bend: *His hair is curly and mine is straight.*

**summer** (n) /ˈsʌmə(r)/ the season that comes between spring and autumn: *I am going to Spain in the summer.*

**tall** (adj) /tɔːl/ higher than other people or things: *Richard is taller than his brother.*

**thirsty** (adj) /ˈθɜːsti/ wanting or needing a drink: *I'm thirsty. Can I have a drink of water, please?*

**tired** (adj) /ˈtaɪəd/ needing to rest or sleep: *I've been working all day and I'm really tired now.*

**uncle** (n) /ˈʌŋkl/ the brother of your mother or father, or the husband of your aunt: *Uncle Steve works for a big software company in California.*

**wife** (n) /waɪf/ the woman that a man is married to: *This is my wife, Josephine.*

**winter** (n) /ˈwɪntə(r)/ the coldest part of the year: *It often snows in winter.*

**young** (adj) /jʌŋ/ in the early part of life; not old: *They have two young children.*

## Unit 1

**(check your) answer** (n) /ˈɑːnsə(r)/ a reply to a question in a test or an exam: *Check your answers are at the back of the book.*

**art** (n) /ɑːt/ the activity of producing things such as paintings, designs, etc.: *I am really good at art.*

**assembly** (n) /əˈsembli/ a regular meeting for all the students and teachers of a school: *We have assembly three times a week.*

**(by) bike** (n) /baɪk/ a bicycle; a vehicle with two wheels. You sit on it and move your legs to make the wheels turn: *I go to school by bike.*

**bin** (n) /bɪn/ a thing that you put rubbish in: *Put your rubbish in the bin.*

**blackboard** (n) /ˈblækbɔːd/ a dark board that a teacher writes on with a white substance called chalk: *Look at the blackboard.*

**(look at the) board** (n) /bɔːd/ a thin flat surface on the wall that a teacher writes on: *All the new vocabulary is on the board.*

**break** (n) /breɪk/ a short period of rest between lessons: *I went to see the teacher at break.*

**(by) bus** (n) /bʌs/ a large vehicle that carries a lot of people along the road and stops often so they can get on and off: *We went to town by bus.*

**(by) car** (n) /kɑː(r)/ a vehicle with four wheels, usually with enough space for four or five people: *She travels to work by car.*

**calculator** (n) /ˈkælkjuleɪtə(r)/ a small piece of electronic equipment that you use for finding amounts or numbers using mathematics: *We're not allowed to use calculators in the test.*

**chair** (n) /tʃeə(r)/ a piece of furniture for one person to sit on, with four legs, a seat and a back: *The chairs were arranged in a circle.*

**citizenship** (n) /ˈsɪtɪzənʃɪp/ the study of the responsibilities and rights of the people in a country: *We have citizenship classes twice a week.*

**clock** (n) /klɒk/ an object that shows you the time: *I set my alarm clock for 6.30 a.m.*

**desk** (n) /desk/ a type of table that you sit at to write or work: *The students sat quietly at their desks.*

**(listen to a) dialogue** (n) /ˈdaɪəlɒg/ a conversation between people: *Listen to this short dialogue between a shop assistant and a customer.*

**diary** (n) /ˈdaɪəri/ a book where you write what you are going to do: *I never forget my diary.*

**dictionary** (n) /ˈdɪkʃənri/ a book, website or piece of software that explains what words mean: *Look up the words in your dictionary.*

**door** (n) /dɔː(r)/ the way into a building or room; a piece of wood, glass or metal that you use to open and close the way in to a building or room: *Can you close the door, please?*

**drama** (n) /ˈdrɑːmə/ the study of plays and acting: *Mrs Weston teaches drama at our school.*

**DT** (n) /ˌdiː ˈtiː/ design and technology: the study of making drawings that show how sth should be made, how it will work, etc. and the activity of making it: *George made a beautiful table in DT.*

**English** (n) /ˈɪŋglɪʃ/ the study of the English language: *English is my favourite subject at school.*

**(do an) exercise** (n) /ˈeksəsaɪz/ a piece of work that you do to learn sth: *Please do exercises 1 and 2.*

**exercise book** (n) /ˈeksəsaɪz ˌbʊk/ a book that you use at school for writing in: *Please write these sentences in your exercise book.*

**folder** (n) /ˈfəʊldə(r)/ a cover made of cardboard or plastic for keeping papers in: *The teacher opened the folder and took out three sheets of paper.*

**geography** (n) /dʒiˈɒgrəfi/ the study of the Earth and everything on it, such as mountains, rivers, land and people: *Have you revised for the geography test?*

**get dressed** (v) /ˌget ˈdrest/ to put clothes on yourself: *I got dressed and had my breakfast.*

**get home** (v) /ˌget ˈhəʊm/ to come back to the place where you live: *When did he get home?*

**get up** (v) /ˌget ˈʌp/ to get out of bed: *What time do you usually get up?*

**glue** (n) /gluː/ a thick liquid that you use for sticking things together: *Stick the picture to the card with glue.*

**go to bed** (v) /ˌgəʊ tə ˈbed/ to lie in a bed and go to sleep: *It's time to go to bed.*

**have a shower** (v) /ˌhæv ə ˈʃaʊə(r)/ to wash yourself by standing under water that falls from above you: *I had a shower after the tennis match.*

**have breakfast** (v) /ˌhæv ˈbrekfəst/ to eat the first meal of the day: *I never have breakfast.*

**have dinner** (v) /ˌhæv ˈdɪnə(r)/ to eat the largest meal of the day, usually in the evening: *What time do you usually have dinner?*

**have lunch** (v) /ˌhæv ˈlʌntʃ/ to eat the meal that you eat in the middle of the day: *What time do you usually have lunch?*

**history** (n) /ˈhɪstri/ the study of things that happened in the past: *Albert is a history teacher.*

**(do) homework** (n) /ˈhəʊmwɜːk/ work that a teacher gives to you to do at home: *Have you done your French homework?*

**ICT** (n) /ˌaɪ siː ˈtiː/ information and communication technology: the study of the use of computer, the internet, video and other technology: *We're learning how to make simple websites in ICT at the moment.*

**interactive whiteboard** (n) /ˌɪntəræktɪv ˈwaɪtbɔːd/ a piece of classroom equipment using a computer connected to a large screen that you can write on or use to control the computer by touching it with your finger or a pen: *Nearly every classroom has an interactive whiteboard.*

**(use) the internet** (n) /ˈɪntənet/ the international system of computers that makes it possible for you to see information from all around the world on your computer and to send information to other computers: *The internet is a useful study tool.*

**map** (n) /mæp/ a drawing of a town, a country or the world that shows things like mountains, rivers and roads: *Can you find Glasgow on the map?*

**maths** (n) /mæθs/ the study of numbers, measurements and shapes: *Maths is great!*

**meet (friends)** (v) /miːt/ to come together with other people: *I often meet friends at the weekend.*

**modern languages** (n) /ˌmɒdn ˈlæŋgwɪdʒɪz/ the study of languages that are spoken now: *Ms James is Head of Modern Languages at our school.*

# Wordlist

**music** (n) /'mjuːzɪk/ the study of the sounds that you make by singing, or by playing instruments: *Our music teacher plays the guitar in a band.*

**on foot** /ˌɒn 'fʊt/ walking: *We'll go on foot.*

**(work in) pairs** (n) /peəz/ groups of two people together: *I'd like you to work in pairs for this task.*

**PE** (n) /ˌpiː 'iː/ physical education: sport and exercise that are done as a subject at school: *We have PE on Tuesdays.*

**pen** (n) /pen/ an object that you use for writing with a coloured liquid called ink: *Can I borrow your pen, please?*

**pencil** (n) /'pensl/ a thin object that you use for writing or drawing. Pencils are usually made of wood and have a black or coloured point: *Bring a pencil and paper with you.*

**pencil case** (n) /'pensl ˌkeɪs/ a small bag or box that you keep pens, pencils, etc. in: *Do you like my new pencil case?*

**pencil sharpener** (n) /'pensl ˌʃɑːpnə(r)/ a small device that you use for making pencils sharp: *Have you got a pencil sharpener I could borrow?*

**(chat on the) phone** (n) /fəʊn/ a piece of equipment that you use for talking to sb who is in another place: *I love chatting on the phone.*

**(by) plane** (n) /pleɪn/ an aeroplane; a vehicle with wings that can fly through the air: *I like travelling by plane.*

**poster** (n) /'pəʊstə(r)/ a big piece of paper on a wall, with a picture or words on it: *We designed a poster on the theme of healthy eating.*

**RE** (n) /ˌɑːr 'iː/ religious education: the study of religion: *We study different systems of belief in RE.*

**registration** (n) /ˌredʒɪ'streɪʃn/ the time when a teacher looks at the list of students in a class and checks that they are all there: *Registration is at 8.45 a.m.*

**rubber** (n) /'rʌbə(r)/ a small piece of rubber that you use for taking away marks that you have made with a pencil: *Do you have a rubber?*

**ruler** (n) /'ruːlə(r)/ a long piece of plastic, metal or wood that you use for drawing straight lines or for measuring things: *Use a ruler to measure the sides of the triangle.*

**school bag** (n) /'skuːl ˌbæg/ a bag that you use for carrying school books, a pencil case, etc.: *I'm getting a new school bag for my birthday.*

**science** (n) /'saɪəns/ the study of natural things: *We did an interesting experiment in our science class.*

**scissors** (n) /'sɪzəz/ a tool for cutting that has two sharp parts that are joined together: *These scissors aren't very sharp.*

**(write a) sentence** (n) /'sentəns/ a group of words that tells you sth or asks a question: *In this exercise you have to fill in the gaps in the sentences.*

**sheet of paper** (n) /ʃiːt əv 'peɪpə(r)/ a thin flat piece of paper (= thin material for writing or drawing on) : *Take out a sheet of paper and write your name at the top.*

**start school** (v) /ˌstɑːt 'skuːl/ start being at school: *What time do you start school each day?*

**student** (n) /'stjuːdnt/ a person who is studying at a school, college or university: *Every student takes a test in English at the end of the course.*

**teacher** (n) /'tiːtʃə(r)/ a person whose job is to teach: *Mr Morton is my English teacher.*

**(study for a) test** (n) /test/ an exam that you do in order to show what you know or what you can do: *We have a vocabulary test every Friday.*

**(read a) text** (n) /tekst/ a short piece of writing that you study: *Read the text quickly.*

**textbook** (n) /'tekstbʊk/ a book that teaches you about sth: *Open your textbooks at page 151.*

**(by) train** (n) /treɪn/ a vehicle that is pulled by an engine along a railway line: *I'm going to Bristol by train.*

**(learn) vocabulary** (n) /və'kæbjələri/ the words in a language: *Remember to learn vocabulary.*

**watch TV** (v) /ˌwɒtʃ tiː 'viː/ to look at progammes and films on the television: *Grandma always watches TV in the evenings.*

**window** (n) /'wɪndəʊ/ an opening in a building with glass in it: *Open the window. It's hot in here.*

**(read the) word** (n) /wɜːd/ a letter or group of letters that has a meaning: *Read the word carefully.*

# Unit 2

**acting** (n) /'æktɪŋ/ performing in plays or films: *Have you ever done any acting?*

**aerobics** (n) /eə'rəʊbɪks/ physical exercises that people often do in classes, with music: *I do aerobics twice a week to keep fit.*

**archery** (n) /'ɑːtʃəri/ the sport of shooting arrows: *The centre offers archery courses.*

**athletics** (n) /æθ'letɪks/ sports like running, jumping and throwing: *Sam goes to an athletics club after school on Tuesdays.*

**bad** (adj) /bæd/ not able to work or do sth well: *He's a bad teacher.*

**badminton** (n) /'bædmɪntən/ a game for two or four players who try to hit a kind of light ball with feathers on it (called a shuttlecock) over a high net, using a racket (= a piece of equipment which you hold in your hand): *Do you want to play badminton?*

**basketball** (n) /'bɑːskɪtbɔːl/ a game for two teams of five players who try to throw a ball into a high net: *Who won the basketball match?*

**canoeing** (n) /kə'nuːɪŋ/ the activity of moving through water in a light narrow boat for one or two people, using a flat piece of wood called a paddle: *Canoeing is an exciting watersport.*

**cello** (n) /'tʃeləʊ/ a large wooden musical instrument with strings. You sit down to play it and hold it between your knees: *I play the cello.*

**clarinet** (n) /ˌklærə'net/ a musical instrument made of wood with holes in it. You play it by blowing into it: *I'm learning to play the clarinet.*

**(play a) computer game** (n) /kəm'pjuːtə(r) ˌgeɪm/ a game that you play on a computer: *They play computer games every evening.*

**cooking** (n) /'kʊkɪŋ/ making food ready to eat: *Who does the cooking in your family?*

**dancing** (n) /'dɑːnsɪŋ/ moving to music: *We both like dancing.*

**different** (adj) /'dɪfrənt/ many and not the same: *They sell 30 different sorts of ice cream.*

**difficult** (adj) /'dɪfɪkəlt/ not easy to do or understand: *The exam was very difficult.*

**drawing** (n) /'drɔːɪŋ/ the art of drawing pictures with a pen or a pencil: *Sue is very good at drawing.*

**(play the) drums** (n) /drʌm/ a musical instrument made of empty containers with plastic stretched across the ends. You play the drums by hitting them with sticks: *She plays the drums in a band.*

**easy** (adj) /'iːzi/ not difficult to do or understand; not causing problems: *The homework was easy.*

**enjoy** (v) /ɪn'dʒɔɪ/ to like sth very much: *I enjoy playing football.*

**flute** (n) /fluːt/ a musical instrument that you hold out to the side and play by blowing: *Suzanne plays the flute in an orchestra.*

**good** (adj) /gʊd/ able to do sth well: *She's a good driver.*

**guitar** (n) /gɪ'tɑː(r)/ a musical instrument with strings: *Ben played the guitar and Isabel sang.*

**gymnastics** (n) /dʒɪm'næstɪks/ physical exercises that are done inside a building, often using special equipment such as bars and ropes: *She won a gold medal in gymnastics.*

**hockey** (n) /'hɒki/ a game that is played on a field by two teams of eleven players who try to hit a small hard ball into a goal with a curved wooden stick: *Rosie is a member of the school hockey team.*

**interested (in sb / sth)** (adj) /'ɪntrəstɪd/ wanting to know or hear more about sth/sb; enjoying or liking sth/sb: *Are you interested in cats?*

**karate** (n) /kə'rɑːti/ a Japanese sport where people fight with their hands and feet: *Jake is taking part in a karate competition on Saturday.*

**keyboards** (n) /'kiːbɔːdz/ a musical instrument like a small electrical piano: *Harry plays keyboards in a band.*

**like** (v) /laɪk/ to enjoy sth: *I like playing tennis.*

**love** (v) /lʌv/ to like sth very much: *I love skiing.*

**new** (adj) /njuː/ different from before: *The teacher usually explains the new words to us.*

**noisy** (adj) /'nɔɪzi/ making a lot of noise; full of noise: *The restaurant was too noisy.*

**old** (adj) /əʊld/ done or had before now: *My old job was more interesting than this one.*

**painting** (n) /'peɪntɪŋ/ the act of making pictures using paint (= a coloured liquid that you put on things with a brush) : *Painting is harder than drawing.*

**piano** (n) /pi'ænəʊ/ a big musical instrument that you play by pressing black and white bars called keys: *Can you play the piano?*

**quiet** (adj) /'kwaɪət/ with very little or no noise: *It was very quiet in the library.*

**rock climbing** (n) /'rɒk ˌklaɪmɪŋ/ the sport of climbing rocks and mountains with ropes, etc.: *Have you ever been rock climbing?*

**rugby** (n) /'rʌgbi/ a game like football for two teams of 13 or 15 players. In rugby, you can kick and carry the ball: *Do you prefer rugby or football?*

**running** (n) /'rʌnɪŋ/ the sport of moving very quickly on your legs: *How often do you go running?*

**sailing** (n) /'seɪlɪŋ/ the sport of controlling a boat with sails: *They do a lot of sailing.*

**same** (adj) /seɪm/ not different; not another: *Emma and I like the same kind of music.*

**saxophone** (n) /'sæksəfəʊn/ a musical instrument made of metal that you play by blowing into it: *I play saxophone in a jazz band.*

**singing** (n) /'sɪŋɪŋ/ making musical sounds with your voice *Natalie takes singing lessons.*

**skateboarding** (n) /'skeɪtbɔːdɪŋ/ the activity of moving over the ground on a long piece of wood or plastic on wheels: *Mark loves skateboarding.*

**skiing** (n) /'skiːɪŋ/ The sport of sliding over snow on a pair of long, flat, narrow pieces of wood or plastic that are fastened to boots: *We go skiing every winter.*

**swimming** (n) /'swɪmɪŋ/ the sport or activity of moving your body through water: *Swimming is my favourite sport.*

**(play) tennis** (n) /'tenɪs/ a game for two or four players who hit a ball to each other over a net using a piece of equipment called a racket: *Let's play tennis.*

**trumpet** (n) /'trʌmpɪt/ a musical instrument that is made of metal and that you blow: *My brother is learning to play the trumpet.*

**unusual** (adj) /ʌn'juːʒuəl/ not expected or normal: *A field is an unusual place for a violin lesson.*

**usual** (adj) /'juːʒuəl/ happening or used most often: *I sat in my usual seat.*

**violin** (n) /ˌvaɪə'lɪn/ a musical instrument that you hold under your chin and play by moving a stick (called a bow) across the strings: *Erica plays the violin in the school orchestra.*

**volleyball** (n) /'vɒlibɔːl/ a game where two teams try to hit a ball over a high net with their hands: *We played volleyball on the beach.*

# Unit 3

**after that** (n) /ˌɑːftə 'ðæt/ used to introduce the next item in a list of things: *After that, have a drink and a snack in the museum café.*

**armchair** (n) /'ɑːmtʃeə(r)/ a soft comfortable chair with side parts where you can put your arms: *She was asleep in an armchair.*

**bank** (n) /bæŋk/ a place that keeps money safe for people: *I've got £500 in the bank.*

**bath** (n) /bɑːθ/ a large container that you fill with water and sit in to wash your body: *Can you answer the phone? I'm in the bath!*

**bathroom** (n) /'bɑːθruːm/ a room where you can wash and have a bath or shower: *Go and wash your hands in the bathroom.*

**bed** (n) /bed/ a piece of furniture that you sleep on: *This is a very comfortable bed.*

**bedroom** (n) /'bedruːm/ a room where you sleep: *I share a bedroom with my sister.*

**bedside table** (n) /ˌbedsaɪd 'teɪbl/ a small piece of furniture for a lamp, clock, etc. next to a bed: *There was a glass of water on the bedside table.*

**bidet** (n) /ˈbiːdeɪ/ a large bowl in the bathroom that you can sit on in order to wash your bottom: *Each bathroom has a bath, a bidet and a washbasin.*

**bus stop** (n) /ˈbʌs ˌstɒp/ a place where buses stop and people get on and off: *The bus stop is five minutes' walk from here.*

**café** (n) /ˈkæfeɪ/ a place where you can buy a drink and sth to eat: *There's a nice café near here.*

**capital** (n) /ˈkæpɪtl/ the most important city in a country, where the government is: *Tokyo is the capital of Japan.*

**carpet** (n) /ˈkɑːpɪt/ a piece of thick material that is used for covering floors and stairs: *Oh no, I've spilt coffee on the new carpet!*

**ceiling** (n) /ˈsiːlɪŋ/ the top part of the inside of a room: *We painted the ceiling white.*

**chest of drawers** (n) /ˌtʃest əv ˈdrɔːz/ a large piece of furniture with parts that you can pull out (called drawers). A chest of drawers is usually used for keeping clothes in: *Put your clothes away in your chest of drawers.*

**cinema** (n) /ˈsɪnəmə/ a place where you go to see a film: *Let's go to the cinema tonight.*

**city** (n) /ˈsɪti/ a large and important town: *Venice is one of the most beautiful cities in the world.*

**city centre** (n) /ˌsɪti ˈsentə(r)/ the most important part of a city, usually in the middle, where most of the shops and offices are: *It is very expensive to park your car in the city centre.*

**cooker** (n) /ˈkʊkə(r)/ a piece of kitchen equipment for cooking using electricity or gas. It has places for heating pans on the top and an oven for cooking food inside it: *The kitchen has a gas cooker, a fridge and a dishwasher.*

**countryside** (n) /ˈkʌntrɪsaɪd/ land with fields, woods, farms, etc., that is away from towns and cities: *There are magnificent views over open countryside.*

**cupboard** (n) /ˈkʌbəd/ a piece of furniture with shelves and doors, where you keep things like clothes or food: *We put the sugar, flour and jam away in the kitchen cupboard.*

**curtains** (n) /ˈkɜːtnz/ two pieces of cloth that you can move to cover a window: *Could you draw the curtains, please?*

**cushion** (n) /ˈkʊʃn/ a cloth bag filled with sth soft, which you put on a chair: *She sat back in the armchair with a cushion behind her head.*

**dining room** (n) /ˈdaɪnɪŋ ˌruːm/ a room where people eat meals: *We are waiting for you in the dining room.*

**dishwasher** (n) /ˈdɪʃwɒʃə(r)/ a machine that washes things like plates, glasses, knives and forks: *Could you empty the dishwasher, please?*

**finally** (n) /ˈfaɪnəli/ used to introduce the last in a list of things: *Finally, after dinner, enjoy some traditional Irish music in the hotel bar.*

**fireplace** (n) /ˈfaɪəpleɪs/ the open place in a room where you light a fire: *There's a rug in front of the fireplace.*

**first** (n) /ˈfɜːst/ used to introduce what happens before anything else: *First fry the onions, then add the potatoes.*

**floor** (n) /ˈflɔː(r)/ the part of a room that you walk on: *There weren't any chairs so we sat on the floor.*

**freezer** (n) /ˈfriːzə(r)/ an electric container which keeps food very cold (below 0° Celsius) so that it stays fresh for a long time: *There's some ice cream in the freezer.*

**fridge** (n) /ˈfrɪdʒ/ a metal container, usually electric, which keeps food cold, but not frozen: *Can you put the milk in the fridge, please?*

**front door** (n) /ˌfrʌnt ˈdɔː(r)/ the main door at the front of a house: *Jo's at the front door.*

**garden** (n) /ˈɡɑːdn/ a piece of land by your house where you can grow flowers, fruit, and vegetables: *Let's have lunch in the garden.*

**hall** (n) /hɔːl/ the room in a house that is near the front door and has doors to other rooms *You can leave your coat in the hall.*

**hospital** (n) /ˈhɒspɪtl/ a place where doctors and nurses look after people who are ill or hurt: *My brother is in hospital – he's broken his leg.*

**kitchen** (n) /ˈkɪtʃɪn/ a room where you cook food: *We usually eat in the kitchen.*

**lamp** (n) /ˈlæmp/ an electric light that stands on a table: *It was dark, so I switched on the lamp.*

**leisure centre** (n) /ˈleʒə ˌsentə(r)/ a public building where people can go to do sports and other activities in their free time: *On Saturdays, we usually go swimming at the leisure centre.*

**library** (n) /ˈlaɪbrəri/ a room or building where you go to borrow or read books: *My library books are due back tomorrow.*

**living room** (n) /ˈlɪvɪŋ ˌruːm/ a room in a house where people sit together and watch television or talk, for example: *There's a sofa in the living room.*

**mirror** (n) /ˈmɪrə(r)/ a piece of special glass where you can see yourself: *Look in the mirror.*

**museum** (n) /mjuˈziːəm/ a building where people can look at old or interesting things: *Have you ever been to the Science Museum in London?*

**next** (n) /ˈnekst/ used to introduce a new or different item in a list of things: *Next, take a bus to the City Museum.*

**park** (n) /pɑːk/ place with grass and trees, where anybody can go to walk, play games or relax: *We had a picnic in the park.*

**police station** (n) /pəˈliːs ˌsteɪʃn/ an office where police officers work: *They took the men to the police station for questioning.*

**restaurant** (n) /ˈrestrɒnt/ a place where you buy a meal and eat it: *We went to a Chinese restaurant.*

**roof** (n) /ruːf/ the top of a building, that covers it *All the houses have red tiled roofs.*

**rug** (n) /rʌɡ/ a small piece of thick material that you put on the floor: *The dog sat on the rug.*

**shelf** (n) /ʃelf/ a long flat piece of wood on a wall or in a cupboard, where things can stand: *Put the plates on the top shelf.*

**shopping centre** (n) /ˈʃɒpɪŋ ˌsentə(r)/ a place where there are many shops, either outside or in a covered building: *I often meet friends at the shopping centre on Saturday afternoons.*

**shower** (n) /ˈʃaʊə(r)/ a place where you can wash by standing under water that falls from above you: *There's a shower in the bathroom.*

**shutters** (n) /ˈʃʌtəz/ wooden or metal covers on the outside of a window: *Close the shutters at night.*

**sink** (n) /sɪŋk/ the place in a kitchen where you wash dishes: *Leave the dirty plates in the sink.*

**sofa** (n) /ˈsəʊfə/ a long soft seat for more than one person: *Jane and Bob were sitting on the sofa.*

**stadium** (n) /ˈsteɪdiəm/ a place with seats around it where you can watch sport: *As you leave the city centre, the football stadium is on your left.*

**stairs** (n) /steəz/ steps that lead up and down inside a building: *I ran up the stairs to the bedroom.*

**suburb** (n) /ˈsʌbɜːb/ one of the parts of a town or city outside the centre: *We live in the suburbs.*

**table** (n) /ˈteɪbl/ a piece of furniture with a flat top on legs: *Let me help you clear the table.*

**theatre** (n) /ˈθɪətə(r)/ a building where you go to see plays: *I'm going to the theatre this evening.*

**then** (n) /ðen/ used to introduce the next item in a list of things: *We had dinner. Then we watched a movie.*

**toilet** (n) /ˈtɔɪlət/ a large bowl with a seat, that you use when you need to empty waste from your body: *Excuse me, I'm just going to the toilet.*

**town** (n) /taʊn/ a place where there are a lot of houses, shops and other buildings: *I live in a small town near Oxford.*

**train station** (n) /ˈtreɪn ˌsteɪʃn/ a place where trains stop so that people can get on and off: *Is the train station far from the city centre?*

**university** (n) /ˌjuːnɪˈvɜːsəti/ a place where people go to study more difficult subjects after they have left school: *I'm going to university soon.*

**village** (n) /ˈvɪlɪdʒ/ a very small town in the countryside: *She lives in a village in the mountains.*

**wall** (n) /wɔːl/ a side of a building or room: *There's a poster on the wall.*

**wardrobe** (n) /ˈwɔːdrəʊb/ a cupboard where you hang your clothes: *My clothes are in the wardrobe.*

**washbasin** (n) /ˈwɒʃbeɪsn/ the large bowl in a bathroom where you wash your hands and face: *In the bathroom, there is a bath, a washbasin and a toilet.*

**washing machine** (n) /ˈwɒʃɪŋ məˌʃiːn/ a machine that washes clothes: *Put your dirty clothes in the washing machine now!*

**window** (n) /ˈwɪndəʊ/ an opening in a building with glass in it: *It was cold, so I closed the window.*

# Unit 4

**background** (n) /ˈbækɡraʊnd/ the things at the back in a picture: *This is a photo of my house with the mountains in the background.*

**bear** (n) /beə(r)/ a big wild animal with thick fur: *A large brown bear came out of the forest.*

**bite** (n) /baɪt/ If an insect or snake bites you, it hurts you by pushing a small sharp part into your skin. *I've been bitten by a mosquito.*

**bouldering** (n) /ˈbəʊldərɪŋ/ the sport of rock climbing on low rocks without special equipment: *Bouldering is quite popular amongst young people.*

**budgie** (n) /ˈbʌdʒi/ a small blue or green bird that people often keep as a pet: *I have to clean out the budgie's cage once a week.*

**bungee jumping** (n) /ˈbʌndʒi dʒʌmpɪŋ/ a sport in which you jump from a high place, for example a bridge, with a thick elastic (= material that can stretch) rope tied round your feet: *Have you ever tried bungee jumping?*

**butterfly** (n) /ˈbʌtəflaɪ/ an insect with big coloured wings: *Caterpillars develop into butterflies.*

**cactus** (n) /ˈkæktəs/ a plant with a lot of sharp points that grows in hot dry places: *The bears eat cacti, fruit, mice and ants.*

**carry** (n) /ˈkæri/ to hold sth and take it to another place or keep it with you: *I carried my bag upstairs.*

**cat** (n) /kæt/ a small animal with soft fur that people keep as a pet: *A cat ran across the road.*

**caving** (n) /ˈkeɪvɪŋ/ the sport of walking and climbing through caves under the ground: *There are some areas around here that are good for caving.*

**centre** (n) /ˈsentə(r)/ the part in the middle of sth: *There was a candle in the centre of the table.*

**chicken** (n) /ˈtʃɪkɪn/ a bird that people often keep for its eggs and its meat: *We keep free-range chickens on our farm.*

**cloud** (n) /klaʊd/ a white or grey shape in the sky that is made of small drops of water: *Look at those dark clouds. It's going to rain.*

**cloudy** (adj) /ˈklaʊdi/ If the weather is cloudy, the sky is full of clouds: *The day will be cloudy, with occasional heavy showers.*

**cold** (adj) /kəʊld/ not hot or warm; with a low temperature: *Put your coat on – it's cold outside.*

**cool** (adj) /kuːl/ a little cold; not hot or warm: *It's hot outside but it's nice and cool in here.*

**cow** (n) /kaʊ/ a big female farm animal that is kept for its milk or meat: *There were some cows in the field next to our camp site.*

**desert** (n) /ˈdezət/ a large, dry area of land with very few plants: *I crossed the Sahara desert on foot.*

**dig** (v) /dɪɡ/ to move earth and make a hole in the ground: *They dug a tunnel through the mountain for the new railway.*

**diving** (n) /ˈdaɪvɪŋ/ the sport of swimming underwater wearing breathing equipment, collecting or looking at things: *The main purpose of his holiday to Greece was to go diving.*

**dog** (n) /dɒɡ/ an animal that many people keep as a pet or to guard buildings: *I love dogs!*

**eagle** (n) /ˈiːɡl/ a large bird that can see very well. It catches and eats small birds and animals: *A golden eagle flew overhead.*

**elephant** (n) /ˈelɪfənt/ a very big wild animal from Africa or Asia, with a long nose (called a trunk) that hangs down: *An elephant can live for up to eighty years.*

**fish** (n) /fɪʃ/ an animal that lives and breathes in water, and has thin flat parts (called fins) that help it to swim: *Jack keeps exotic fish.*

**flower** (n) /ˈflaʊə(r)/ the brightly coloured part of a plant that comes before the seeds or fruit: *She gave me a bunch of flowers.*

# Wordlist

**follow** (v) /ˈfɒləʊ/ to come or go after sb or sth: *Follow me and I'll show you the way.*

**foreground** (n) /ˈfɔːɡraʊnd/ the things at the front of a picture: *The man in the foreground is my father.*

**forest** (n) /ˈfɒrɪst/ a large area of land covered with trees: *We went for a walk in the forest.*

**fox** (n) /fɒks/ a wild animal like a small dog with a long thick tail and red fur: *Foxes have a keen sense of smell.*

**giraffe** (n) /dʒəˈrɑːf/ a big animal from Africa with a very long neck, long legs and big dark spots on their skin: *Male giraffes often fight each other using their long necks.*

**grass** (n) /ɡrɑːs/ a plant with thin green leaves that covers fields and gardens. Cows and sheep eat grass: *Don't walk on the grass.*

**grassland** (n) /ˈɡrɑːslænd/ a large area of land where grass grows: *There's nothing there except open grassland and a few sheep.*

**guinea pig** (n) /ˈɡɪni pɪɡ/ a small animal with short ears and no tail, that people often keep as a pet: *We keep guinea pigs in our back garden.*

**hamster** (n) /ˈhæmstə(r)/ a small animal that people keep as a pet. A hamster can keep food in the sides of its mouth: *This is my pet hamster, called Nibbles.*

**horse** (n) /hɔːs/ a big animal that can carry people and pull heavy things: *Can you ride a horse?*

**horse riding** (n) /ˈhɔːs raɪdɪŋ/ the sport or activity of riding a horse for pleasure: *Kate goes horse riding at the weekends.*

**hot** (adj) /hɒt/ having a high temperature: *It's hot today, isn't it?*

**hunt** (v) /hʌnt/ to chase animals to kill them for food: *Young lions have to learn to hunt.*

**ice** (n) /aɪs/ water that has become hard because it is frozen: *I slipped on a patch of ice.*

**(on the) left** (n) /left/ the left side or direction: *Our house is on the left as you enter the village.*

**lizard** (n) /ˈlɪzəd/ a small animal that has four legs, a long tail and rough skin: *Lizards basked on rocks in the hot sun.*

**look for** (v) /ˈlʊk fə(r)/ to try to find sth: *I'm looking for my keys.*

**(in the) middle** (n) /ˈmɪdl/ the part that is the same distance from the sides or ends of sth: *I'm in the middle of my class photo.*

**monkey** (n) /ˈmʌŋki/ an animal with a long tail, that can climb trees: *Monkeys were swinging from the trees.*

**mountain** (n) /ˈmaʊntən/ a very high hill: *Everest is the highest mountain in the world*

**mountain biking** (n) /ˈmaʊntən baɪkɪŋ/ the sport of riding a bicycle with a strong frame and wide tyres over rough ground: *Ross and Ben often go mountain biking at the weekends.*

**mouse** (n) /maʊs/ a small animal with a long tail: *Our cat caught a mouse.*

**parrot** (n) /ˈpærət/ a bird with very bright feathers that can copy what people say: *Does your parrot speak?*

**pig** (n) /pɪɡ/ a fat animal that people keep on farms for its meat: *My Uncle Joe is a pig farmer.*

**plant** (n) /plɑːnt/ anything that grows from the ground: *Don't forget to water the plants.*

**rabbit** (n) /ˈræbɪt/ a small animal with long ears. Rabbits live in holes under the ground: *The dog ran after a rabbit.*

**rainy** (adj) /ˈreɪni/ with a lot of rain: *It was a cold, rainy day.*

**(on the) right** (n) /raɪt/ the right side or direction: *We live in the first house on the right.*

**rock** (n) /rɒk/ the very hard material that is in the ground and in mountains: *These layers of rock were formed over millions of years.*

**run away** (v) /ˌrʌn əˈweɪ/ to go quickly away from sb or sth: *The rabbit ran away from the dog.*

**sand** (n) /sænd/ powder made of very small pieces of rock, that you find on beaches and in deserts: *We played in the sand and swam in the sea.*

**sheep** (n) /ʃiːp/ an animal that people keep on farms for its meat and its wool: *They keep sheep and pigs on their farm.*

**snake** (n) /sneɪk/ an animal with a long thin body and no legs: *Do these snakes bite?*

**snow** (n) /snəʊ/ soft white pieces of frozen water that fall from the sky when it is very cold: *Eight centimetres of snow fell during the night.*

**snowboarding** (n) /ˈsnəʊbɔːdɪŋ/ the sport of moving down mountains that are covered in snow using a large board that you fasten to both your feet: *Have you ever been snowboarding?*

**snowy** (adj) /ˈsnəʊi/ with a lot of snow: *The school bus is often late on snowy days.*

**spider** (n) /ˈspaɪdə(r)/ a small animal with eight legs, that catches and eats insects: *Spiders spin webs to catch flies.*

**stormy** (adj) /ˈstɔːmi/ with strong wind and rain: *The plane was delayed due to stormy weather.*

**sunny** (adj) /ˈsʌni/ bright and warm with light from the sun: *Tomorrow will be warm and sunny.*

**surfing** (n) /ˈsɜːfɪŋ/ the sport of riding on waves while standing on a board (called a surfboard): *His hobbies include surfing and photography.*

**tiger** (n) /ˈtaɪɡə(r)/ a wild animal like a big cat, with yellow fur and black stripes. Tigers live in Asia: *Tigers are nearly extinct in the wild.*

**tortoise** (n) /ˈtɔːtəs/ an animal with a hard shell on its back, that moves very slowly: *Tortoises can live to over 100 years old.*

**tree** (n) /triː/ a big plant that can live for a long time. Trees have a central part (called a trunk) and many smaller parts (called branches): *Apples grow on trees.*

**warm** (adj) /wɔːm/ having a pleasant temperature that is fairly high, between cool and hot: *It's nice and warm by the fire.*

**whale** (n) /weɪl/ a very big animal that lives in the sea and looks like a very big fish: *Whales, dogs and humans are all mammals.*

**white water rafting** (n) /ˌwaɪt ˈwɔːtə ˈrɑːftɪŋ/ the sport of travelling in a rubber boat down a section of a river where water is moving very fast: *We went white water rafting down the river.*

**windy** (adj) /ˈwɪndi/ with a lot of wind: *It's very windy today!*

**wolf** (n) /wʊlf/ a wild animal like a big dog: *I've seen wolves in the zoo, but not in the wild.*

**zorbing** (n) /ˈzɔːbɪŋ/ the sport or activity of rolling down a hill in a large clear plastic ball: *I've never tried zorbing before.*

## Unit 5

**(a) bottle (of water)** (n) /ˈbɒtl/ a glass or plastic container for liquids, with a thin part at the top: *They drank two bottles of water.*

**boring** (adj) /ˈbɔːrɪŋ/ not interesting: *I thought that film was a bit boring.*

**bowl** (n) /bəʊl/ a deep round dish that is used for holding food or liquids: *I had a bowl of soup for lunch.*

**bread** (n) /bred/ food made from flour and baked in an oven: *I like bread and butter with my soup.*

**(a) can (of coke)** (n) /kæn/ a metal container for food or drink that keeps it fresh: *Two cans of lemonade, please.*

**carrot** (n) /ˈkærət/ a long thin orange vegetable that grows under the ground: *I'd like a kilo of carrots, please.*

**(a) carton (of juice)** (n) /ˈkɑːtn/ a container made of very thick paper (called cardboard) or plastic: *I'll open a new carton of juice.*

**cheese** (n) /tʃiːz/ a yellow or white food made from milk: *Can I have extra cheese on my pizza?*

**chocolate** (n) /ˈtʃɒklət/ a dark brown sweet food that is made from seeds (called cocoa beans) that grow on trees in hot countries: *Do you like chocolate?*

**chocolate cake** (n) /ˈtʃɒklət ˌkeɪk/ a sweet food that you make from flour, eggs, sugar and butter and chocolate, and bake in the oven: *I ordered a slice of chocolate cake and a cup of coffee.*

**coffee** (n) /ˈkɒfi/ a brown drink that you make by adding water to a powder made from cocoa beans (= seeds from a tree that grows in hot countries): *Would you like another cup of coffee?*

**cream** (n) /kriːm/ the thick liquid on the top of milk: *We had strawberries and cream for dessert.*

**crisps** (n) /krɪsps/ very thin pieces of potato cooked in hot oil and eaten cold. Crisps are sold in bags and have many different flavours: *I had a sandwich and a packet of crisps in my lunch box.*

**cucumber** (n) /ˈkjuːkʌmbə(r)/ a long vegetable with a green skin, that we often eat in salads: *Slice the cucumber and add it to the salad.*

**cup** (n) /kʌp/ a small round container with a handle, that you can drink from: *Would you like a cup of tea?*

**delicious** (adj) /dɪˈlɪʃəs/ very good to eat: *This soup is delicious.*

**disgusting** (adj) /dɪsˈɡʌstɪŋ/ very unpleasant: *What a disgusting smell!*

**exciting** (adj) /ɪkˈsaɪtɪŋ/ Sth that is exciting makes you have strong feelings of happiness and enthusiasm: *We watched an exciting film last night.*

**fork** (n) /fɔːk/ an object with long points at one end, that you use for putting food in your mouth: *Please use your knife and fork.*

**fruit salad** (n) /ˌfruːt ˈsæləd/ a mixture of prepared fruit that you eat as a dessert: *For dessert, we had a choice of fruit salad or ice cream.*

**glass** (n) /ɡlɑːs/ a cup without a handle that is made of glass: *Could I have a glass of water, please?*

**grape** (n) /ɡreɪp/ a small green or purple fruit that we eat or make into wine: *I bought some apples, some pears and a bunch of grapes.*

**ham sandwich** (n) /ˌhæm ˈsænwɪtʃ/ two pieces of bread with a slice of ham between them: *Would you like a ham sandwich?*

**ice cream** (n) /ˌaɪs ˈkriːm/ very cold sweet food made from milk: *Do you like ice cream?*

**interesting** (adj) /ˈɪntrəstɪŋ/ enjoyable and entertaining; holding your attention: *This book is very interesting.*

**(a) jar (of jam)** (n) /dʒɑː(r)/ a glass container for food: *I can't open this jar of jam.*

**jug** (n) /dʒʌɡ/ a container with a handle that you use for holding or pouring liquids: *There was a jug of milk on the table.*

**ketchup** (n) /ˈketʃəp/ a cold sauce made from tomatoes: *Do you want ketchup on your chips?*

**(a) kilo (of apples)** (n) /ˈkiːləʊ/ a kilogram: a measure of weight. There are 1,000 grams in a kilo: *I bought a kilo of apples.*

**knife** (n) /naɪf/ a sharp metal object with a handle that you use for cutting things: *I need a sharp knife to cut this meat.*

**lettuce** (n) /ˈletɪs/ a plant with big green leaves that you eat cold in salads: *Wash the lettuce and mix in the salad sauce.*

**(a) litre (of oil)** (n) /ˈliːtə(r)/ a measure of liquid: *Try to drink a litre of water a day.*

**(a) loaf (of bread)** (n) /ləʊf/ bread that has been baked in one piece: *How much is a loaf of bread?*

**lovely** (adj) /ˈlʌvli/ beautiful or very nice: *We had a lovely holiday.*

**mug** (n) /mʌɡ/ a big cup with straight sides: *Lisa sat in front of the fire with a mug of hot chocolate.*

**mushroom** (n) /ˈmʌʃrʊm/ a plant with a flat top and no leaves that you can eat as a vegetable: *Mushrooms are very good for you.*

**mushroom pizza** (n) /ˌmʌʃrʊm ˈpiːtsə/ a flat round piece of bread with tomatoes, cheese and mushrooms on top, that is cooked in an oven: *I ordered a mushroom pizza and some juice.*

**nut** (n) /nʌt/ a dry fruit that has a hard outside part with a seed inside *This chocolate contains nuts.*

**olive oil** (n) /ˌɒlɪv ˈɔɪl/ oil that is produced from olives (= small green or black fruit): *Fry the onions in a little olive oil.*

**onion** (n) /ˈʌnjən/ a round vegetable with many layers and a strong smell. Cutting onions can make you cry: *Can I have some onions, please?*

**orange** (n) /ˈɒrɪndʒ/ a round fruit with a colour between red and yellow, and a thick skin: *I bought six juicy oranges at the market.*

**orange juice** (n) /ˈɒrɪndʒ ˌdʒuːs/ the liquid from an orange that you can drink: *I'd like a glass of orange juice, please.*

**(a) packet (of sweets)** (n) /ˈpækɪt/ a small box or bag that you buy things in: *We ate a packet of biscuits between us.*

**pasta** (n) /ˈpæstə/ an Italian food that is made from flour, water and sometimes eggs, which comes in many different shapes: *We had pasta and tomato sauce for lunch.*

**peach** (n) /piːtʃ/ a soft round fruit with a yellow and red skin and a large stone in the centre: *I opened a tin of peaches.*

**peas** (n) /piːz/ very small round green vegetables. Peas grow in long, thin cases (called pods): *There are some frozen peas in the freezer.*

**pepper** (n) /ˈpepə(r)/ a red, green or yellow vegetable that is almost empty inside: *Add red peppers to the salad to give it some colour.*

**plate** (n) /pleɪt/ a round dish that you put food on: *Careful! The plate is very hot.*

**potato** (n) /pəˈteɪtəʊ/ a white vegetable with a brown or red skin that grows underground: *I bought two kilos of potatoes.*

**rice** (n) /raɪs/ short, thin white or brown grain from a plant that grows on wet land in hot countries. We cook and eat rice: *Would you like rice or potatoes with your chicken?*

**salmon** (n) /ˈsæmən/ a big fish with pink meat that lives in the sea and in rivers: *Would you like some smoked salmon?*

**salt** (n) /sɔːlt/ a white substance that comes from sea water and from the earth. We put it on food to make it taste better: *Add a little salt and pepper.*

**scary** (adj) /ˈskeəri/ frightening: *Patrick told us a scary ghost story.*

**(a) slice of pizza** (n) /slaɪs/ a thin piece that you cut off bread, meat or other food: *Would you like a slice of pizza?*

**spinach** (n) /ˈspɪnɪtʃ/ a vegetable with big green leaves: *For a healthy diet you should eat lots of cabbage, spinach and other greens.*

**spoon** (n) /spuːn/ an object with a round end that you use for eating, serving or mixing food: *Give each person a knife, a fork and a spoon.*

**steak** (n) /steɪk/ a wide flat piece of meat, especially meat from a cow (called beef): *I'd like steak and chips, please.*

**strange** (adj) /streɪndʒ/ unusual or surprising: *Did you hear that strange noise?*

**strawberry** (n) /ˈstrɔːbəri/ a soft red fruit with seeds near the surface: *Strawberries are my favourite fruit.*

**sugar** (n) /ˈʃʊgə(r)/ a sweet substance that comes from certain plants: *Do you take sugar in your coffee?*

**sweets** (n) /swiːts/ small pieces of sweet food: *He bought a packet of sweets for the children.*

**(a) tin (of peaches)** (n) /tɪn/ a metal container for food that keeps it fresh: *I opened a tin of beans.*

**tomato** (n) /təˈmɑːtəʊ/ a soft red fruit that you cook or eat cold in salads: *My mum makes the most delicious tomato soup.*

**tomato sauce** (n) /təˌmɑːtəʊ ˈsɔːs/ a cold sauce made from tomatoes: *Would you like tomato sauce on your chips?*

**yoghurt (also yogurt)** (n) /ˈjɒgət/ a thick liquid food made from milk: *Do you like yoghurt?*

## Unit 6

**alarm clock** (n) /əˈlɑːm klɒk/ a clock that makes a noise to wake you up: *She set the alarm clock for half past six.*

**baggy** (adj) /ˈbægi/ If clothes are baggy, they are big and loose: *He wore jeans and a baggy T-shirt.*

**baker's** (n) /ˈbeɪkəz/ a shop that sells bread and cakes: *I went to the baker's to buy some bread.*

**bargain** (n) /ˈbɑːgən/ sth that is cheaper than usual: *At just £10, the dress was a real bargain!*

**bookshop** (n) /ˈbʊkʃɒp/ a shop that sells books: *She went to the bookshop to buy a London guide book.*

**boots** (n) /buːts/ a shoe that covers your foot and ankle and sometimes part of your leg: *I need a new pair of boots for the winter.*

**butcher's** (n) /ˈbʊtʃəz/ a shop that sells meat: *She went to the butcher's for some lamb chops.*

**calculator** (n) /ˈkælkjuleɪtə(r)/ a small electronic instrument that you use for finding amounts or numbers using mathematics: *Use a calculator to check your answers.*

**camera** (n) /ˈkæmərə/ a piece of equipment that you use for taking photographs or moving pictures: *I need a new film for my camera.*

**cap** (n) /kæp/ a soft hat with a hard curved part at the front: *He always wore a baseball cap.*

**cardigan** (n) /ˈkɑːdɪgən/ a piece of clothing which fastens at the front like a jacket and is usually made of wool: *Where's my cardigan? It's getting cold in here.*

**cheap** (adj) /tʃiːp/ costing little money: *That restaurant is very good and quite cheap.*

**chemist's** (n) /ˈkemɪsts/ a shop that sells medicines, soap and other personal goods: *I'm just going to the chemist's to get my tablets.*

**clear** (adj) /klɪə(r)/ easy to see or hear: *We get a very clear picture on our new TV.*

**clothes shop** (n) /ˈkləʊðz ʃɒp/ a shop that sells clothes (= things like trousers, shirts and coats) : *Katie works in a clothes shop on the High Street.*

**coat** (n) /kəʊt/ a piece of clothing that you wear over your other clothes when you are outside: *Put your coat on – it's cold today.*

**consumer** (n) /kənˈsjuːmə(r)/ a person who buys or uses sth: *Consumers want more information about the food they buy.*

**credit card** (n) /ˈkredɪt kɑːd/ a plastic card from a bank that you can use to buy sth and pay for it later: *Can I pay by credit card?*

**debt** (n) /det/ money that you must pay back to sb: *He's borrowed some money but he still has debts.*

**department store** (n) /dɪˈpɑːtmənt stɔː(r)/ a big shop that sells a lot of different things: *Harrods is a famous department store in London.*

**designer** (n) /dɪˈzaɪnə(r)/ used before another noun to describe sth that is expensive, with a famous fashion name on the label: *She wears designer sunglasses.*

**discount** (n) /ˈdɪskaʊnt/ money that sb takes away from the price of sth to make it cheaper: *Students often get a discount on rail travel.*

**do sth up** (v) /duː ˈʌp/ to fasten sth: *Do up the buttons on your shirt.*

**dollar** (n) /ˈdɒlə(r)/ a unit of money that people use in the US, Canada, Australia and some other countries. There are 100 cents in a dollar: *You will be paid in American dollars.*

**donate** (v) /dəʊˈneɪt/ to give sth, especially money, to people who need it: *They donated $10,000 to the hospital.*

**dress** /dres/ a piece of clothing with a top part and a skirt, that a woman or girl wears: *I bought a new dress for the wedding.*

**DVD player** (n) /ˌdiː viː ˈdiː pleɪə(r)/ a piece of equipment that you use for playing DVDs (= small plastic discs that you record films and music on): *Put the DVD into the DVD player and press 'play'.*

**e-reader** (n) /ˈiːriːdə(r)/ a device for reading electronic books: *My e-reader is very convenient.*

**excellent** (adj) /ˈeksələnt/ very good: *She speaks excellent Spanish.*

**expensive** (adj) /ɪkˈspensɪv/ costing a lot of money: *She always wears expensive clothes.*

**fashionable** (adj) /ˈfæʃnəbl/ popular or in a popular style at the time: *She was wearing a fashionable black hat.*

**fishmonger's** (n) /ˈfɪʃmʌŋgəz/ a shop that sells fish: *Is there a fishmonger's near here?*

**fuzzy** (adj) /ˈfʌzi/ not clear: *The photo was a bit fuzzy.*

**games console** (n) /ˈgeɪmz kɒnsəʊl/ a piece of equipment with buttons and switches on it which you connect to a computer to play games: *The company is selling a new games console.*

**greengrocer's** (n) /ˈgriːngrəʊsəz/ a shop that sells fruit and vegetables: *We went to the greengrocer's and bought a lettuce.*

**half price** (adj) /hɑːf praɪs/ for half the usual price: *These jeans were half price in the sale!*

**hang sth up** (v) /hæŋ ˈʌp/ to put an item of clothing on a hook or a hanger: *Hang your coat up over there.*

**hat** (n) /hæt/ a thing that you wear on your head: *She's wearing a hat.*

**incomplete** (adj) /ˌɪnkəmˈpliːt/ not finished; with parts missing: *This list is incomplete.*

**inconvenient** (adj) /ˌɪnkənˈviːniənt/ causing you problems or difficulty: *Is this an inconvenient time? I can call back later.*

**incorrect** (adj) /ˌɪnkəˈrekt/ not right or true: *There were several incorrect answers.*

**inexpensive** (adj) /ˌɪnɪkˈspensɪv/ low in price: *This is a very inexpensive little car.*

**intolerant** (adj) /ɪnˈtɒlərənt/ not able to accept behaviour or opinions that are different from your own: *She's very intolerant of young children.*

**jacket** (n) /ˈdʒækɪt/ a short coat with sleeves: *He wore a denim jacket and jeans.*

**jeans** /dʒiːnz/ trousers made of strong cotton material (called denim). Jeans are usually blue: *He wore jeans and a T-shirt.*

**jumper** (n) /ˈdʒʌmpə(r)/ a warm piece of clothing with sleeves, that you wear on the top part of your body. Jumpers are often made of wool: *She wore a red jumper with a blue scarf.*

**laptop** (n) /ˈlæptɒp/ a small computer that is easy to carry: *Moira took her laptop to the lecture.*

**leather** (n) /ˈleðə(r)/ the skin of an animal that is used to make things like shoes, jackets or bags: *He wore jeans and a leather jacket.*

**look for sth** (v) /ˈlʊk fə(r)/ to try to find sb or sth: *I'm looking for my keys. Have you seen them?*

**loyalty card** (n) /ˈlɔɪəlti kɑːd/ a card that a supermarket gives you. You use it to buy things at a cheaper price in that shop: *All the big supermarkets offer their customers loyalty cards.*

**make-up** (n) /ˈmeɪk ʌp/ special powders and creams that you put on your face to make yourself more beautiful: *She put on her make-up.*

**market** (n) /ˈmɑːkɪt/ a place where people go to buy and sell things, usually outside: *There is a fruit and vegetable market in the town.*

**MP3 player** (n) /ˌem piː ˈθriː pleɪə(r)/ a small piece of computer equipment that can play music: *I usually take my MP3 player on long journeys.*

**necklace** (n) /ˈnekləs/ a piece of jewellery that you wear round your neck: *He bought the necklace as a present for his wife.*

**new** (adj) /njuː/ recently made; not used before: *I bought a new pair of shoes yesterday.*

**newsagent's** (n) /ˈnjuːzeɪdʒənts/ a shop that sells things like newspapers, magazines, sweets and cigarettes: *I went to the newsagent's and bought a magazine and a bar of chocolate.*

**old** (adj) /əʊld/ that has existed for a long time; that has been used a lot: *I gave away all my old clothes.*

**perfect** (adj) /ˈpɜːfɪkt/ Sth that is perfect is so good that it cannot be better: *Her English is perfect.*

**phone shop** (n) /ˈfəʊn ʃɒp/ a shop that sells mobile phones: *Harry works at a phone shop in town.*

**post office** (n) /ˈpəʊst ɒfɪs/ a building where you go to send letters and packages and to buy stamps: *Where's the main post office?*

**purchase** (n) /ˈpɜːtʃəs/ sth that you have bought: *Sophie showed me her purchases.*

**put sth away** (v) /pʊt əˈweɪ/ to put sth back in its usual place: *She put her socks away in the drawer.*

**put sth on** (v) /pʊt ˈɒn/ to take clothes and wear them: *Put your coat on.*

**radio** (n) /ˈreɪdiəʊ/ a piece of equipment that brings voices or music from far away so that you can hear them: *We listened to an interesting programme on the radio.*

**reuse** (v) /ˌriːˈjuːz/ to use sth again: *Please reuse your envelopes.*

**rucksack** (n) /ˈrʌksæk/ a bag that you carry on your back, for example when you are walking or climbing: *She was carrying a rucksack on her back.*

**sale** (n) /seɪl/ a time when a shop sells things for less money than usual: *In the sale, everything is half price.*

**sandals** (n) /'sændlz/ a light open shoe that you wear in warm weather: *She was wearing shorts and sandals.*

**sandwich shop** (n) /'sænwɪtʃ ʃɒp/ a shop that sells sandwiches, drinks and other snacks: *There's a sandwich shop opposite my office.*

**scarf** (n) /skɑːf/ a piece of material that you wear around your neck or head: *Kay wore her new scarf.*

**scruffy** (adj) /'skrʌfi/ untidy and perhaps dirty: *She was wearing scruffy jeans.*

**second-hand** (adj) /sekənd-'hænd/ not new; used by another person before: *I want to buy a second-hand car.*

**shirt** (n) /ʃɜːt/ a thin piece of clothing that you wear on the top part of your body: *He wore a blue shirt.*

**shorts** (n) /ʃɔːts/ short trousers that end above your knees *She wore shorts and a T-shirt.*

**skirt** (n) /skɜːt/ a piece of clothing for a woman or girl that hangs from the waist and covers part of the leg: *She wore a dark blue skirt.*

**smart** (adj) /smɑːt/ right for a special or an important time; clean and tidy: *I need a smart suit for the wedding.*

**smartphone** (n) /'smɑːt fəʊn/ a mobile phone that can also do some of the things that a computer can do: *You can use your smartphone to access the internet.*

**sock** (n) /sɒk/ an item of clothing that you wear on your foot, inside your shoe: *I can't find any socks!*

**sports shop** (n) /'spɔːts ʃɒp/ a shop that sells sports equipment and clothes: *I went to the sports shop and bought some new tennis balls.*

**tablet** (n) /'tæblət/ a small, flat computer that you can carry with you and that you work by touching the screen: *This game can be played on a tablet or a smartphone.*

**take sth back** (v) /teɪk 'bæk/ to return sth to the place that you got it from: *I took the dress back because it didn't go with my shoes.*

**take sth off** (v) /teɪk 'ɒf/ to remove sth, especially clothes: *Come in and take your coat off.*

**take sth out** (v) /teɪk 'aʊt/ to remove sth from a bag or a cupboard, drawer, etc.: *She opened the drawer and took out a T-shirt.*

**tidy** (adj) /'taɪdi/ with everything in the right place: *Her room is very tidy.*

**tight** (adj) /taɪt/ Tight clothes fit very closely in a way that is often uncomfortable: *These shoes are too tight.*

**tights** (n) /taɪts/ a thin piece of clothing that a woman or girl wears over her feet and legs: *There's a hole in these tights.*

**top** (n) /tɒp/ a piece of clothing that you wear on the top part of your body: *I like your top – is it new?*

**trainers** (n) /'treɪnəz/ soft shoes that you wear for doing sport or with informal clothes: *She wore jeans and trainers.*

**trousers** (n) /'traʊzəz/ a piece of clothing for your legs and the lower part of your body: *Your trousers are on the chair.*

**try sth on** (v) /traɪ 'ɒn/ to put on a piece of clothing to see if you like it and if it is big enough: *I tried the jeans on but they were too small.*

**unattractive** (adj) /ˌʌnə'træktɪv/ not nice to look at: *His office was in an unattractive grey building.*

**undo** (v) /ʌn'duː/ to open sth that was tied or fixed: *I can't undo this zip.*

**unfair** (adj) /ˌʌn'feə(r)/ not treating people in the same way or in the right way: *It was unfair to give chocolates to my brother and not to me.*

**unfashionable** (adj) /ʌn'fæʃnəbl/ in a style that is not popular at a particular time: *He wore an unfashionable black suit.*

**unfriendly** (adj) /ʌn'frendli/ not friendly; not kind or helpful to other people: *Our new neighbours seemed rather unfriendly.*

**unhappy** (adj) /ʌn'hæpi/ not happy: *He was very unhappy when he failed the exam.*

**unimportant** (adj) /ˌʌnɪm'pɔːtnt/ not important: *Anyone can enter the competition; age is unimportant.*

**unkind** (adj) /ˌʌn'kaɪnd/ unpleasant and not friendly: *It was unkind of you to laugh at her.*

**unlucky** (adj) /ʌn'lʌki/ having bad luck: *They were unlucky to lose because they played very well.*

**unzip** (v) /ˌʌn'zɪp/ if you unzip a bag, piece of clothing, etc., you open it by pulling on the zip (= the device that fastens the opening, with two rows of metal or plastic teeth): *She unzipped her bag and took out a key.*

**wallet** (n) /'wɒlɪt/ a small flat case for money and bank cards: *Somebody stole my wallet.*

**watch** (n) /wɒtʃ/ a small clock that you wear on your wrist: *She kept looking at her watch nervously.*

**zip sth up** (v) /zɪp 'ʌp/ to fasten sth together with a zip: *She zipped up her dress.*

## Unit 7

**ankle** (n) /'æŋkl/ the part of your leg where it joins your foot: *She fell and broke her ankle.*

**antibiotics** (n) /ˌæntibaɪ'ɒtɪks/ a type of medicine which fights illness in a person's body: *The doctor gave me some antibiotics for my cough.*

**arm** (n) /ɑːm/ the part of your body from your shoulder to your hand: *Put your arms in the air.*

**back** (n) /bæk/ the part of your body that is between your neck and your bottom: *He lay on his back and looked up at the sky.*

**bandage** (n) /'bændɪdʒ/ a long piece of white cloth that you tie around a part of the body that is hurt: *A nurse put a bandage around my knee.*

**blocked nose** (n) /ˌblɒkt 'nəʊz/ the problem you have when it is difficult to breathe through your nose because you have a cold: *I've got a blocked nose.*

**broken arm** (n) /ˌbrəʊkən 'ɑːm/ If you have a broken arm, one of the bones in your arm is damaged: *Lisa has a broken arm.*

**broken leg** (n) /ˌbrəʊkən 'leg/ If you have a broken leg, one of the bones in your leg is damaged: *I was taken to hospital with a broken leg.*

**bruise** (n) /bruːz/ a dark mark on your skin that comes after sth hits it: *How did you get that bruise on your knee?*

**burn** (n) /bɜːn/ a place on your body where fire or heat has hurt it: *I've got a burn on my arm.*

**(wash the) car** (n) /kɑː(r)/ a vehicle with four wheels, usually with enough space for four or five people: *Dad washes the car once a week.*

**chest** (n) /tʃest/ the top part of the front of your body: *She held the baby against her chest.*

**competitor** (n) /kəm'petɪtə(r)/ a person who is trying to win a competition: *There are ten competitors in the first race.*

**cough** (n) /kɒf/ an illness that makes you send air out of your throat with a sudden loud noise: *I've got a bad cough.*

**cut** (n) /kʌt/ an injury on the skin, made by sth sharp like a knife: *He had a deep cut on his leg.*

**dangerous** (adj) /'deɪndʒərəs/ Sth that is dangerous may hurt you: *It's dangerous to drive a car at night without any lights.*

**dizzy** (adj) /'dɪzi/ If you feel dizzy, you feel that everything is turning round and round and that you are going to fall: *The room was hot and I started to feel dizzy.*

**do the ironing** (n) /ˌduː ði: 'aɪənɪŋ/ making clothes smooth using an iron: *I usually do the ironing on Sunday evenings.*

**do the shopping** (n) /ˌduː ðə 'ʃɒpɪŋ/ to buy the things you need from shops: *She does her shopping after work.*

**do the washing up** (n) /ˌduː ðə wɒʃɪŋ 'ʌp/ to wash the plates, knives, forks, and pans after a meal: *I'll do the washing up if you cook the meal.*

**downhill** (adj) /ˌdaʊn'hɪl/ going downwards: *The race follows a downhill course.*

**elbow** (n) /'elbəʊ/ the part in the middle of your arm where it bends: *She fell and broke her elbow.*

**endurance** (n) /ɪn'djʊərəns/ the ability to continue doing sth painful or difficult for a long period of time without complaining: *You need endurance to play a four-hour match.*

**extreme** (adj) /ɪk'striːm/ Extreme sports are more dangerous or more difficult than other sports: *I'm into extreme sports like skydiving.*

**face** (n) /feɪs/ the front part of your head: *Have you washed your face?*

**feel sick** (v) /fiːl 'sɪk/ to feel that food is going to come up from your stomach: *The motion of the boat made her feel sick.*

**finger** (n) /'fɪŋgə(r)/ one of the five parts at the end of your hand: *She cut her finger on some glass.*

**fit** (adj) /fɪt/ healthy and strong: *I keep fit by jogging every day.*

**flu** (n) /fluː/ an illness like a very bad cold that makes your body sore and hot: *I think I've got flu.*

**foot** (n) /fʊt/ the part of your leg that you stand on: *I've been walking all day and my feet hurt.*

**hand** (n) /hænd/ the part at the end of your arm that has four fingers and a thumb: *She held the letter in her hand.*

**hard-working** (adj) /ˌhɑːd 'wɜːkɪŋ/ working with effort and energy: *My sister is very hard-working.*

**have a temperature** (v) /hæv ə 'temprətʃə(r)/ to feel very hot because you are ill: *She felt sick and she had a temperature.*

**hay fever** (n) /'heɪ fiːvə(r)/ an illness like a cold. Grass and other plants can cause hay fever: *I've got hay fever.*

**head** (n) /hed/ the part of your body above your neck: *She turned her head to look at me.*

**(have a) headache** (n) /'hedeɪk/ a pain in your head: *I've got a headache.*

**hip** (n) /hɪp/ the place where your leg joins the side of your body: *I put my hands on my hips.*

**ill** (adj) /ɪl/ not well; not in good health: *Mark is in bed because he is ill.*

**injection** (n) /ɪn'dʒekʃn/ If you have an injection, a doctor or nurse puts a drug into your body using a special needle (called a syringe): *The doctor gave the baby an injection.*

**knee** (n) /niː/ the part in the middle of your leg where it bends: *I fell and cut my knee.*

**lazy** (adj) /'leɪzi/ A person who is lazy does not want to work: *Don't be so lazy – come and help me!*

**leg** (n) /leg/ one of the long parts of the body that is used for walking and standing: *She sat down and crossed her legs.*

**medicine** (n) /'medsn/ special liquid that helps you to get better when you are ill: *Take this medicine every morning.*

**neck** (n) /nek/ the part of your body between your shoulders and your head: *Helen wore a silver chain round her neck.*

**(have a) nosebleed** (n) /'nəʊzbliːd/ a sudden flow of blood that comes from your nose: *What's the best thing to do when you have a nose bleed?*

**painkiller** (n) /'peɪnkɪlə(r)/ a drug that makes pain less strong: *She's on painkillers.*

**plaster** (n) /'plɑːstə(r)/ a small piece of sticky material that you put over a cut on your body to keep it clean: *You should put a plaster on that cut.*

**player** (n) /'pleɪə(r)/ a person who plays a game: *She's an excellent tennis player.*

**poor** (adj) /pɔː(r)/ with very little money: *She was too poor to buy clothes for her children.*

**rash** (n) /ræʃ/ a lot of small red spots on your skin: *He came out in a rash where the plant had touched him.*

**rich** (adj) /rɪtʃ/ having a lot of money: *He wants to be rich and famous.*

**(take out the) rubbish** (n) /'rʌbɪʃ/ things that you do not want any more: *Could you take out the rubbish, please?*

**runner** (n) /'rʌnə(r)/ a person who runs: *The French runner is in the lead.*

**safe** (adj) /seɪf/ not dangerous: *Is it safe to swim in this river?*

**shivery** (adj) /'ʃɪv(r)i/ shaking because you are cold or ill: *I went to bed feeling cold and shivery.*

**shoulder** (n) /'ʃəʊldə(r)/ the part of your body between your neck and your arm: *She fell asleep with her head on his shoulder.*

**skater** (n) /skeɪtə(r)/ a person who skates: *One of the skaters fell.*

**sneeze** (v) /sniːz/ to make air come out of your nose and mouth with a sudden loud noise, for example because you have a cold: *Pepper makes you sneeze.*

**(have a) sore throat** (n) /ˌsɔː(r) ˈθrəʊt/ a pain in your throat: *I've got a sore throat.*

**(have a) sprained ankle** (n) /spreɪnd ˈæŋkl/ If you have a sprained ankle, you have hurt and damaged it by turning it suddenly or falling: *What's the best treatment for a sprained ankle?*

**sprinter** (n) /ˈsprɪntə(r)/ a person who runs short distances very fast: *There were four 100-metre sprinters in the England team.*

**stomach** (n) /ˈstʌmək/ the part inside your body where food goes after you eat it: *Lie on your stomach and lift your arms off the ground.*

**(have) stomach ache** (n) /ˈstʌmək eɪk/ a pain in your stomach: *I've got stomach ache.*

**swimmer** (n) /ˈswɪmə(r)/ a person who swims: *He's a good swimmer.*

**take part (in sth)** (v) /teɪk ˈpɑːt/ to join with other people in an activity: *We all took part in the discussion.*

**thick** (adj) /θɪk/ far from one side to the other: *The walls are very thick.*

**toe** (n) /təʊ/ one of the five parts at the end of your foot: *Did I tread on your toe? Sorry.*

**(have) toothache** (n) /ˈtuːθeɪk/ a pain in your tooth: *I've got toothache.*

**(the) toughest** (n) /ˈtʌfɪst/ (the) strongest: *Only the toughest go climbing here in winter.*

**unwell** (adj) /ʌnˈwel/ not well; ill: *I feel unwell.*

**(hang out/bring in the) washing** (n) /ˈwɒʃɪŋ/ clothes that you have washed: *Shall I hang the washing out?*

**weak** (adj) /wiːk/ not powerful or strong: *She felt very weak after her long illness.*

**well** (adj) /wel/ healthy: *'How are you?' 'I'm very well, thanks.'*

**wrist** (n) /rɪst/ the part of your body where your arm joins your hand: *I wear a bracelet on my wrist.*

## Unit 8

**accountant** (n) /əˈkaʊntənt/ a person whose job is to make lists of all the money that people or businesses receive and pay: *Nicky is an accountant.*

**architect** (n) /ˈɑːkɪtekt/ a person whose job is to design and plan buildings: *Sam wants to be an architect when he grows up.*

**article** (n) /ˈɑːtɪkl/ a piece of writing in a newspaper or magazine: *Did you read the article about young fashion designers?*

**be born** (v) /bi ˈbɔːn/ to start your life: *He was born in 1990.*

**beautiful** (adj) /ˈbjuːtɪfl/ very nice to see, hear or smell: *She has a beautiful voice.*

**builder** (n) /ˈbɪldə(r)/ a person whose job is to make buildings: *The builders are starting work on the new school today.*

**die** (v) /daɪ/ to stop living: *She died of cancer.*

**doctor** (n) /ˈdɒktə(r)/ a person whose job is to make sick people well again: *The doctor will see you soon.*

**electrician** (n) /ɪˌlekˈtrɪʃn/ a person whose job is to make and repair electrical systems and equipment *John's an electrician.*

**engineer** (n) /ˌendʒɪˈnɪə(r)/ a person whose job is to plan, make or repair things like machines, roads or bridges: *My brother is an engineer.*

**factory worker** (n) /ˈfæktri ˌwɜːkə(r)/ a person who works in a place where things are made with machines: *He works at the car factory.*

**fall in love (with sb)** (v) /ˌfɔːl ɪn ˈlʌv/ to begin to love sb: *He fell in love with Anna immediately.*

**fiction** (n) /ˈfɪkʃn/ stories that sb writes and that are not true: *I enjoy reading fiction.*

**get a job** (v) /get ə ˈdʒɒb/ to start working in a place: *She got a job as a waitress.*

**get divorced** (v) /get dɪˈvɔːst/ to end a marriage by law: *They got divorced last year.*

**get married** (v) /get ˈmærɪd/ to take sb as your husband or wife: *Kat and Paul got married last year.*

**go to university** (v) /gəʊ tə ˌjuːnɪˈvɜːsəti/ to regularly attend university (= a place where people go to study more difficult subjects after they have left school): *I'm hoping to go to university.*

**grow up** (v) /grəʊ ˈʌp/ to become an adult; to change from a child to a man or woman: *I want to be a doctor when I grow up*

**have a baby** (v) /hæv ə ˈbeɪbi/ When a woman has a baby, she produces a child from her body: *She's going to have a baby.*

**lawyer** (n) /ˈlɔːjə(r)/ a person who has studied the law and who helps people or talks for them in a court of law: *Susan is training to be a lawyer.*

**musical** (adj) /ˈmjuːzɪkl/ connected with music: *Do you play a musical instrument?*

**natural** (adj) /ˈnætʃrəl/ finding sth easy: *She's a natural dancer: strong and graceful.*

**non-fiction** (n) /nɒn ˈfɪkʃn/ writing that is about real people, events and facts: *You'll find biographies in the non-fiction section of the library.*

**novel** (n) /ˈnɒvl/ a book that tells a story about people and things that are not real: *'David Copperfield' is a novel by Charles Dickens.*

**nurse** (n) /nɜːs/ a person whose job is to look after people who are sick or hurt: *My sister works as a nurse in a hospital.*

**office worker** (n) /ˈɒfɪs ˌwɜːkə(r)/ a person who works at a desk in an office: *The train was full of office workers on their way home.*

**peaceful** (adj) /ˈpiːsfl/ with no fighting: *The two countries found a peaceful solution to the dispute.*

**play** (n) /pleɪ/ a story that you watch in the theatre or on television, or listen to on the radio: *We went to see a play at the National Theatre.*

**plumber** (n) /ˈplʌmə(r)/ a person whose job is to put in and repair things like water pipes and baths: *The plumber came to mend the broken pipes.*

**poem** (n) /ˈpəʊɪm/ words arranged in lines in an artistic way, often with sounds repeated at the ends of lines: *I wrote poems about the countryside.*

**political** (adj) /pəˈlɪtɪkl/ connected with politics or the government: *Do you belong to a political party?*

**powerful** (adj) /ˈpaʊəfl/ having a lot of strength or power: *Richard is a very powerful swimmer.*

**professional** (adj) /prəˈfeʃnl/ doing sth for money as a job: *He is a professional footballer.*

**retire** (v) /rɪˈtaɪə(r)/ to stop working because you are a certain age: *My grandfather retired last year.*

**scientist** (n) /ˈsaɪəntɪst/ a person who studies science or works with science: *Scientists have made an important new discovery.*

**script** (n) /skrɪpt/ the written words that actors speak in a play or film: *Who wrote the film script?*

**shop assistant** (n) /ˈʃɒp əˌsɪstənt/ a person who works in a shop: *The shop assistant helped me.*

**short story** (n) /ˌʃɔːt ˈstɔːri/ a piece of writing that is shorter than a novel: *He gave me a collection of short stories by Thomas Hardy.*

**successful** (adj) /səkˈsesfl/ If you are successful, you have got or done what you wanted, or you have become popular, rich, etc.: *Her uncle is a successful actor.*

**take care** (v) /ˌteɪk ˈkeə(r)/ to be careful: *Take care when you cross the road.*

**take control (of sth)** (v) /ˌteɪk kənˈtrəʊl/ to use your power to deal with sth: *The police have now taken control of the situation.*

**take photos (of sth)** (v) /ˌteɪk ˈfəʊtəʊz/ to use a camera to record pictures: *I took photos of all the famous sights.*

**take place** (v) /ˌteɪk ˈpleɪs/ to happen: *The wedding of Katherine and Warren will take place on 19 July.*

**take turns** (v) /ˌteɪk ˈtɜːnz/ to do sth one after the other: *You can't both use the computer at the same time. Why don't you take turns?*

**vet** (n) /vet/ a doctor for animals: *Mary is training to be a vet.*

**waiter** (n) /ˈweɪtə(r)/ a man who brings food and drink to your table in a restaurant: *The waiter took our order.*

**waitress** (n) /ˈweɪtrəs/ a woman who brings food and drink to your table in a restaurant: *The waitress cleared the table.*

**wonderful** (adj) /ˈwʌndəfl/ extremely good; great: *What a wonderful present!*

## Unit 9

**achievement** (n) /əˈtʃiːvmənt/ sth that sb has done after trying hard: *Climbing Mount Everest was his greatest achievement.*

**attraction** (n) /əˈtrækʃn/ sth that is interesting or enjoyable: *Big Ben is a major tourist attraction.*

**bald** (adj) /bɔːld/ with no hair or not much hair: *My dad is going bald.*

**beard** (n) /bɪəd/ the hair on a man's chin: *He has got a beard.*

**blonde** (adj) /blɒnd/ with light-coloured hair: *She is tall and blonde.*

**cardboard** (n) /ˈkɑːdbɔːd/ very thick paper that is used for making boxes, etc.: *Put the books in a cardboard box.*

**celebration** (n) /ˌselɪˈbreɪʃn/ a time when you enjoy yourself because you have a special reason to be happy: *We had a big family celebration when Uncle Tony came home.*

**clay** (n) /kleɪ/ a kind of heavy earth that becomes hard when it is dry: *She shaped the clay into a pot.*

**come up with sth** (v) /kʌm ˈʌp wɪð/ to find an answer or a solution to sth: *Engineers have come up with new ways of saving energy.*

**cut sb off** (v) /kʌt ˈɒf/ to stop or interrupt sb's telephone call: *We were cut off before I could give her my message.*

**decoration** (n) /ˌdekəˈreɪʃn/ a beautiful thing that you add to sth to make it look nicer: *When shall we put up the Christmas decorations?*

**disappointment** (n) /ˌdɪsəˈpɔɪntmənt/ a feeling of sadness because what you wanted did not happen: *She couldn't hide her disappointment when she lost the match.*

**dyed** (adj) /daɪd/ dyed hair is not its natural colour: *Diane has dyed blonde hair.*

**enjoyment** (n) /ɪnˈdʒɔɪmənt/ a feeling of enjoying sth: *I get a lot of enjoyment from travelling.*

**entertainment** (n) /ˌentəˈteɪnmənt/ sth that entertains people, for example films, concerts or television: *There isn't much entertainment for young people in this town.*

**find sth out** (v) /faɪnd ˈaʊt/ to get information about something: *Can you find out what time the train leaves?*

**foam** (n) /fəʊm/ a light rubber material that is used inside seats, etc. to make them comfortable: *We slept on foam mattresses on the floor.*

**freckled** (adj) /ˈfrekld/ Freckled skin has a lot of small light brown spots on it: *She has curly brown hair and a freckled face.*

**get off the line** (v) /ˌget ɒf ðə ˈlaɪn/ to stop using a telephone line: *I'll get off the line in case somebody else is trying to call.*

**get through** (v) /ˌget ˈθruː/ to be able to speak to somebody on the telephone: *I tried to call Kate but I couldn't get through.*

**give up** (v) /gɪv ˈʌp/ to stop trying to do something: *I give up – what's the answer?*

**glasses** (n) /ˈglɑːsɪz/ two pieces of glass or plastic (called lenses) in a frame that people wear over their eyes to help them see better: *Does she wear glasses?*

**go ahead** (v) /gəʊ əˈhed/ to begin or continue to do something: *We decided to go ahead with the match in spite of the heavy rain.*

**hold on** (v) /həʊld ˈɒn/ to wait: *Could you hold on a moment, please?*

**look like sb** (v) /ˈlʊk laɪk/ to have a similar appearance to sb: *John looks like his father.*

**marble** (n) /ˈmɑːbl/ a hard attractive stone that is used to make statues (= models of people) and parts of buildings: *Marble is always cold when you touch it.*

**medium-height** (adj) /ˌmiːdiəm ˈhaɪt/ not tall and not small: *He's medium-height with dark hair.*

**medium-weight** (adj) /ˌmiːdiəm ˈweɪt/ not fat and not thin: *He's medium-weight with blonde hair.*

# Wordlist

**metal** (n) /'metl/ a solid substance that is usually hard and shiny, such as iron, tin or gold: *This chair is made of metal.*

**moustache** (n) /mə'stɑːʃ/ the hair above a man's mouth, below his nose: *He has got a moustache.*

**overweight** (adj) /ˌəʊvə'weɪt/ too heavy or fat: *The doctor said I was overweight.*

**paper** (n) /'peɪpə(r)/ thin material for writing or drawing on or for wrapping things in: *Take a sheet of paper and write your name at the top.*

**pick up (the phone)** (v) /pɪk 'ʌp/ to answer the telephone: *I called her office but nobody picked up.*

**plastic** (n) /'plæstɪk/ an artificial material that is used for making many different things: *These chairs are made of plastic.*

**prediction** (n) /prɪ'dɪkʃn/ what you think will happen: *The results confirmed our predictions.*

**put sb through (to sb)** (v) /pʊt 'θruː/ to connect somebody on the telephone to the person they want to speak to: *Can you put me through to the manager, please?*

**put sth together** (v) /pʊt tə'geðə(r)/ to produce sth: *They put together a list of good hotels nearby.*

**set sth up** (v) /set 'ʌp/ to start something: *The company was set up in 1981.*

**slim** (adj) /slɪm/ thin, but not too thin: *Her father was a tall slim man in his forties.*

**speak up** (v) /spiːk 'ʌp/ to talk louder: *Can you speak up? I can't hear you!*

**stone** (n) /stəʊn/ the very hard material that is in the ground. Stone is sometimes used for building: *There is a high stone wall around the garden.*

**tanned** (adj) /tænd/ If you are tanned, your skin has become brown because you have spent time in the sun: *He had dark hair and a tanned face.*

**thin** (adj) /θɪn/ not fat: *He's tall and thin.*

**wax** (n) /wæks/ the substance that is used for making candles (= tall sticks that you burn to give light) or for making things shine: *I bought a tin of wax floor polish.*

**what is ... like?** (v) /wɒt ɪz '... laɪk/ words that you say when you want to know more about sb or sth: *'What's your new teacher like?' 'She's really nice.'*

**wood** (n) /wʊd/ the hard substance that trees are made of *The table is made of wood.*

**work sth out** (v) /wɜːk 'aʊt/ to find the answer to something: *We worked out the cost of the holiday.*

## Unit 10

**activity holiday** (n) /æk'tɪvəti ˌhɒlədeɪ/ a holiday where you do things like sailing, diving and climbing: *We are planning an activity holiday.*

**apartment** (n) /ə'pɑːtmənt/ the American English word for flat: a group of rooms for living in, usually on one floor of a house or big building: *Their apartment is on the fifth floor.*

**beach** (n) /biːtʃ/ a piece of land next to the sea that is covered with sand or stones: *We lay on the beach in the sun.*

**beach holiday** (n) /'biːtʃ ˌhɒlədeɪ/ a holiday where you spend a lot of time on the beach and in the sea: *I don't really like beach holidays; I prefer walking in the countryside.*

**bed and breakfast** (n) /ˌbed ənd 'brekfəst/ a private house or small hotel where you pay for a room to sleep in and a meal the next morning: *I stayed in a bed and breakfast.*

**camper van** (n) /'kæmpə(r) væn/ a vehicle that you use for sleeping in on holiday: *We travelled across Europe in a camper van.*

**camping holiday** (n) /'kæmpɪŋ ˌhɒlədeɪ/ a holiday where you sleep in a tent: *We're planning a camping holiday in France.*

**campsite** (n) /'kæmpsaɪt/ a place where you can stay in a tent: *We found a lovely campsite by a lake.*

**candy** (n) /'kændi/ the American English word for sweets: small pieces of sweet food: *The children eat too much candy.*

**caravan** (n) /'kærəvæn/ a large vehicle that is pulled by a car. You can sleep, cook, etc. in a caravan when you are travelling or on holiday: *The caravan site was full.*

**check into (a hotel)** (v) /tʃek 'ɪntu/ to tell the person at the desk in a hotel that you have arrived: *We checked into our hotel at 3 p.m.*

**check out of** (v) /tʃek 'aʊt əv/ to pay your bill and leave a hotel: *Please check out by 10 a.m.*

**chill out** (v) /tʃɪl 'aʊt/ to relax and not feel angry or nervous: *I work hard all week so on Sundays I just chill out.*

**chips** (n) /tʃɪps/ the American English word for crisps: very thin pieces of potato cooked in hot oil and eaten cold. They are sold in bags and have many different flavours: *He bought a bag of potato chips and a bar of chocolate.*

**coast** (n) /kəʊst/ the part of the land that is next to the sea: *Their holiday house is near the coast.*

**cruise** (n) /kruːz/ a holiday when you travel on a ship and visit a lot of different places: *They went on a world cruise.*

**day trip** (n) /'deɪ trɪp/ a visit to place that lasts one day: *We didn't go away on holiday; we just went on day trips.*

**drop off** (v) /drɒp 'ɒf/ to stop a vehicle so that sb can leave it: *Can you drop me off here, please?*

**eraser** (n) /ɪ'reɪzə(r)/ the American English word for rubber: a small piece of rubber that you use for taking away marks that you have made with a pencil: *May I borrow your eraser, please?*

**fall** (n) /fɔːl/ the American English word for autumn: the part of the year between summer and winter: *I'm starting university next fall.*

**farm holiday** (n) /'fɑːm ˌhɒlədeɪ/ a holiday where you stay on a farm: *The children would like to go on a farm holiday.*

**fries** (n) /fraɪz/ the American English word for chips: thin pieces of potato cooked in hot oil: *Do you want fries with your burger?*

**garbage** (n) /'gɑːbɪdʒ/ the American English word for rubbish: things that you throw away because you do not want them any more: *Don't forget to put the garbage out.*

**get away** (v) /get ə'weɪ/ to go on holiday: *I'm hoping to get away for a few days in May.*

**get back** (v) /get 'bæk/ to return: *When did you get back from your holiday?*

**get into** (v) /get 'ɪntu/ to enter a vehicle: *I saw the man getting into a blue van.*

**get off** /get 'ɒf/ to leave something such as a bus or train: *Where did you get off the bus?*

**get on** (v) /get 'ɒn/ to climb onto a bus or train: *I got on the train.*

**get out of** (v) /get 'aʊt əv/ to leave a vehicle: *A woman got out of the car.*

**go abroad** (v) /gəʊ ə'brɔːd/ to go to another country: *Are you going abroad this summer?*

**go away** (v) /gəʊ ə'weɪ/ to leave the place where you live for at least one night: *They have gone away for the weekend.*

**guided tour** (n) /ˌgaɪdɪd 'tʊə(r)/ a visit of a building or city with a person who tells you about the place: *We went on a guided tour of the castle.*

**harbour** (n) /'hɑːbə(r)/ a place where ships can stay safely in the water: *We went to look at the boats in the harbour.*

**holiday** (n) /'hɒlədeɪ/ a time when you do not go to work or school, and often go and stay away from home: *I'm going to Spain for my holiday.*

**hotel** (n) /həʊ'tel/ a place where you pay to sleep and eat: *I stayed at a hotel near the airport.*

**island** (n) /'aɪlənd/ a piece of land with water all around it: *We visited the Greek islands last summer.*

**lake** (n) /leɪk/ a big area of water with land all around it: *We went swimming in the lake.*

**look forward to** (v) /lʊk 'fɔːwəd tə/ to wait for something with impatience and pleasure: *I'm looking forward to seeing you again.*

**movie theater** (n) /'muːvi ˌθɪətə(r)/ the American English word for cinema: a place where you go to see a film: *Is there a movie theater in town?*

**pants** (n) /pænts/ the American English word for trousers: a piece of clothing for your legs and the lower part of your body: *Lewis wore black pants with a yellow T-shirt.*

**postcard** (n) /'pəʊstkɑːd/ a card with a picture on one side, that you write on and send by post: *She sent me a postcard from California.*

**queue up** (v) /kjuː 'ʌp/ When people queue up they stand in a line waiting for sth: *People queued up outside the ticket office.*

**river** (n) /'rɪvə(r)/ a long wide line of water that flows into the sea: *People were fishing along the banks of the river.*

**set off** (v) /set 'ɒf/ to start a journey: *We set off for Oxford at two o'clock.*

**sightseeing holiday** (n) /'saɪtˌsiː ɪŋ 'trɪp/ a holiday where you visit the famous places and things of interest in a city or country: *Rose's parents went on a sight-seeing trip to Prague.*

**ski resort** (n) /'skiː rɪˌzɔːt/ a place where a lot of people go on holiday to ski: *We stayed at a ski resort in the Alps.*

**ski trip** (n) /'skiː trɪp/ a holiday where you ski (= move along on snow on long flat pieces of metal or plastic that you fix to boots): *The school organizes a ski trip every winter.*

**soccer** (n) /'sɒkə(r)/ the American English word for football: a game for two teams of eleven players who try to kick a round ball into the other team's goal on a field (called a pitch): *Ben plays for the university soccer team.*

**souvenir** (n) /ˌsuːvə'nɪə(r)/ something that you keep to remember a place or a special event: *I bought this cowboy hat as a souvenir of Texas.*

**study holiday** (n) /'stʌdi ˌhɒlədeɪ/ a holiday where you learn about a subject: *The company offers study holidays for young people in the UK.*

**summer camp** (n) /ˌsʌmə(r) 'kæmp/ a place where children spend their holidays away from home: *The children go on summer camp in June.*

**sweater** (n) /'swetə(r)/ the American English word for jumper: a warm piece of clothing with sleeves, that you wear on the top part of your body. Sweaters are often made of wool: *She wore a red sweater with a blue scarf.*

**temple** (n) /'templ/ a building where people go to say prayers to a god or gods: *Please remove your shoes before entering the temple.*

**theme park** (n) /'θiːm pɑːk/ a type of amusement park (= a large park which has a lot of things that you can ride and play on) where the activities are all based on a single idea: *We went to a theme park called Waterland.*

**tower** (n) /'taʊə(r)/ a tall narrow building or a tall part of a building: *Did you go up the Eiffel Tower?*

**train** (n) /treɪn/ a vehicle that is pulled by an engine along a railway line: *I'm going there by train.*

**vacation** (n) /və'keɪʃn/ the American English word for holiday: a time when you do not go to work or school, and often go and stay away from home: *They're on vacation in Hawaii.*

**volcano** (n) /vɒl'keɪnəʊ/ a mountain with a hole in the top where fire, gas and hot liquid rock (called lava) sometimes come out: *Is Mount Etna an active volcano?*

**walking holiday** (n) /'wɔːkɪŋ ˌhɒlədeɪ/ a holiday where you walk from one place to another and sleep in a tent or a cheap hotel in each place: *We went on a walking holiday in the Alps.*

**waterfall** (n) /'wɔːtəfɔːl/ a place where water falls from a high place to a low place: *Come to Niagara and see the spectacular waterfall.*

**yard** (n) /jɑːd/ the American English word for garden: a piece of land by your house where you can play, relax, or grow flowers and vegetables: *The children were playing out in the yard.*